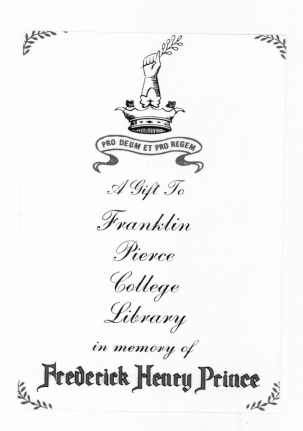

The Origin of Terrestrial Vertebrates

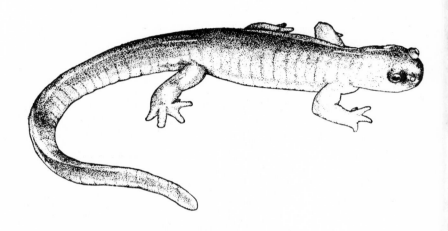

Terrestrial Vertebrates

I. I. SCHMALHAUSEN

TRANSLATED FROM THE RUSSIAN BY LEON KELSO
EDITED BY KEITH STEWART THOMSON
WITH A PREFACE TO THE ENGLISH EDITION BY CARL GANS

ACADEMIC PRESS · New York and London · 1968

First published in the Russian language in 1964 under the title
PROISHOŽDENIE NAZEMNYH POZVONOČNYH
by Izdatel'stvo Nauka, Moscow.

ACADEMIC PRESS INC.
111 Fifth Avenue, New York, New York 10003

United Kingdom Edition published by
ACADEMIC PRESS INC. (LONDON) LTD.
Berkeley Square House, London W.1

LIBRARY OF CONGRESS CATALOG CARD NUMBER 67-31044

PRINTED IN THE UNITED STATES OF AMERICA

Foreword to the Russian Edition

The problem of the origin of terrestrial vertebrates has concerned me for quite some time. My first works on the problem of the origin of the limbs of terrestrial vertebrates were done over fifty years ago. Later on I investigated the structure of the suspensorial apparatus of fishes and took up the subject of the origin of the sound transmission organs in terrestrial vertebrates. The whole problem acquired interest anew following a succession of outstanding paleontological discoveries and the reinvestigation of fossil remains with the aid of new methods of research. However, comparison with modern forms was not always easy owing to inadequacies in our knowledge of them. New investigations of the ontogeny of modern Amphibia were needed. Portions of such studies were published by myself in a series of papers in the 1950's and 1960's. The composition of a planned monograph was interrupted on account of my illness. The original plan had to be curtailed; the ontogeny of the anuran Amphibia was omitted; the description of the development of the skull of urodele Amphibia was cut short; the ontogeny and evolution of the organs of locomotion and their musculature was omitted; the reviews of the evolution of the olfactory organs and the organs of vision were cut short. In addition, all those questions that could not be decided by comparison with fossil forms were omitted.

In my work essential assistance was rendered me by my collaborators, especially E. D. Regel, who prepared a series of plastic reconstructions and figures. Several figures were prepared for this book by N. S. Lebedkina. I. M. Medvedeva and S. M. Epstein assisted me considerably in the preparation of the manuscript for printing. To all my collaborators I here extend my heartfelt gratitude. I also thank the management of the Zoological Institute collectively, and in particular my old friend Academician E. N. Pavlovskii, who unwaveringly supported me in my work and created for the activities of the Embryological Laboratory and its collaborators a peaceful and benevolent environment.

Moscow   I. I. SCHMALHAUSEN

Preface to the English Edition[1]

Carl Gans

Ivan Ivanovich Schmalhausen died on October 7, 1963, at the age of 79 after a long illness. At the time of his death the Russian edition had just gone to press. The appearance in print of the Russian edition, during the fall of 1964, thus marked the end of the long productive period of one of the most broadly interested of Russian morphologists and evolutionary biologists.

I. I. Schmalhausen was born in Kiev on April 23, 1884. His father was Ivan Fedorovich Schmalhausen (1849–1894), Professor of Botany at Kiev University, perhaps best known for his "Flora of Central and Southern Russia, Crimea and Northern Caucasus" and extensive paleobotanical studies mentioned prominently in Krishtoforovich's "History of Paleobotany in the USSR" (1956). The father died when his son was only ten, but young Schmalhausen soon began to show an interest in the problems of biology. He graduated with honors from the Kiev Gymnasium in 1901 and commenced work in the laboratory of Aleksei Nikolaevich Severtsov at Kiev University. Here he participated in the early phases of the studies into the morphology and evolution of fishes and lower chordates that were to culminate in the several editions of Severtsov's "Morphologische Gesetzmässigkeiten der Evolution," an important work that, perhaps because of the absence of an English edition, has received relatively little attention in the United States.

Schmalhausen's study, "The Development of Appendages in Amphibia," was awarded the Kiev University Gold Medal. His master's dissertation dealt with "The Unpaired Fins of Fishes and their Phylogenetic Development," and his doctoral dissertation was entitled "The Development of Appendages in Amphibia and their Significance in the Problem of the Origin of Terrestrial Vertebrates."

[1] I am grateful to the several colleagues who provided me with the biographical data abstracted here and to Drs. L. Kelso and E. Kochva for translations of some of these. I am informed that a detailed biography of Schmalhausen, including a list of his more than 200 publications, is now being prepared by Dr. A. A. Makhotin.

The last-mentioned two were defended at Moscow University (1914, 1916) where he, in 1912, had taken on the position of senior lecturer. In 1917, Schmalhausen was appointed to a professorship at Yurev University, and in 1920 he returned as professor to Kiev where he remained until 1937. In that year he assumed the directorship of the A. N. Severtsov Institute of Evolutionary Morphology of Moscow, later changing to the Zoological Institute of the Akademiya Nauk USSR when he was dismissed from the former institution following the strong attacks upon him by T. D. Lysenko during the 1948 USSR Biological Congress. He remained at the Zoological Institute until just before his death.

His early years as an instructor saw additional studies in the comparative anatomy of lower vertebrates. Numerous papers traced the development of the hyomandibular apparatus and, in particular, the phylogenetic development of the auditory ossicles. These studies were soon followed by the appearance of a textbook of comparative anatomy which was apparently widely accepted and ran through four editions. In 1922, Schmalhausen was elected Academician of the all-Ukrainian Akademiya Nauk.

The return to a professorship at Kiev marked a gradual change in research emphasis. He and his students started a series of investigations into the regulation, dynamics, and determination of morphogenetic processes. Various studies in experimental embryology were begun by a consideration of the role of nervous tissues on limb regeneration in amphibians; these studies ultimately led to his papers on growth as an exponential process and later caused him to consider character differentiation. In 1935, this work was recognized when he received the title of Honored (Preeminent) Scientist and was elected Academician in the Akademiya Nauk USSR.

After his move to Moscow, Schmalhausen devoted himself almost entirely to synthetic work which resulted in his books, "The Organism as a Whole, in Individual and Historical Development" (1938), "Ways and Laws of Evolution" (1939), and "Factors of Evolution" (1946), the last reprinted in an English edition in 1949. Throughout, his concern with techniques for numerical expression of the factors of morphogenesis logically led him into discussions of the applicability of cybernetics to such biological systems. Many of his ideas were summarized in the semipopular book, "Regulation of Morphogenesis in Individual Development," which also appeared posthumously in 1964.

Schmalhausen's interests paralleled those of his teacher and long-time associate, A. N. Severtsov, in combining considerations of a particular phase in phylogeny with a concern for broader problems. In spite of active concern with general theoretical questions relating to processes of morphogenesis and evolution, he retained an interest in more specific questions regarding the origin of lower vertebrates. Shortly after his 65th birthday, there appeared the first of a new cycle of studies intended to define the nature of the fish–amphibian transition. This was planned as a review of all facets of the problem. Specifically, its approach included a re-examination of critical aspects of amphibian development, and its ultimate aim was the present volume. In

1963, the first of these papers on fish–amphibian transition was recognized by the award of the I. I. Mechnikov Medal.

The foreword to the Russian edition indicates and it is quite clear, from the relative space devoted to the various topics, that Schmalhausen's illness (and perhaps the after effects of his involvement in the controversy with T. D. Lysenko[2]) forced him to begin this book before he had a chance to start or complete investigation of numerous aspects. Most critical of these is the question of anuran development. Even so, the publication of this recapitulation of the earlier work of Schmalhausen and that of his students is an important event.

This volume is of particular interest because Schmalhausen here argues for a monophyletic origin of the Amphibia from a viewpoint that differs from various recent treatments of this topic, and because he presents many new and speculative ideas. Except for cursory abstracts and privately distributed translations, most of the Russian papers upon which this monograph is based have not before been available in English. The publication of an organized and expanded version of these studies in English is especially useful since it occurs at a time when the origin of the amphibia is again being dealt with in numerous papers and symposia.

A preface is not the place for an extended critique of the multiplicity of anatomical and functional details analyzed in this volume. It is perhaps permissible to note that the method of presentation and argument, particularly of functional hypotheses, is somewhat more general than is now customary in the English literature. More critical is that Schmalhausen makes no mention of much recent non-Russian literature. One wonders, for instance, how some of the early chapters might have been modified if the implications of Francis' work on amphibian intermaxillary glands had been known to the author.

Yet these are minor difficulties of a major work that the author began at an age when most students retire from active investigation. This translation is welcomed precisely because it allows English-reading workers to study and consider an extended version of the studies of I. I. Schmalhausen and his students; it makes available the expression of an important school so that their results may be taken into account in subsequent analyses.

[2] Cf. C. Zirkle, "Death of a Science in Russia," 1962.

Editor's Note

The role of the editor in the preparation of this volume has been to remain as invisible as possible. However, it is necessary to note one change from the Russian original. Figures 8 and 9 of the original work (representations of an Upper Devonian and a Carboniferous landscape) were not technically suitable for reproduction and have been omitted. Thus in the present volume Figures 8 to 165 represent Figures 10 to 167 of the original.

KEITH STEWART THOMSON
Yale University

Introduction

The problem of the origin of terrestrial vertebrates represents a most complex and intriguing division of phylogeny, touching upon many fundamental areas of evolution. The reason for this is that there occurred pronounced change in habitat which led to a complete revision of the animal's organization. The possibility that the vertebrate animal could make the transition from the aquatic to the terrestrial–aerial medium seems almost incredible if one considers the profundity of the necessary rearrangement. Such a transition would actually have been impossible if there had not been unique conditions which first paved the way for emergence into the aerial medium and thence led very gradually to the formation of the coastal type of stegocephalian amphibian from which there later arose both palustrine and wholly terrestrial reptiles and higher vertebrates.

That terrestrial vertebrates arose from fishes became clear with the establishment of the evolutionary theory of Darwin. Ample evidence of a "unified plan" of all vertebrates had accumulated since early in the preceding period of "idealistic morphology." Special significance was attached to the very first embryological researches of Rathke (1825) and von Baer (1828, 1837). They showed a vast similarity in the development of all vertebrate animals. Rathke made the amazing discovery in bird embryos of anlagen of gill slits and arches with arterial arches passing through them. These facts could only be satisfactorily explained in the light of the evolutionary theory. The embryonic gill slits of terrestrial vertebrates serve as undoubted proof of an origin from pisciform ancestors respiring by gills.

Notwithstanding this triumph of comparative embryology, the problem of the origin of terrestrial vertebrates could not advance beyond the most general sense of this conclusion. Comparative morphological information merely permitted the assertion that terrestrial vertebrates arose from primitive fish with a bony skeleton. Morphologists of the past century cited in the latter role the Dipnoi, which, according to embryological evidence, show a striking similarity to the lower terrestrial vertebrates—the Amphibia—in the development of the chondrocranium, in the connection of the palatoquadrate cartilage to the braincase, in pulmonary respiration, and particularly in the structure of the heart and the blood vascular system.

On the other hand, however, in some characteristics—the structure of the jaw and teeth and the composition of the osteocranium—the Dipnoi are so specialized and so different from terrestrial vertebrates that the origin of Amphibia from Dipnoi is out of the question (even in consideration of all the known fossil forms). One can only assert that the Amphibia and Dipnoi arose from some common ancestor.

These common ancestors are to be found among the most primitive of bony fishes.

Only in the present century have the discoveries of paleontologists shed light upon the problem of the origin of terrestrial vertebrates. The contributions of Moodie, Stensiö, Gregory, Watson, and Romer came from work with fossil crossopterygians on the one hand and from remains of Stegocephalia on the other. Of special significance was the work of Watson (1919, 1926b) in which the first detailed comparison of the organization of the crossopterygian fishes and the most primitive Carboniferous Stegocephalia was given. Valuable new data was also obtained by Steen (1934, 1938) who gave a detailed description of the very interesting stegocephalian *Dendrerpeton*, and in addition made a revision of the old descriptions of Stegocephalia made by Dawson (1863), Cope (1882–1887), and Fritsch (1883–1901). In recent times this material has been supplemented by remarkable discoveries in Greenland of Devonian Stegocephalia described by Säve-Söderbergh (1932), and after his untimely death, by Jarvik (1952, 1955). Finally, of no slight significance was the study and description of discoveries of crossopterygian fishes, Stegocephalia, and lower reptiles in the Soviet Union. Among many authors we note here only the outstanding works of P. Sushkin, I. Efremov, and A. Bystrov, the significance of which in resolving our problems could hardly be overestimated.

All this paleontological material should already have permitted the settlement of the problem of the origin of terrestrial vertebrates quite definitely. However, in the fossil remains there are represented only the solid parts of the animal—its skeleton. In some cases the skeletal structure permits one to draw conclusions concerning the associated soft parts, but it is rarely possible to do this with all desirable completeness and reliability. In this case the comparative embryological method occasionally gives additional results which may be utilized for a more complete definition of phylogenetic changes.

Lastly, only by a synthesis of all data, with the biology of modern forms and their paleoecology included, may the whole succession of biological stages in the establishment of terrestrial vertebrates be restored.

In the present treatise material pertaining to different organ systems is elaborated unequally. Principal attention is given to the skeleton. Sense organs are examined only to the extent that their presence is manifest in the skeleton. Such a treatment of the material is dictated by the necessity of comparison with paleontological data. In other respects attention is devoted to certain process of fundamental significance in the transition of crossopterygian fishes to a terrestrial-aerial existence.

I. I. SCHMALHAUSEN

A Bibliography of the More Significant and Available Publications of I. I. Schmalhausen[1]

1905. The development of lungs in *Tropidonotus natrix* (Die Entwicklung der Lungen bei *Tropidonotus natrix*). *Anat. Anz.* Nos. 20–21, 511–520.

1907. The development of the skeletons of the anterior extremities of anuran Amphibia (Die Entwicklung des Skellettes der vorderen Extremität der anuren Amphibien). *Anat. Anz.* **31**, Nos. 7–8, 177–187.

1923. The fundamentals of comparative anatomy. Manual for universities (Osnovy sravnitelnoi anatomii. Rukovodstvo dlya Vyzov). Gosizdat, Moscow and Petrograd. 425 pp.

1925. On the influence on morphogenesis of the extremities of the axolotl by various factors (Weber die Beeinflussung der Morphogenese der Extremiläten von Axolotl durch verschiedene Faktoren). *Arch. Entwicklungsmech. Organ.*, **105**, hft. 3: 483–500.

1926. Problems of death and immortality (Problema smerti i bessmertiya). Gosizdat, Moscow and Leningrad. 92 pp.

1932. The growth of organisms (Rist organizmiv). Medvidav, Kiev and Kharkov. 80 pp. (in Ukrainian).

1934. On the phenogenetics of some morphological characters in domestic fowl (K fenogenetike nekotorykh morfologicheskykh priznakov v domashnikh kur). *Dokl. Akad. Nauk. SSSR*, **2**, No. 5, 311–336.

1937. Modern tasks of phenogenetics (Sovremennye zadachi fenogenetiki). *Izv. Akad. Nauk, Otd. Mat. i Estestv. Nauk. Biol. Ser.* No. 3, 895–906.

1938. The organism as a whole in individual and historical development (Organizm kak tseloe v individualnom i istoricheskom razvitii). Akad. Nauk SSSR, Moscow and Leningrad, 144 pp.

1939. The significance of correlations in animal evolution (Znachenie korrelyatsii v evolyutsii zhiovotnykh). Sbornik in commemoration of A. N. Severtsov, I, 175–230. Akad. Nauk SSSR, Moscow and Leningrad.

1939. The ways and laws of the evolutionary process (Puti i zakono-

[1] In addition to those cited in this volume.

mernostei evolyutsionnogo protsessa). Akad. Nauk SSSR. Moscow and Leningrad, 231 pp.

1946.   The problems of Darwinism (Problemy darvinisma). Gosizdat,
Moscow, 528 pp.

1946.   The factors of evolution: The theory of stabilizing selection (Fac-
tory evolyutsii: Teoriya stabiliziruyushchego otbora). Akad. Nauk SSSR,
Moscow and Leningrad, 396 pp.

1947.   The fundamentals of comparative anatomy (Osnovy sravnitelnoi
anatomii). 4th ed. Sovetskaya Nauka, Moscow, 540 pp.

1949.   The factors of evolution: The theory of stabilizing selection.
(English translation). McGraw-Hill (Blakiston), New York, 327 pp.

1960.   Evolution and cybernetics (in English). *Evolution* **14**, No. 4,
509–524.

1961.   The integration of biological systems and their self-regulation
(Integratsiya biologicheskikh sistem i ikh samoregulyatsiya). *Byul. Mosk.
Obshchestva Ispytatelei Prirody, Otd. Biol.*, **66**, No. 2, 104–134.

1964.   The regulation of morphogenesis in individual development
(Regulyatsiya formoobrazovaniya v individualnom razvitii). Akad. Nauk SSSR,
Moscow, 136 pp.

Contents

CHAPTER 1

Principal Modes of Evolution in Lower Vertebrates

CHAPTER 2

Ecological Conditions That Allowed the Vertebrates to Emerge from the Aquatic Medium into the Air

CHAPTER 3

The Origin of Accessory Respiratory Organs in Fishes and Amphibia

CHAPTER 4

Organization and Position of the Brachiopterygii

CHAPTER 5

The Organization and Position of the Dipnoi

I

Principal Modes of Evolution in Lower Vertebrates

Primitive chordate animals were undoubtedly microphagous, as are both modern tunicates and lancelets. In contrast to modern forms they were undoubtedly also free-swimming nektonic forms. They were, consequently, active planktonivorous animals.

The presence in all chordate animals of a flexible skeletal axis—the notochord—and powerfully built, metameric, lateral body muscles reflects a capacity for rapid movement in the water. These movements were accomplished by means of wavelike flexures of the whole trunk, the effective surface of which was increased by the formation of median fin folds. Modern lancelets have retained this capacity for rapid swimming. However, they utilize this ability only in sudden changes of their resting place in the sand. When the animal is buried in the sand its oral hood projects outward, and detrital particles and small benthic organisms are collected through it. This passive mode of life in lancelets is the result of a definite regression. The presence of a well-developed musculature does not accord with such a mode of life. There can be no doubt that it was inherited from a period of more aggressive activity among ancestral forms. The tunicates underwent an even greater regression. They changed to the modern sedentary life, and then, again, to a free existence, but only in a passive form, as plankton. That the simplicity of organization in this case is epigenetic (a regression) is shown by the structure of the active free-swimming larvae of the Ascidia, which have both a notochord and a central nerve trunk, and (especially) the lateral musculature.

The free-swimming lower chordate animals progressed rapidly and (in the Ordovician and Silurian) gave rise to more highly organized vertebrates. Chordates are not to be found as fossil remains from the Cambrian (when these ancestral forms should have been living) because the absence of a solid skeleton obviously made their preservation impossible. The whole organization of the living lancelets allows one to draw certain well-founded conclusions concerning the structure and mode of life of the primordial chordates

1

which gave rise to the vertebrates. We will emphasize only those essential features of their biology which determined the further mode of progressive evolution.

The existence of a flexible skeletal axis had considerable significance for a rapidly swimming animal. Serving as a fulcrum for the action of the lateral trunk muscles, it afforded at the same time considerable economy in the energy used in swimming. For in lateral flexions of the trunk, the energy expended in bending the flexible notochord is released and utilized in succeeding undulations. The wavelike succession of these undulations is achieved by alternating contraction of individual segments of the lateral trunk muscles. The segmented structure of these particular muscles is the most essential feature of the organization of aquatic chordates, and determined their metamery and progressive evolution as they became the most motile organisms of any given epoch. To this motility was also related the transition to more and more active forms of taking food and the progressive development of the nervous system and sense organs. The lower chordate animals, like many invertebrates, fed on small organisms suspended in the water—plankton. Planktonivorous organisms (e.g., sponges, rotifers, lamellibranchiate molluscs, ascidians, and lancelets) either had adaptations for the utilization of existing water currents or, more often, were able to create controlled currents by the use of ciliated or mucous epithelia. The planktonivorous Crustacea create a strong water current by strokes of appendages provided with tufts of setae. In all cases the water current is guided into special filters in which the particles suspended in the water are trapped. The latter are usually collected by mucous and thereby carried into the oral opening. Modern lower chordates also utilize ciliated epithelia for creating water currents, and mucous epithelia on the endostyle (ventral groove) for agglutinating the particles and transferring them along with the mucous into the pharynx. As in many invertebrates, the water current is used not only for extracting particles of food material suspended in the water, but also as a source of oxygen dissolved in the water. The filter is simultaneously an organ of respiration.

In modern lower chordates the accumulation of detritus and sometimes of plankton takes place only through the activity of the ciliated epithelium without involving muscular action. In immobile or sedentary forms, for the most part, non-nutritious detritus and mud particles are taken up. This creates a considerable overload for the intestine. The pharyngeal cavity with its filter apparatus attains considerable size, the intestine evacuates rapidly, and the nutritious material is poorly utilized. In the more active forms of the remote past, however, there was undoubtedly developed a more effective means of extracting plankton which was of critical importance in further evolution.

Water movement was created in these forms not only by action of the ciliate epithelium, but also by *action of the musculature of the anterior element of the intestine.* By a transverse closure of the oral opening and the branchial slits, the anterior intestine acted alternately as a suction pump, filling the oral cavity with water, and as a force pump driving this water outward through the gill slits. Thus a periodic water current was created, and directed through the branchial apparatus which served on the one hand as a filter for food material and on the other hand as an organ of respiration. The plankton strained out was retained in the pharynx from which it was then carried into the intestine. The use of muscular energy greatly improved the mechanism of extracting plankton since, first, it increased the rate of water filtration and, second, the suction action created a water current so powerful that it could draw along with it many small actively swimming organisms (which were not captured by the ciliary method of filtration). In this, a prerequisite for the much later transition to a predatory way of life was already fulfilled. The transition from these chordates to the present vertebrates was very gradual. The first agnathous vertebrates were also actively planktonivorous animals.

This mechanism of plankton extraction was developed through an increase in the activity of the animals themselves, in particular by improvement of the action of the branchial apparatus in which separate filtration and respiratory elements (gill fringes) were differentiated. The complicated structure of the gill pouches and the strengthening of their skeleton and musculature was accompanied by reduction in the number of gill clefts and by a more compact arrangement of the whole branchial apparatus.

Certain skeletal formations were present in the lower chordates (they are also present in modern forms), but they did not have the more solid tissues such as cartilage, bone, and dentine. Cartilaginous and bony skeletons are new acquisitions of vertebrate animals. Among the lower members of the latter, in the Agnatha, the notochord is supplemented by small cartilaginous arches which are elements of simple vertebrae, serving as some protection for the central nervous system, the spinal chord. In the head region a more solid protection for the brain has evolved in the form of a cartilaginous braincase. In addition, the gill pouches and gill musculature have acquired a firmer support in the form of a system of gill arches. All these supporting structures were present in a rudimentary fashion in the lower chordates also; in the vertebrates, however, they achieved further development as new, more durable, endoskeletal (primarily cartilaginous) structures. The acquisition of highly developed sense organs and the evolution of the brain was of very great significance.

The complex paired structure of the inverted organs of vision first appeared only in vertebrate animals. Also first appearing here were the organs of equilibrium (ears) and the paired olfactory organs (associated in the jawless Agnatha with the hypophysial duct) which were developed progressively.

In the modern fauna, agnathous vertebrates are present only as extremely specialized forms, the lampreys and the hagfishes. The fossil Agnatha were very diversified, however, only forms with fairly strong armor in the dermal skeleton are represented. The discovery of numerous scattered dermal teeth just within the more ancient Silurian deposits (Ordovician) indicates the existence of numerous more primitive forms not having such strong armor and which therefore are not more completely preserved. Many fossil Agnatha were benthic forms. Their remains have long been known but, owing to the difficulty of preparation, their organization was ascertained only in recent times by the use of binocular microscopes and methods of reconstruction of cross sections. As a result of the existence of bony tissue both on the inner surface of the braincase and on the surface of vessels and nerves in closely examined Osteostraci, it has been possible to reconstruct the shape of the brain from the nerves leading off from it, and the structure of the visceral apparatus from its nerves and vessels (Stensiö, 1927). The similarity of their organization to that of modern lampreys turns out to be remarkable. Nevertheless fossil Agnatha prove to be much more primitive forms, lacking the unique specialization of modern cyclostomes.

The most primitive of the Agnatha preserved in the fossil state were the Coelolepida (Fig. 1), animals with well-developed dermal teeth, paired eyes, an unarmed mouth, a hypocercal tail, and sometimes a small anal fin. Among them were very active forms with a fusiform trunk (*Phlebolepis elegans*) and less motile benthic forms with a broad and flat head (*Thelodus*). Evidently the Coelolepida stand at the base of the phylogenetic development of all the Agnatha (Obruchev, 1945). In higher Agnatha the dermal teeth are fused into larger plates with a bony foundation (noncellular aspidine) which usually form a large cranial shield. The most motile of these armored forms were the Heterostraci. They had a streamlined body form (*Pteraspis*), a hypocercal tail, and evidently could swim rapidly. The eyes were placed at the sides of the head, the mouth was located on the ventral side, and anterior to the mouth were the paired olfactory organs, connected to the hypophysis.

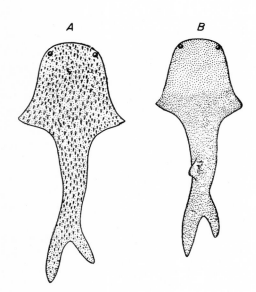

FIG. 1. Primitive Agnatha (Coelolepida —Silurian); *Lanarkia* (A) and *Thelodus* (B). From von Zittel.

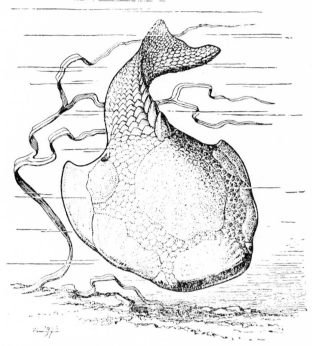

FIG. 2. The heterostracan *Psammolepis venjukovi* (Devonian). From Bystrov, after Obruchev.

There was only one external gill opening. The Heterostraci also changed to a benthic life and the armored anterior part of the trunk became flattened (*Psammolepis*, Fig. 2; *Drepanaspis* and others).

Stensiö (1927) suggested that modern hagfishes originated from fossil Heterostraci, and modern lampreys from Osteostraci, by reduction of the dermal armor and the bony tissue in the endoskeleton.

Thus the cyclostomes may perhaps have had a diphyletic origin. However, the opinions of Stensiö have been criticized by some authors (Severtsov, 1939; Obruchev, 1945, 1948; Balabai, 1956; Bystrov, 1956; and others) and can hardly be maintained at present.

The ancestral relationships of the various Agnatha are now relatively well clarified as the result of studies of the structure of the dermal armor (Gross, 1935; Obruchev, 1945, 1948; Bystrov, 1955, 1956). The Heterostraci are undoubtedly a lateral branch of specialized Agnatha which completely died out.

Of great interest to us is another fairly primitive branch of ostracoderm Agnatha—the Anaspida (Fig. 3). These were free-swimming, quite fishlike forms with a relatively light dermal armor of comparatively small plates of bony tissue (aspidine). The paired eyes were located on the sides of the head; between them was the pineal organ, and in front of the latter a large unpaired nasohypophysial opening. This last fact may not justify one in

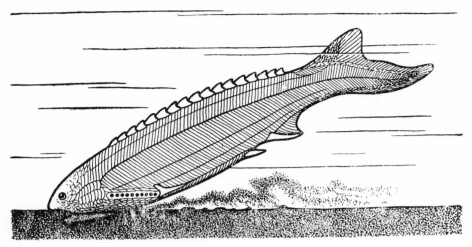

Fig. 3. The ostracoderm *Pterolepis nitida* (Anaspida—Silurian). From Bystrov.

regarding the Anaspida as an ancestral form giving rise to fishes. It was a highly mobile microphage with 6 to 15 pairs of gill clefts on the sides of the anterior part of the trunk. The tail in the Anaspida was hypocercal. A group of specialized benthic forms, the Osteostraci, having a thick cranial shield on the sides of which electric organs were apparently situated, probably originated from the Anaspida. The organization of the Osteostraci has been studied in detail by Stensiö (1927) in particular, who emphasized their exceptional similarity to modern lampreys. For all their primitiveness, however, the Osteostraci were nevertheless uniquely specialized animals and it is difficult to conceive that from the known Osteostraci there could have originated both the Anaspida and also the cyclostomes (as Stensiö suggested). This idea is opposed by the existence of electrical organs in the Osteostraci, and in particular by the appearance of real bony tissue instead of the aspidine which was present in all lower Agnatha including Anaspida (Bystrov, 1956). It is much more likely therefore that the cyclostomes, as did the Osteostraci, arose directly from Anaspida.

In all Ostracodermi the tail had a hypocercal structure. This might indicate the presence of a swim bladder or even lungs (Schmalhausen, 1916a), which would have fully harmonized with life in overheated fresh waters rich in the detritus on which they fed. There is another possibility, however, which is fully established in the particular case of the Devonian psammosteids. In these forms, the arrangement of the branchial plates on the sides of the anteriorly expanded division of the trunk obscured the outer margin. This occurred on the water bed and, according to Obruchev (1945), is explained by the fact that the psammosteids faced into the current at a certain angle to the floor and fed passively in the oncoming mud. This seems very probable to me, particularly if one takes into account the shape of the branchial plates. Moreover, the shape of the caudal fin indicates active movement on the water bed with the oral opening pressed to the floor (i.e., in such a position as

Obruchev illustrates). Bystrov suggests that the Anaspida also fed in the same inclined position, burrowing in the soft ground of the bed. This, so it seems, also explains the inclined position of the series of external gill openings, which in this case are all located at the same level above the bottom; the nasohypophysial openings were also located at the same level, which prevented the blocking of these openings by mud. Perhaps the hypocentral shape of the caudal fin of all Ostracodermi is explained by a similar mode of feeding on the floor of the waterways.

The Anaspida undoubtedly had large highly distensible oral cavities. Obviously they drew into the mouth and swallowed large masses of detritus. The adaptation of the mouth to sucking action could also have led to temporary attachment to other benthic animals (e.g., *Bothriolepis,* Fig. 4 by which they could have been carried about, as in the modern forms. This could have led to the semiparasitic feeding habits of the cyclostomes (Bystrov, 1956). In any case the presence of large oral cavities in the Anaspida indicates a more active feeding with an intake not only of detritus, but probably of small living organisms also.

In all these pisciform creatures the mouth had no special support (except plates in the dermal skeleton). The branchial apparatus was situated directly behind the buccal orifice, supported by the arches of the endoskeleton. In modern fishes one of the primitive pairs of gill arches is transformed into a prehensile oral apparatus, the jaws. Action of the musculature of the branchial apparatus created a strong water current which drew in plankton suspended in the water as well as small free-swimming organisms. The latter were then retained by the action of the anterior pair of visceral arches and were sometimes macerated and swallowed. The progressive development of jaws with a covering of dermal teeth was accompanied by a transition from feeding on

FIG. 4. Representative armored fishes (Antiarchi); *Bothriolepis* (Devonian) and several ostracoderm *Endeiolepis*. From Bystrov.

plankton to feeding on nektonic organisms. Along with the progressive development of paired olfactory organs this also led to the establishment of primitive jawed vertebrates, i.e., true fishes. Feeding on nekton required not only an increase of speed (since *Pteraspida* and *Anaspida* were mediocre swimmers), but also precision of movement. This was achieved by the development of unpaired dorsal fins as rudders for horizontal movements, and paired fins as rudders controlling movements in the vertical plane. This likewise required progressive development of the organs of equilibrium which were supplemented by a new, horizontal, semicircular canal.

Unpaired fins in the form of simple folds were also present in the free-swimming lower chordates. They were gradually developed in the caudal region in which they gave rise to the powerful tail and in some cases an anal fin. Distinct dorsal fins were also developed in jawed vertebrates. The development of unpaired fins meant an increase of the surface of effective water resistance during active swimming. In the posterior part of the body it was the source of motive power; and in the anterior part it was utilized for controlling the direction of movement. From the same folds, paired fins should also inevitably have been developed as horizontal surfaces providing lift for supporting a heavier body in the water and for regulating movements in the vertical plane. *Paired fins obviously arose repeatedly in the form of unpaired folds along the sides of the free-swimming nektonic animals.* Such folds apparently were present in certain small enigmatic chordates, *Jaymoytius*, from the lower Silurian (Ordovician). They could have originated completely independently in the Agnatha. Of the anaspid group such unpaired lateral folds were described in *Endeiolepis*. Fig. 4 (Stensiö, 1939). It is likely, however, that the lateral lobes on the body of *Thelodus* should be regarded in the same light. Turning to modern fishes we find paired fins, the pectoral and the pelvic, which in no way can be linked to the above folds already fully formed in the Agnatha.

The most ancient members of the jawed vertebrates were the Acanthodii (Fig. 5), fossil remains of which are known as far back as the Silurian. The Acanthodii were contemporaries of the specialized agnathous vertebrates

FIG. 5. A representative acanthodian—*Euthacanthus* (Lower Devonian); lateral and ventral views; between the spines of the pectoral and pelvic fins there are five other pairs of fin spines. From Romer.

and could have originated only from the more primitive forms living in the Ordovician which have left their traces only in the form of small scattered dermal teeth.

The Acanthodii were small fishes having skin protected by very small scales. These scales had a laminated denticle-like structure, as if forming a transition between the simple dermal teeth of Agnatha and the large and complex cosmoid and ganoid scales of bony fishes.

The organization of the Acanthodii is comparatively well known owing to the researches of Watson (1937). These fishes were very primitive in many respects and show the fundamental organization of all the higher forms. They are nevertheless not lacking in certain unique specializations appearing in the development of a passive means of defense, which later attained extreme development in other members of the Placodermii. The most characteristic specializations were the powerful spines on the anterior margins of all the fins (with the exception of the caudal). It is interesting that in addition to the spines in the two dorsal and one anal fin there was also a paired series of two to seven spines arranged along the sides of the trunk (Fig. 5). Of these spines, the posterior spines at least were supplied with dermal folds taking the role of the pelvic fins. Undoubtedly the paired series of spines may be regarded as remnants of fins which were developed in continuous lateral fin folds. The latter were acquired from ancestors of the Acanthodii quite independently of the paired folds of the Agnatha.

In the Acanthodii we first encounter the typical structure of the visceral apparatus of the jawed vertebrates and, moreover, in its most primitive form (Fig. 6). The branchial arches consisted of four divisions each, in which the tips of the arches were directed forward as in the Teleostomi (and not backward as in the cartilaginous fishes). The maxillary arch was divided into only two divisions, which functioned as the jaws (the palatoquadrate and the mandible). They consisted of a cartilaginous foundation which was covered by superficial ossifications. The hyoid arch apparently did not take part in the strengthening of the jaws and still played the role of a branchial arch. Correspondingly, the spiracle was well developed and functioned as a gill slit. All the gill slits, including the spiracle, were covered by branchial folds with dermal bones, i.e., had gill opercula, cf. Fig. 6 (Watson, 1937). However, the gill operculum of the hyoid arch was the largest (Stensiö, 1947). Throughout their organization the Acanthodii resemble modern cartilaginous (sharklike) fishes although features similar to the higher fishes are also found in them, and bony tissue was indeed well developed. The other more specialized members of the Placodermi, the Arthrodira, developed strong external armor and stronger ossification of the endoskeleton also, but the general organization nevertheless was very close to the sharklike fishes (*Macropetalichthys;* Stensiö, 1925). The skull, platybasic in form, was mainly cartilaginous, but on all sides the cartilage was covered by complete perichondrial ossification. Since the braincase completely enclosed the brain, one can restore not only the skull structure and the brain with its sense organs, but also the exits of the cranial nerves and the position of many vessels and other organs. The

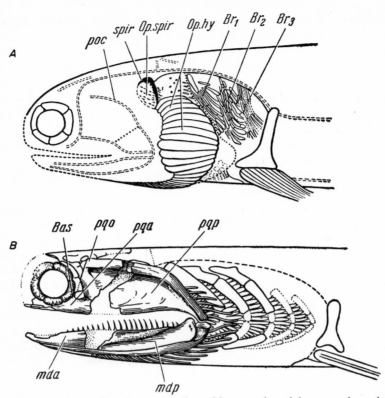

FIG. 6. Head of *Euthacanthas* showing the lateral line canals and the opercula on the mandibular, hyoid, and branchial arches (A). The visceral skeleton of *Acanthodes* (B). Br_1—Br_3, Opercular ossifications; *Bas*, basal articulation; *mda, mdp*, anterior and posterior ossifications in the lower jaw; *Op.hy*, operculum of hyoid arch; *Op.spir*, spiracular operculum; *poc*, preopercular canal; *pqa, pqo, pqp*, anterior, dorsal, and posterior ossifications in the palatoquadrate cartilage; *spir*, spiracle. From Watson, with revisions by Stensiö.

paired appendages of Arthrodira, e.g., Macropetalichthyida, had a primitive structure with many parallel rays. In all these characteristics the Arthrodira show exceprional similarity to elasmobranch fishes. In these fishes, and especially in the Antiarchi (Fig. 4), dermal armor in the form of a cranial shield and a pectoral girdle of large shieldlike plates attained very pronounced development, and this undoubtedly was a specialized characteristic which in its extreme form was incompatible with adequate mobility. Therefore these forms also shifted to benthic life. On the other hand, the more mobile members of the Arthrodira, the Macropetalichthyida and Stegoselachii, evidently gave rise (by reduction of bony tissue and external arnor) to modern cartilaginous fishes (Stensiö, 1925).

We are interested, however, in the particular case of another line of evolution from primitive fishes close to the fossil Acanthodii. It is without question that the higher bony fishes (the Teleostomi) are closely related to the latter.

The Osteichthyes appeared in freshwater deposits of the Devonian, show-ing quite a diversity of forms at first. They all show a certain organizational similarity to the Acanthodii and their kinship with them is very likely. A more precise connection can not yet be established, however, owing to gaps in the geological record. Transitions between the most ancient members of the Osteichthyes and the Dipnoi, the crossopterygians or the chondrostean fishes, were not preserved either. The most ancient members of these groups are, however, rather similar in their organization and have probably de-scended from one stock (Fig. 7). The sudden appearance of a diversity of forms is probably explained by their evolution in conditions not favoring the preservation of fossil remains. In the Silurian, according to the Romer hy-pothesis, fishes pursued by the merostomes (Gigantostraca) migrated upward along river courses, became good swimmers, and after the extinction of the Gigantostraca again descended to the lowlands of rivers and lakes (Romer, 1933). We only note that the main features of their organization are related to the mode of life and the general trend of evolution of the Osteichthyes.

. A number of progressive modifications clearly distinguish all Osteichthyes from the Acanthodii. The complex cranial armor of the Acanthodii was re-tained in the bony fishes in the form of a more limited number of typical bony plates in the skull and pectoral girdle. On the body, small dermal teeth fused into groups and were transformed into thick cosmoid scales of rhombic shape, articulated to each other and forming a very firm but nevertheless flexible dermal armor. In the most recent forms the scales have become thinner, rounded, and have gradually lost their dentine layer. On the jaws the teeth formed a more or less powerful armor, allowing a change-over to predatory life. On the hyoid arch operculum, covering the first gill slit in the Acanthodii, only a little more bone developed, but the operculum itself spread out and came to cover the whole branchial apparatus laterally. The paired appendages were limited to two pairs but acquired great mobility.

The Osteichthyes at once began divergent evolution. Some of them pro-gressed rapidly and gave rise to a great diversity of fossil and modern ray-finned fishes. The others retained a relatively primitive organization and

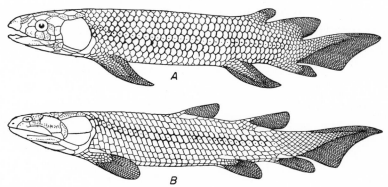

FIG. 7. The typical Devonian dipnoan *Dipterus* (A) and the crossopterygian *Osteolepis* (B).

survived to modern times as "living fossils" (Brachiopterygii—*Polypterus* and *Calamoichthys*). Some bony fishes changed to feeding on vegetable food along with which were seized, crushed, and eaten the Crustacea and molluscs also contained in the waterweed. The inner series of teeth fused together and formed laminated macerating dental plates. These are the dipnoan fishes, surviving in the form of several representatives to the present day (*Ceratodus*) and in some cases shifting over anew to predation in restricted environments (*Protopterus*).

Finally, of especial interest to us is another group of relatively primitive extinct fishes—the crossopterygians (Crossopterygii). These freshwater predators first appeared as three allied branches: Coelacanthiformes, Porolepiformes, and Osteolepiformes. The first branch, having arisen in fresh waters, then passed over to life at sea, attained some dominance, but became specialized and almost died out in the late Mesozoic. Only one representative of this branch of crossopterygian fishes has survived to the present time—*Latimeria chalumnae*—recently found in the Indian Ocean. The latter two branches are more closely allied to each other (Rhipidistia). The Coelacanthiformes stand somewhat apart and in some respects are perhaps close to the Brachiopterygii. In other very distinctive features of organization, however, the crossopterygian fishes form a quite natural group of related organisms. This applies first of all to the structure of the paired appendages. They take the form of elongated and evidently very mobile fins with narrow bases and articulated skeletal axes. The fins had a well-differentiated musculature. Such fins undoubtedly could have served as organs of support in locomotion along the water floor, for creeping over undergrowth, and even for crawling out on the shore. In this respect crossopterygian fishes were similar (and undoutedly related) to dipnoan fishes. They are also linked to the latter in the presence of organs of aerial respiration—the lungs. These organs are present along with gills and serve as auxiliary organs which supplement or even replace the organs of aquatic respiration during deficiency of oxygen in the water. The latter condition is usually found in overheated fresh waters, especially in the presence of large amounts of decomposing organic substances. Crossopterygian fishes, like the Dipnoi, elaborated their organization under the difficult conditions of the Devonian climate and in some respects developed in parallel.

2

Ecological Conditions That Allowed the Vertebrates to Emerge from the Aquatic Medium into the Air

In the Silurian and Devonian, almost all the land was lifeless desert. Only along the shores of freshwater basins were there dense growths of primitive herbaceous terrestrial plants. Appearing in the Silurian (and perhaps in the Cambrian also), the unique psilophytes, the first arrivals of a terrestrial flora, were small plants, 20–30 cm high, attached to the soil by small rhizoids and extending upward by dichotomously branched stalks. These primitive plants had neither real roots nor leaves. In the Lower Devonian, fairly numerous representatives of these forms (species of *Rhynia, Horneophyton* and *Psilophyton*) were already flourishing, sometimes reaching 50 cm in height. In the Lower Devonian several more complex members of the psilophytes also appeared, such as *Asteroxylon*, which had branches covered with small scalelike leaves. These plants probably gave rise to the later lycopods (Lycopsida), which, like the early ferns (Pteropsida) and horsetails (Articulata), followed the psilophytes in the Upper Devonian. However, all these were still mostly herbaceous plants. In the Upper Devonian there were only scattered representatives of the first arborescent species, the primitive lepidodendrons and sigillarias. Only in the wet climate of the Carboniferous did the filicales, lepidodendrons, sigillarias, arborescent horsetails (calamites), and numerous herbaceous ferns grow abundantly and the first representatives of the bryophytes (Bryopsida) appear. Since the possibility of animals populating dry land was determined at all times by the presence of plants, the first terrestrial animals, consequently, could only have appeared in the Silurian.

At present, in the coastal surf zone of the sea numerous Crustacea, mainly amphipods (Amphipoda) and crabs, always accumulate in masses of vegetable detritus. It is likely that it was always thus in the past. Of the typical Crustacea, however, the only fully terrestrial forms that originated were the

13

Isopoda. Their predecessors were evidently the Syncarida, known from Devonian freshwater deposits. On the other hand, the early Palaeozoic Eurypterida gave rise to the richest variety of terrestrial Chelicerata, beginning with the scorpions and ending with the spiders and a multitude of mites. The scorpions are known from the Silurian; many spiders have been described from the Carboniferous, and mites were living as early as the Devonian. All these invertebrates could have served as food for the early terrestrial vertebrates. However, obviously the tracheate arthropods were of greatest significance in this regard. Their origin is associated with the emergence into the aerial medium of annelid worms. On the sea coasts, during high tide, numerous seaweeds were cast up, the wet decaying masses of which formed favorable conditions for vegetable-detritus-feeding invertebrates cast up or actively crawling there. Annelid worms formed a large part of these forms. The low shores of freshwater basins that were inundated at times when algae were flourishing were probably of even greater significance for the emergence from the water. Algae, bacteria, and lower fungi penetrated the wet soil and annelid worms and other small invertebrates moved in later. The first detritus-feeding terrestrial invertebrates, the tracheate arthropods, probably arose from the earthworms (Gilyarov, 1949). The fossil remains of primitive Tracheata (Protracheata) are known from the Cambrian (*Reynella, Xenusion,* and *Ayshenia*).

In the Silurian the millepedes appeared, which in the Devonian, and especially in the Carboniferous, attained a great diversity and great abundance. In the Devonian, wingless insects (Apterygota) had already appeared; primitive winged forms (Order Archaeoptera) are known from the Upper Devonian, and many groups of Palaeoptera and Neoptera from the Carboniferous. Thus, even in the Devonian, there was a potential food base which could support the first terrestrial vertebrates in their emergence from the water and their occupancy of the land. The worms, the primitive Tracheata, and the myriapods were obviously of fundamental significance in this respect. In the Late Devonian and Carboniferous the insects were added to this.

I. CLIMATIC CONDITIONS IN THE DEVONIAN AND CARBONIFEROUS

After the Caledonian Period of mountain building, in the Devonian, a continental climate with pronounced daily and seasonal fluctuations in temperature was established on the great expanses of dry land. Only in the equatorial zone was there a humid climate without marked seasonal changes. Erosion phenomena, unfavorable to the flourishing of vegetation, prevailed on the surface of the earth. The water level in rivers and freshwater basins fluctuated seasonally. Many waters dried out completely in summer. The terrestrial (then exclusively coastal) vegetation froze in winter and its remains were easily washed away by spring floods. Aquatic vegetation perished during the summer through the heating and drying up of the waters. Thus an increased accumulation of vegetable remains formed, which served as good "fertilizer" for ground waters and coastal soils. This promoted a dense development of the flora and fauna of these waters. Abrupt, periodic, seasonal changes of the water level and temperature corresponded to the seasonal changes of the conditions of organic life expressed in periods of flowering and dying-down. For longer-lived animals, such as fishes, there was, there-fore, an alternation of optimal conditions with ample food and periods of very difficult conditions. The latter were created not so much as the direct result of high water temperatures in the summer season, as by the indirect effects of this heating. The high temperature accelerated the decay of vege-table remains and led to a rapid reduction of the oxygen content of the water. This caused a massive mortality among the animals which decayed in the water, and a complete reduction of free oxygen. Survival under such con-ditions was possible only through the development of adaptations for the respiration of atmospheric air. With drying out of the waters, the only means of escape was by burrowing into wet ground (hibernation) and enduring until a return of the water, or migration on the chance of reaching new waters. The latter was a difficult task at any time, but could be accomplished at night in humid air, and even then only for very short distances. In the dry air of the Devonian such migration could hardly have taken place on a large scale.

In the Carboniferous, the humid, warm and therefore equable climate in which there were no pronounced seasonal variations, could have favored such migrations. The rich vegetation would have maintained and increased the atmospheric humidity. There was actually no necessity for migrations in search of water, however, since broad expanses were given over to extensive swamps and permanent waters. This, however, did not mean that for aquatic animals, and above all for fishes, optimal conditions had set in. A vast quan-tity of organic material accumulated in the shallow waters, underwent decay, and led to an almost total elimination of free oxygen from the water. Respira-tion of atmospheric air was the sole means of sustaining existence.

II. REASONS FOR THE EMERGENCE OF FISHES INTO THE AERIAL MEDIUM

As a rule fishes are so adapted to the aquatic habitat that under normal conditions it is impossible for them to emerge into the air. The direct cause of emergence onto dry land cannot be either the search for food material, intense competition, or flight from pursuing predators. None of these, or other factors, could have led to positive changes if there had not been some form of organizational preconditioning in the form of adaptations for aerial respiration and locomotion on the ground. A fundamental cause is found in the contrast of ecological conditions, by which aerial respiration as well as temporary emergence from the water is accomplished in modern fishes.

Auxiliary aerial respiration occurs *in freshwater fishes living in well-heated waters with a large quantity of organic material*. In such waters there is occasionally observed, at least periodically, an acute shortage of oxygen, and fishes living in such waters are obliged to rise to the surface and take in atmospheric air which is then expelled through the gill slits or sometimes through the intestine (in *Misgurnus fossilis*, and in some South American catfishes—*Callichthys, Doras, Loricaria,* and *Plecostomus*). This led to the formation, in the most diverse fishes, of adaptations for the retention of atmospheric air in various auxiliary cavities, usually located in the dorsal parts of the branchial apparatus. The walls of these cavities are folded, and supplied with venous blood from the fourth afferent branchial artery. Such organs are present in *Ophiocephalus* and *Anabas scandens*. Similar "labyrinth" organs are present also in some Osphronemidae (*Polyacanthus, Osphronemus,* and *Trichogaster*) to which also belong certain curious aquarium-cultivated macropods. In some catfishes (*Clarias* and *Heterobranchus*) there are dendritically branching highly vascular formations situated at the ends of the first and second gill arches and included in the dorsal outgrowths of the branchial cavity. In some herrings (*Chanos salmoneus*) there is a spirally twisted organ connected to the fourth gill arch. Similar formations have been described in some Osteoglossidae and Characinidae.

Sometimes air is engulfed into spacious air sacs. Thus, in *Amphipnous cuchia* (Symbranchidae) and in *Saccobranchus* (Siluridae) there are paired sacs running from the first gill slit posteriorly along the vertebral column (under the lateral muscles of the trunk) to the tail (*Saccobranchus*). They are supplied with venous blood from the fourth afferent gill artery. In *Amphipnous* this apparatus of aerial respiration is fundamental since gill filaments are present only on the *second* gill arch. Swim bladders are sometimes utilized for aerial respiration. In *Polypterus* there are paired swim bladders (lungs) with short airducts and a muscular "laryngeal" slit on the ventral side of the esophagus. In *Lepidosteus* and *Amia* the swim bladder is unpaired and opens by short ducts into the dorsal surface of the esophagus. There is a "laryngeal" slit with a sphincter. The bladder wall in these cases has an alveolar structure. The lungs are even more differentiated in dipnoan fishes. The unpaired lung of *Ceratodus* and paired lungs of *Protopterus* and *Lepidosiren* communicate by a short duct and a muscular laryngeal slit to the ventral wall of the esophagus. These organs are supplied by venous blood from the fourth afferent gill artery.

In all these cases the auxiliary organs serve for breathing atmospheric air during shortages of oxygen in the water. Since this condition is observed as a rule at high temperatures and high content of readily decomposed organic materials in the waters, all the above adaptations characterize fishes living in tropical fresh waters.

The presence of organs of aerial respiration, however, does not yet indicate a capacity for their use on land and, on the other hand, the absence of such special organs does not mean that the fish could not breathe in the aerial medium. Dipnoan fishes, which have the most highly developed lungs, never crawl out on land. *Ceratodus* uses aerial respiration only when in the water. In the dry season, when the waters in which *Protopterus* lives dry out, they burrow into the mud, enclosing themselves in a cocoon of hardened mucous and respire atmospheric air. Only during this quite passive endurance of an unfavorable season is *Protopterus* in need of utilizing the lungs outside of water.

Many fishes having labyrinth organs, and also *Polypterus, Amia,* and *Lepidosteus* which have alveolar swim bladders, never leave the water. On the other hand, *Periophthalmus* (of the Gobiidae) is one of the fishes most adapted to survival on dry land. Crawling ably and even climbing up on tree trunks, it does not have special distinctive organs for aerial respiration. *Periophthalmus* utilizes dermal respiration. Dermal respiration is probably also used by most catfishes which can spend a fairly long time out of water even if they lack special organs of aerial respiration.

The fishes with air sacs (*Amphipnous* and *Saccobranchus*), which crawl out of the water on to the shore in herbaceous growth and can live for days on land, are well able to survive out of water. Some catfishes burrow in the dry season of the year (*Clarias lazera*) and spend several months out of water, while at night they creep about in search of food. *Doras* migrates from drying-up waters and spends whole nights on the way to new water sources.

The possibility of adaptation to life on dry land is determined not only by the presence of organs of aerial respiration or by the capacity for dermal respiration, but also by the capacity for crawling onto the shore and locomotion on land. Thus for example, the modern Dipnoi, notwithstanding the presence of lungs, could not have transferred to life on land due to the complete unsuitability of their appendages for movement on land. Many fishes utilize their paired appendages as organs of support during movement along the water bed (*Polypterus,* Gobiidae, and Lophiidae). There are also fishes which can not only crawl out of the water but can also move about and travel a fairly considerable distance from the shore.

Some gobies (*Gobius* and especially *Periophthalmus* and *Boleophthalmus*), blennies (*Blennius*), snake-eyes (*Ophiocephalus*), climbing fish (*Anabas scandens*), some catfishes (*Clarias, Doras,* and *Saccobranchus*), and also *Amphipnous,* crawl out of the water. Some of them, when the waters dry up, actively migrate in search of other water. Such migrations are usually accomplished at night.

Almost all these adaptations characterize, as we have said, freshwater fishes, mainly of the tropical zone, which are obliged, at least periodically, to contend with a lack of oxygen in the water. Seawater is always supplied with oxygen in its upper layers, and accordingly marine fishes do not possess special organs for aerial respiration. Some marine fishes, however, habitually crawl out of the water. This is associated with the opportunities for feeding in the surf zone, the high tide zone and, in particular, in mangrove thickets. The fishes most adapted to locomotion on dry land are the gobies, *Periophthalmus* and *Boleophthalmus*, which find an abundance of food in the form of small fishes, crustaceans, annelids, etc., on the shore after ebb tide. They do not have special organs for aerial respiration but dermal respiration is well developed. Capillary blood vessels penetrate the epithelia of the oral and branchial cavities and the cutaneous epidermis of the whole body surface (of *Periophthalmus*), in which there are sometimes found special respiratory papillae (*Boleophthalmus;* Harms, 1934). In this case emergence onto the land is not caused by a shortage of oxygen in the water. It also cannot represent a direct attempt to seek food on land. In any case, in the beginning, there must have been only passive entry into the high tide zone with a gradual adaptation toward enduring the low tide period until the new tide. Later, with successful survival, the decidedly favorable conditions for feeding on the small marine animals stranded on the shore during low tide became important.

In our review of the problem of the transition of freshwater fishes into the aerial environment this mode of adaptation is readily disposed of. All freshwater fishes acquired aerial respiration, and later the capacity to crawl out of the water, solely in correlation with shortage of oxygen in heated waters.

First on the route to this adaptation was the special acquisition of aerial respiratory organs. Apparently however, these organs usually did not become sufficiently developed to provide the fish with oxygen when it was totally absent from the water. In such a situation the fish either remained submerged or, by swimming on the surface or crawling onto the shore, used its capacity for dermal respiration in the air. Simple crawling out on to the shore was the most reliable means of self-preservation for fishes in situations in which oxygen was completely absent from the water.

The particular conditions of existence in warm fresh waters also led (in the Devonian) evidently to the establishment in fishes of respiration (first pulmonary and then dermal) of atmospheric air, to crawling out on the shore, and finally, to complete adaption to terrestrial life.

3

The Origin of Accessory Respiratory Organs in Fishes and Amphibia

I. LUNGS

A characteristic of all bony fishes is the presence of hydrostatic organs in the form of swim bladders which, in the lower fishes, are connected by a duct to the anterior part of the esophagus. Atmospheric air can penetrate to the bladder along this duct. The additional development of the duct in higher fishes, the gases filling it, entering from the blood, and the regulation of the internal pressure are the results of gradual development of this organ as a hydrostatic structure. The presence of this apparatus limits the freedom of action of the fish in vertical planes and therefore it is minimized in some of the better swimmers. It even disappears through disuse in many benthic fishes.

On the other hand, in some lower fishes the swim bladder also serves another function—it is an organ for respiration of atmospheric air. This function cannot be regarded as epigenetic. Obviously the very initiation of the swim bladder is particularly connected with its significance as an accessory organ of respiration. Testifying in support of this is the history of the origin of bony fishes. As we have already stated, they were all first found in fluvial deposits of the Devonian. In shallow fresh water there was perhaps no special need for a hydrostatic structure. In warm fresh waters, however, a shortage of oxygen undoubtedly was felt periodically and fishes were obliged to take in atmospheric air. This air was forced outward through the branchial apparatus, but any of it that was retained in reserve in the oral or pharyngeal regions served as a supplemental supply of oxygen which could be utilized for survival of the fish in the water. Folds of the mucous membrane and saclike diverticula in the dorsal part of the pharyngeal region facilitated such retention of air. The history of the development of the swim bladder in sturgeons plainly shows its origin to be from precisely such folds of mucous membrane of the anterior intestine (Makushok, 1913).

In most fishes the swim bladder develops as an unpaired formation in the

19

dorsal wall of the anterior intestine. In adult fishes the swim bladder is located in the dorsal part of the abdominal cavity directly under the vertebrae, and its duct is usually attached to the dorsal wall of the esophagus. The blood supply of the bladder in bony fishes is provided by branches of the intestinal coeliac artery and veins passing partly to the portal vein of the kidney and partly into the posterior cardiac vein. One may, however, doubt the primitiveness of these relationships, since in the lower bony fishes the duct is found in another position with a different blood supply and sometimes the swim bladder is paired. We can leave the resolution of this question open since it is not closely relevant to our purpose. We also might consider that the swim bladder of fishes perhaps had different origins. However, we have sufficient ground to presume that it arose, in freshwater fishes at any rate, as an auxiliary organ of respiration in an environment of warm water with a periodic shortage of oxygen. It also recently acquired significance as a hydrostatic organ. In marine waters the latter was the sole function. In our considerations the respiratory function of the swim bladder and the history of its development in lower bony fishes is of special significance.

Leaving the aspect of the respiratory function of the swim bladder of some bony fishes as having apparently been acquired epigenetically, we shall dwell simply on the structure and function of this organ in the bony "ganoids" (Holostei and Brachiopterygii) and in the Dipnoi. In *Amia* and *Lepidosteus* the swim bladder has alveolar walls and a definite respiratory function. In *Amia* it is supplied with venous blood from the last, fourth, afferent branchial artery and passes arterial blood into the Cuvierian duct. In *Polypterus* the swim bladder is paired and opens into the esophagus on the ventral side. It is supplied with blood from the hindmost pair of afferent branchial arteries and passes the blood on to the base of the large veins (vena hepatica and ductus Cuvieri) in close proximity to the sinus venosus of the heart. The right pulmonary sac is considerably longer than the left and is moved toward the dorsal side. This indicates a likely mode of origin of the unpaired swim bladder of the Holostei and Teleostei from the paired situation through reduction of the left one; traces of this can be seen in *Acipenser* and *Amia* (Ballantyne, 1927). In view of the exceptional primitiveness of the Brachiopterygii which, according to Goodrich (1928), stand closest to the fossil Palaeoniscidae, one can accept the hypothesis of the dual origin of the swim bladder of teleost fishes as very likely. The blood supply of the bladder in *Polypterus* definitely indicates its original respiratory function. A similarity of position, the same blood supply, and the clearly marked respiratory function, is shown also in the lungs of the dipnoan fishes. In *Protopterus* and *Lepidosiren* it is a paired (more precisely, bipartite or bilobed) organ; in *Ceratodus*, embryonically unpaired. It is connected by the pneumatic duct to the ventral wall of the esophagus, however, it is located on the dorsal side of the abdominal cavity as is the swim bladder in other fishes. From the course of the blood vessels it is clearly evident that the dorsal position of the lungs in dipnoan fishes is the result of their shift from the ventral side around the right side of the esophagus to the dorsal side (Fig. 8). In this arrangement the origi-

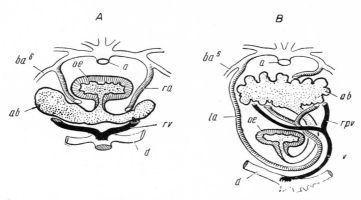

FIG. 8. Pulmonary blood system in *Polypterus* (A) and *Ceratodus* (B). *a*, Aorta; *ab*, lung; *ba*[6], fourth aortic arch; *d*, Curvierian duct; *la*, *ra*, left and right pulmonary arteries; *oe*, oesophagus; *rv*, *rpv*, right pulmonary vein; *v*, pulmonary vein. From Goodrich.

nal right lung is located on the left, and the original left lung on the right. As a result of this shift the left pulmonary artery (arising as does the right from the last pair of arterial arches) skirts in a loop the whole esophagus to the right in order to reach the ventral surface of the lung. The right pulmonary artery supplies the dorsal surface, reaching it by the shortest route (since the lung was rotated to the right). The pulmonary vein also skirts the esophagus to the right to reach the sinus venosus of the heart. This whole picture shows the mode of transformation of the originally ventral and primitively paired respiratory organ, the lung, to the unpaired hydrostatic organ of higher fishes.

The position and blood supply of the lungs of Amphibia are quite similar to their disposition and blood supply in *Polypterus* and the Dipnoi. They communicate with the ventral wall of the anterior intestine (pharynx) through the laryngeal slit and are supplied with blood from the hindmost pair of arterial arches. The pulmonary vein descends, as in the Dipnoi, directly to the left auricle. There can be no doubt of the homology of these organs. However, the Amphibia could only have inherited these organs from crossopterygian fishes. The kinship of the latter to the Dipnoi, and probably to *Polypterus* also, leads one to think that in crossopterygians there actually were paired lungs. However, in the marine Coelacanthidae (as in other higher fishes also) they were naturally transformed into swim bladders, seen also in *Latimeria*. The history of the embryonic development of lungs in Amphibia gives further evidence for our evaluation of the modes of orgin of this organ. In the amphibian embryo the lungs arise as paired diverticula on the ventral wall of the pharynx directly posterior to the anlagen of the hindmost pair of gill pouches (Götte, 1905; Makushok, 1913). These diverticula are connected to an unpaired prolonged furrow representing the rudiment of the airduct (laryngotracheal passage). According to the very credible hypothesis of Spengel (1904), during the history of bony fishes the lungs also arose from the posterior pair of gill pouches in which engulfed air was retained.

II. EXTERNAL GILLS

External gills are present in the larvae of various fishes. We are interested here, however, in the features of fish gills linking them most closely to the crossopterygian fishes. Therefore we will limit ourselves to an examination of the external gills in *Polypterus* and in the Dipnoi.

In the larvae of *Polypterus* there is one pair of large external gills. Their central axis is supported by a short cartilaginous ray, and bears pinnately arranged gill lamellae. These gills develop as processes on the hyoid arch (Kerr, 1907). In the larvae of *Protopterus* and *Lepidosiren* (Fig. 9) there are four pairs of pinnately branched external gills on four gill arteries. Remnants of the three posterior pairs of external gills are also retained in adult *Protopterus* (neoteny; analogous to some urodele Amphibia).

The external gills of the Dipnoi are to a high degree similar to the external gills of Amphibia. Their blood circulation is also similar. Of their homology there is no doubt. In contrast to the Dipnoi, in Amphibia there are only three pairs of external gills, belonging to three anterior branchial arches. In the larvae of *Ranodon*, however, rudiments of external gills also occur on the fourth arch (Schmalhausen, 1955b). There is also an indirect indication of the existence of a fourth gill in the fossil *Dvinosaurus* (Sushkin, 1936). All this evidence gives grounds to the supposition that in general, in the ancestors of the Tetrapoda and Dipnoi, i.e., in crossopterygian fishes, there were also four pairs of external gills on four gill arches.

The question of the origin of external gills is resolved by an analysis of their development and structure in the lower Tetrapoda.

The external gills arise in the form of protuberances in the region of the primordial gill partitions. In these rudiments vascular loops from the corresponding arterial arches grow. Between the forks of the vascular loops are developed, anteriorly and posteriorly, a series of corresponding anastomosing rudiments in the anterior and posterior gill filaments, playing the role of afferent and efferent arteries in the external gills. The anastomosis extends into the filaments, forming afferent and efferent vessels in each filament. Later, among these vessels a complex net of superficial anastomoses is developed in which gas exchange takes place. The filaments of the external gills develop day by day precisely as do the filaments of the internal gills in fishes. They have the same fundamental plan of structure, with distal afferent arteries lying between the bases of the filaments and giving off branches along the inner margin of each lobe, and proximal disposition of the efferent gill arteries gathering blood from the branches and running along the outer

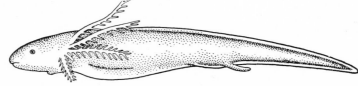

FIG. 9. External gills of the larva of the dipnoan fish *Lepidosiren*. From Kerr (1907).

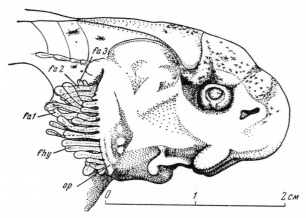

FIG. 10. External gills of the larva of a sturgeon *Acipenser stellatus*. *fa 1–fa 3*, Rudiments of gill filaments on the hyoid semibranch; *op*, rudiment of gill operculum. From O. I. Schmalhausen.

margin of the filament. The axis of the external gills is very short in the primitive urodele Amphibia from mountain streams (*Ranodon* and *Onychodactylus*), and shows straight prolonged gill septa which are simple diverticula from its dorsal margin. The musculature of the external gills develops similarly to the musculature of the branchial septum of fishes (mm. interbranchiales). It is also interesting to note that in the Amphibia, as in the fishes, the musculature of the branchial filaments is frequently attached to the walls of the afferent blood vessels and probably facilitates blood circulation to the gill filaments, or at least takes part in its regulation.

According to all the morphological information the external gills of Amphibia are outgrowths of the branchial septa of fishes, along with their internal gill filaments. The gill septum proper of the Amphibia is the ventral part of the septum of fishes on which the branchial filaments are reduced. The external gills of Amphibia are undoubtedly homologous with the internal gills of fishes (Schmalhausen, 1954, 1955b). While the external gills of Amphibia, and consequently of Dipnoi and crossopterygians also, are the results of transformation of the internal gills, the question then inevitably arises: how was this transformation accomplished and what were its causes?

In the early stages of development of fishes external gills occurred rather frequently. This is seen first during extension of embryonic development in the egg membranes (in the Selachii and some bony fishes) and, second, early in the hatching of larvae from eggs provided with only a small reserve of yolk. In the latter case a larva with an undeveloped branchial apparatus is obliged to lead an independently active way of life. In such larvae there occurs an acceleration of the development of the primordial gill filaments (branchions) and an adaptation arises facilitating flow of water around them even before the establishment of the complex respiratory mechanism of the visceral apparatus. The first transformation in this line is noted in sturgeons. Here the rudiments of branchial filaments, branchions, are developed up to the formation of the gill operculum and they then extend outward in the young larvae (Fig. 10). The external position of the branchions allows a free flow of water and consequently gas exchange on their surface. The cover of ciliated epithelia of the oral cavity and branchial arches, the motion of the larva itself, and later also the action of the gill operculum and membrane, favors a more rapid flow of water. In sturgeon larvae the gill operculum is delayed in development, especially on its dorsal side. Even in the fingerlings of the large stellate sturgeon the branchial operculum leaves the distal ends of the branchia, situated on the upper part of the gill arch, free. The free ends of the dorsal gill filaments are continuously bathed in fresh water. They function as a type of external gills, washed by water externally, but not by water drawn through the oral cavity. Observations show that in the fingerlings of sturgeon the regular rhythmic action of the whole visceral apparatus is discontinued during swallowing of food, and that a very rapid vibration of the gill operculum and membrane occurs instead, inducing a current of water drawn from the dorsal side under the operculum and escaping downward from under the membrane. Thus, during the capturing and swallowing of food, when the normal driving mechanism of respiration of the internal gills cannot operate, a type of external gill respiration mechanism is turned on. These observations (O. I. Schmalhausen, 1955) shed light on the biological significance of external gills. The external gills function without interruption and that gives them clear predominance during the transition to feeding on larger items, i.e., to the predatory life. Prolonged swallowing of captured prey does not disturb normal respiration by the external gills during the time when respiration by internal gills is extensively interrupted.

The external gills of Amphibia were consequently developed as far back as the fishes (in the series Chondrostei to Brachiopterygii to Crossopterygii) as special larval respiratory organs. From their early development and uninterrupted function they acquired significance as the main organs of respiration in the life of predatory larvae. In their origin, however, they only represent a complex of primordial branchions (when anlagen) of the internal gills. Originally their distal ends protruded from under the undeveloped branchial operculum. Along with the gradual development of the external gills these primordial branchions extended farther outward as a consequence of the extension of the dorsal part of the branchial septa bearing them. This part of the septum thickened and gave rise to a separate process, the body (stem) of the external gill, on which the typical gill filaments are distally (ventrally) arranged in two series.

The branchions developing ventrally from the external gills gave rise in fishes to definitive gill filaments, i.e., to the internal gills of the adult animal. In Amphibia, with the emergence of the adult animal onto land, the definitive gills lost their function and degenerated. Therefore, the external gills are developed only in the larval stage. Of the definitive gills, only the supporting structures were retained, the branchial arches and branchial septa with their vessels and muscles.

In the transition from a predatory life to feeding on plankton or vegetation and animal detritus, the predominance of external gills was lost. This was particularly due to their increased vulnerability. Therefore, in anuran Amphibia internal gills of a special type with a dendroid form of branching were developed epigenetically, and the external gills degenerated.

The primary origin of external gills is related, as we saw, to the accelerated development of the larvae and the rudiments of their gill filaments. This was caused by the reduction of the yolk reserve in the egg and the corresponding reduction of the extent of the vitelline vessels which have the function of embryonic respiration organs in fishes. The reduction of egg size, probably accompanied by increase in their number, could have resulted from an increased predation on the larvae or their high mortality in difficult situations (during summer shortage of oxygen in the waters owing to the decay of organic substances). Acceleration of development can also be stimulated by a seasonal limitation of favorable conditions. In a continental climate the larvae were only provided with suitable temperature, a good supply of oxygen, and an optimum of nutrition in the spring. The rapid development of larvae and the establishment of pulmonary respiration before the onset of summer-fall shortage of oxygen was probably a matter of life and death in the Devonian. External gills were therefore developed as special larval organs serving as the main organs of respiration just before the summer "metamorphosis" when they gave up the respiratory role (during oxygen shortage) to the internal gills, the retention of which was all the more necessary since the Devonian waters were probably covered by ice in the winter.

4

Organization and Position of the Brachiopterygii

In turning to known forms of the fishes which gave rise to terrestrial vertebrates we cannot avoid the question of the position of *Polypterus* among the lower bony fishes (Osteichthyes). At the time of Huxley (1861), *Polypterus* and *Calamoichthys* were placed along with the Osteolepidoti and Coelacanthini in one suborder, the Crossopterygii. An attempt was even made to show the possibility of an origin of terrestrial vertebrates from forms close to the Polypterini (Klaatsch, 1896). A review of this matter by Goodrich (1907, 1909) showed that such a combination was based on overly superficial similarities and at present should be rejected (cf. also Berg, 1940). Goodrich (1928) assigned the Polypterini to the Palaeoniscidae and placed them, consequently, in the Actinopterygii. Stensiö (1921) segregated them into an independent order, the Brachiopterygii, placing it between the orders Crossopterygii and Actinopterygii. The latter interpretation undoubtedly portrays their phylogenetic relationship correctly. In reality the Polypterini occupy a quite isolated position among the lower bony fishes (Osteichthyes). The absence of fossil remains of any similar forms removes any possibility of establishing their affinity to other Osteichthyes. On the other hand, they retained certain primitive features of organization characteristic of all lower fishes, for example, the spiracular opening, the well-developed spiral valve in the intestine, and the conus arteriosus of the heart. On the other hand, they show some peculiarities of the organization of the lower Actinopterygii, for example, the covering of rhombic scales of the ganoid type, the location of the nostrils on the dorsal side of the head, and in particular the brain structure, the forebrain with a basal thickening, but with epithelial roof and without hemispheres, the cerebellum with valvula cerebelli, characteristic of the Actinopterygii, projecting into the cavity of the midbrain. This indicates an undoubted affinity to the Actinopterygii.

However, at the same time there are also some similarities to the Crossopterygii, Dipnoi, and even the Tetrapoda. They are evinced first in the presence of paired lungs connected to the ventral wall of the anterior intestine,

26

the existence of a well-developed conus arteriosus, some similarity in the structure and function of the paired fins, and finally in the structure of the skull and its visceral skelton. The limbs and their girdles are built in the same general way as in all primitive Osteichthyes and do not show any special similarity that unites them to the Crossopterygii, but nonetheless the extra development of the clavicle allies them to the latter (as also to Dipnoi and Tetrapoda). The base of the paired fins, especially the pectoral, is a pronounced lobe covered by scales and containing a well-developed internal skelton and the musculature of the free elements. [In the Actinopterygii these parts are less developed and are covered by the lateral part of the body; the free outer stalk of the fin consists only of its dermal skeleton (lepido-trichia).] In this there is some similarity to the crossopterygians (and the Dipnoi) which led previous systematists to include the Polypterini with them into one order. This similarity is explained by identity of function; the paired fins of Polypterini are very mobile and are not only rudders for swimming, but are in part also organs of support in movement along the water bed. There is also a general similarity in structure of the skull (Fig. 11). The skull

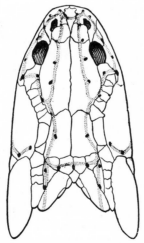

FIG. 11. Skull of *Polypterus,* dorsal view showing canals of seismosensory organs.

roof is built on the same plan as in the Crossopterygii and is even somewhat reminiscent of the skull roof of primitive Embolomeri. This similarity, however, is quite superficial. Thus, for example, the "parietal" bones of *Polypterus* are the result of a progressive fusion of the supratemporals and intertemporals. A series of small bones, the middle one of which covers the spiraculum, runs backward from the orbit. The cheek area, covered by a large bone representing the result of the fusion of the preoperculum with the squamosal, is of unique aspect. The same is sometimes seen in the Osteo-lepida also. The branchial operculum proper consists of two bones, the operculum and the suboperculum. The interoperculum, characteristic of the

Actinopterygii, is absent in Polypterus and the Crossopterygii. Between the forks of the lower jaw in *Polypterus,* as in the Crossopterygii, is one pair of large gular plates (in Rhipidistia there is, in addition, a series of small lateral plates). The skull is underlaid by a large parasphenoid and a pair of anterior vomers. The palatal complex consists of three pterygoid bones (endoptery-goid, ectopterygoid, and metapterygoid) and a small autopalatine which pro-vides a broad but nonetheless movable connection to the base of the skull. The hyomandibular does not play the dominant role in the jaw suspension which is so characteristic of the Actinopterygii. There is no symplectic; apparently this was never present in Crossopterygii either. Besides such primitive characters, which ally the Polypterini to the Crossopterygii, we note, however, the existence of some characteristics of evolution on the route of the Actinopterygii (mainly in the brain structure), some features of progressive development (especially in the complete ossification of the vertebral column), and some characteristics of distinctive specialization (division of the dorsal fin into separate fins; the unique caudal fin, gephyro-cercal in the dorsal half and diphycercal in the ventral half).

On the whole we should recognize a certain degree of distinctness in the Polypterini fully justifying their separation as a distinct suborder, Brachi-opterygii. We would emphasize their primitiveness among the lower Oste-ichthyes, but at the same time we may also note a similarity to the Crossop-terygii and lower Tetrapoda, which is of some importance to our problem of relationships. The paired lungs, supplied with blood from the last arterial arch, the well-developed conus arteriosus, the poorly developed hyostyly, the firm connection of the maxillary bones (premaxilla and maxilla) to the skull roof bones, some similarity in the structure of the skull roof and the construction of the palate, the occurrence of a pair of large gular plates, the more highly developed ventral divisions of the gill arches (hypo- and cerato-branchials), some solidification of the structure of the branchial operculum, and the supporting function of the paired fins, may be noted. All these organi-zational characteristics were of no little importance, representing transfor-mations similar to those which lead through the crossopterygian fishes to the terrestrial vertebrates. In addition, there are also similarities to the Crossopterygii in some of the more specialized characteristics. Jarvik, in particular, states that the dermal bones of *Polypterus* are similar in both appearance and structure to the bones of the Coelacanthini (Jarvik, 1942, 1947, 1954).

Notwithstanding these undoubted indications of the affinity of *Polypterus* to the crossopterygian fishes, and consequently to the ancestors of terrestrial vertebrates, all nonetheless emphasize also its distinctness, and its affinity to the ray-finned fishes. Of especially great significance is the differentiation in brain structure between the crossopterygians and the ray-finned fishes. In this most important organizational characteristic *Polypterus* is similar to the Actinopterygii. *Polypterus* is also allied to the Actinopterygii in the arrange-ment of the lateral line system of the head.

5

The Organization and Position of the Dipnoi

In some respects the Dipnoi are more primitive than the Polypterini, and they are perhaps even more primitive than the known Crossopterygii. In their organization evolution has proceeded along the same lines that were shown in the establishment of the terrestrial vertebrates. However, the phenomena of early and quite unique specialization are even more sharply portrayed in them.

The primitiveness of the Dipnoi is displayed in the retention of a permanent notochord even in the modern forms. The vertebrae consisted only of cartilaginous elements, the bases of the upper and lower arches. In the most ancient members (*Dipterus*), the skull roof consisted of a very large number of small bones (Fig. 12). Between the rami of the lower jaws there were, as in crossopterygians also, a pair of large gular plates. The dermal bones and dermal scales consisted of true bone and had an outer layer of typical cosmine (as in Crossopterygii also). There was a well-developed conus arteriosus in the heart. There was a spiral valve in the intestine. There was a cloaca. The nostrils were located ventrally on the edge of the mouth. In addition, there are also numerous, more specialized characteristics in the Dipnoi linking them to the crossopterygian fishes and to the original terrestrial vertebrates, the Amphibia. Above all there were organs of aerial respiration, lungs, which were supplied with blood from the last pair of arterial arches. The blood returned from the lungs along the pulmonary vein to the left side of the sinus venosus and entered into the left part of the auricle. In the heart itself there was an adaptation in the conus arteriosus for separating the currents of arterial and venous blood. Arterial blood was mainly carried through anterior arches of the aorta to the carotid artery and the dorsal aorta, and venous blood was sent through the posterior arches to the respiratory organs, the gills and lungs (Fig. 13). Even in such details as the structure of the elongate valve of the conus arteriosus of *Protopterus* there is seen an astonishing similarity to modern Amphibia. The venous system, with the unpaired ventral vein, with the first appearance of the posterior half of the vein and well-developed dermal vessels, is also similar. There is also some similarity in the structure of the paired appendages. They possess an articulated skeletal axis with

29

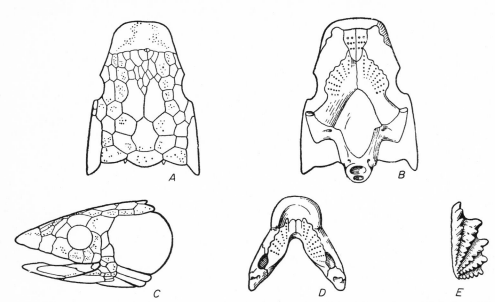

FIG. 12. Skull of the Devonian dipnoan fish *Dipterus*. Skull roof from above (*A*); below (*B*); showing palatine teeth and side (*C*); lower jaw (*D*); tooth plate of lower jaw (*E*). Dots on dermal bones indicate exit of canals of the seismosensory organs. From Goodrich.

lateral rays and distinctive musculature in the axial element of the fin. The fin is very mobile and is articulated to the girdle by a single basal section of the skeleton. These fins are organs of support for the movement of the fishes along the water floor and through aquatic plant growth. In the skull there is a distinctly developed autostyly, the palatoquadrate is fused to the skull axis, and the hyomandibular is reduced (Fig. 14). Moreover, in the Dipnoi there are well-developed hemispheres in the cerebrum, and the brain structure in general greatly resembles the structure in the Amphibia (especially in urodeles). All these resemblances lead to an attempt to find the ancestors of terrestrial vertebrates among the Dipnoi. However, even the most ancient

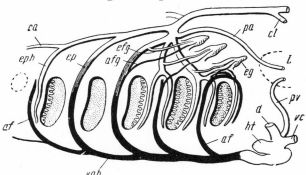

FIG. 13. Circulatory system of *Protopterus*. *af*, Afferent branchial artery; *afg*, afferent artery of external gill; *ca*, carotid artery; *cl*, subclavian artery; *d*, Cuvierian duct; *efg*, efferent artery of external gill; *eg*, external gill; *ep*, arterial arch; *eph*, hyoid artery; *ht*, heart; *L*, lung; *pa, pv*, pulmonary artery and vein; *vab*, arterial trunk; *vc*, inferior vena cava. From Goodrich.

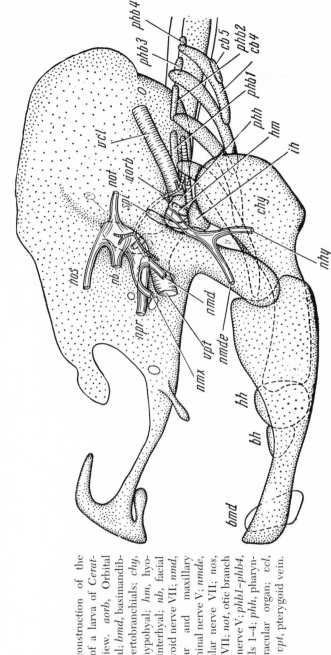

FIG. 14. Reconstruction of the chondrocranium of a larva of *Ceratodus*. Lateral view. *aorb*, Orbital artery; *bh*, basihyal; *bmd*, basimandibular; *cb4*, *cb5*, certobranchials; *chy*, ceratohyal; *hh*, hypohyal; *hm*, hyomandibular; *ih*, interhyal; *nb*, facial nerve VII; *nhy*, hyoid nerve VII; *nmd*, *nmx*, mandibular and maxillary branches of trigeminal nerve V; *nmde*, external mandibular nerve VII; *nos*, suborbital branch VII; *not*, otic branch V; *npr*, profundus nerve V; *phb1–phb4*, pharyngobranchials 1–4; *phh*, pharyngohyal; *spi*, spiracular organ; *vcl*, lateral head vein; *vpt*, pterygoid vein.

31

of their representatives possess specialized characteristics which quite exclude the possibility of their evolution toward the Tetrapoda.

This specialization was linked to a transition to vegetable nutrition, which
led to a reorganization of the dental system and to considerable modification
in the jaw structure. The inner series of teeth were fused at their bases and
formed a laminate dental plate on the palate (Fig. 12) (the pterygoid) and
on the lower jaw (the prearticular, to which the coronoids were probably

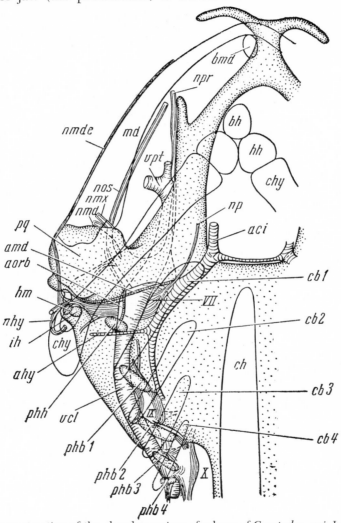

FIG. 15. Reconstruction of the chondrocranium of a larva of *Ceratodus*. *aci*, Internal carotid
artery; *ahy*, hyoid artery; *amd*, mandibular artery; *aorb*, orbital artery; *bh*, basuhyal; *bmd*, basimandibular; *cb1–cb4*, ceratobranchials 1–4; *ch*, notochord; *chy*, ceratohyal; *hh*, hypohyal; *hm*,
hyomandibular; *ih*, interhyal; *md*, lower jaw; *nhy*, hyoid nerve; *nmd*, *nmx*, lower and upper
branches of trigeminal nerve; *nmde*, mandibular branch of hyomandibular nerve VII; *nos*, supraorbital nerve VII (lateralis); *np*, palatine nerve VII; *npr*, orbitoprofundus nerve V; *phb1*,–*phb4*,
pharyngobranchials 1–4; *phh*, pharyngohyal; *pq*, palatoquadrate; *vcl*, lateral head vein, *vpt*,
pterygoid vein; *VII, IX, X*, ganglia of facial, glossopharyngeal and vagus nerves.

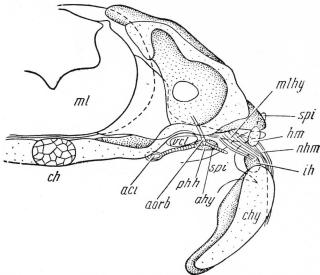

FIG. 16. Reconstruction (from cross sections) of part of the otic region of a larva of *Ceratodus*. Side view. *aci*, Internal carotid artery; *ahy*, hyoid artery; *aorb*, orbital artery; *ch*, choana; *chy*, hyoid; *hm*, hyomandibular; *ih*, interhyal; *ml*, prolongation of the brain; *mlhy*, m. levator hyiodeus; *nhm*, hyomandibular nerve VII; *phh*, pharyngohyal; *spi*, position of the spiracular organ; *vcl*, lateral head vein.

fused). The outer series of teeth which was arranged on the maxillary bones (premaxilla and maxilla) above and on the dentary below in fishes and terrestrial vertebrates disappears in the Dipnoi. The bones bearing them were correspondingly reduced. In the Devonian Dipnoi the anterior part of the skull formed a bony shield, probably consisting of the fused premaxillae, maxillae, and nasals. In the most recent forms this shield disappears altogether. In the most ancient Dipnoi there was still a dentary bone (but without teeth): in the modern *Ceratodus* its rudiment is present, but in other Dipnoi it had disappeared altogether. The dental plates with their alternating fan-shaped series of dental protuberances served for macerating aquatic plants. Along with the vegetable matter Mollusca and Crustacea accompanying it were also chewed and swallowed. As a result, the powerful crushing apparatus with laminate ridged teeth of modern Dipnoi was developed. Autostyly reached a much more marked development than in the Tetrapoda (complete merging of the palatoquadrate with the braincase) and of the suspensorium (hyomandibular) there remained only a rudimentary cartilage (in *Ceratodus*, Figs. 14, 15, and 16).

All this was associated with specialization for feeding and consequently with adaptive divergence at an early stage in the evolution of the forms which approached the closest relationship to the most ancient crossopterygian fishes. Resemblances in the organization of dipnoan fish and Amphibia are portrayed in parallel evolution on the basis of the gradual development of pulmonary respiration and some other biological distinctions of the common ancestors of the dipnoan and crossopterygian fishes.

6

The Organization of the Crossopterygian Fishes and Their Basic Biology

The crossopterygian fishes are characterized by a certain number of primitive features. The permanent notochord forms the principal part of the spine and only in the higher representatives was it surrounded by bony vertebral centra (the hypocentra). The dermal bones of the skull and the dermal scales, from the thick rhombic to the thin cycloid scales, consisted of bone with a covering of cosmine (Fig. 17) (just as in the Dipnoi). The skull had the typical arrangement of dermal bones, fairly numerous in the nasal region, in which there was a tendency toward their fusion with the jaw bones (similar to that seen in the Dipnoi). Between the rami of the lower jaws a pair of large gular plates was located and, at the sides, some small plates passing posteriorly to the gill membrane connected with the gill cover (suboperculum and operculum).

All these are primitive characteristics connecting the crossopterygian fishes to the oldest Dipnoi and also, by many transitions, to the original terrestrial vertebrates. The nostrils lay at the side of the head, close to the rim of the mouth. Lungs were present. The mobile appendages had a scale-covered central lobe supported by a skeleton consisting of an articulated axis with lateral rays. No doubt they functioned not only as rudders for swimming, but also movable organs of support for moving over the water bed, crawling through vegetation, and even for climbing out onto the shore.

Crossopterygian fishes appear first in the freshwater deposits of the Devonian, in the form of two well-marked branches, the Rhipidistia and the Coelacanthini. The first branch contains more primitive forms, closely allied to the terrestrial vertebrates (Fig. 18). It is characterized by the presence of internal nostrils, that is, choanae. The second branch is a specialized group of forms lacking internal nostrils. They arose in fresh water, later passed to the sea, reached some predominance, and almost vanished in the late Meso-zoic. At the present time only one living representative of this branch of crossopterygian fishes survives, *Latimeria chalumnae*, found not long ago in

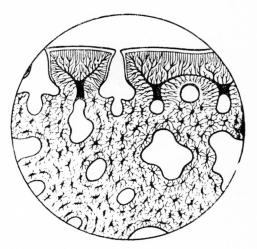

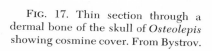

FIG. 17. Thin section through a dermal bone of the skull of *Osteolepis* showing cosmine cover. From Bystrov.

the waters of the Indian Ocean off the coast of the Comoro Islands. The Coelacanthini occupy an isolated position in some respects; perhaps they are close to the Brachiopterygii. However, on the basis of their general structure, all the crossopterygian fishes form a quite natural group of related organisms. The most distinctive feature of their organization is the division of the skull into two parts, movably articulated with each other (Figs. 19 and 20). The anterior division, the ethmosphenoid, contained the olfactory organs and the anterior part of the brain with the organs of vision. The posterior division, the otico-occipital, contained the organs of hearing (and equilibrium) and the posterior part of the brain. Both divisions were ossified, in primitive forms, as solid blocks. The notochord passed through the base of the posterior division of the skull and its anterior end extended into the anterior division. It formed a powerful but nonetheless flexible connection between the two units of the braincase. Otherwise the two units were connected by the joint developed around the notochord, between the sphenoid anteriorly and the anterior surface of the antotic portion of the skull posteriorly (Figs. 20 and 21). In all the most ancient crossopterygian fishes (*Porolepis, Osteolepis, Eusthenopteron,* and *Diplocercides*) both divisions of the braincase are completely ossified, so that the ethmosphenoid and otico-occipital represented

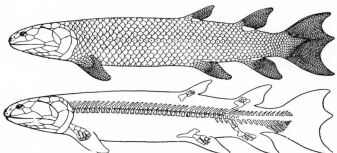

FIG. 18. *Eusthenopteron,* an Upper Devonian crossopterygian fish.

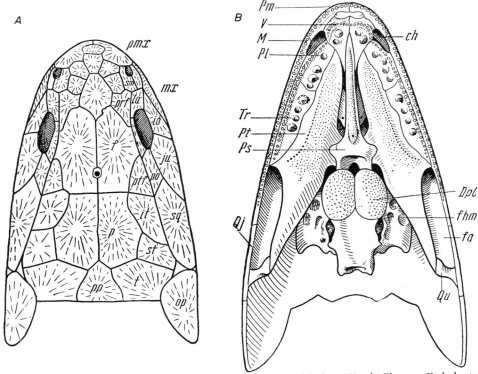

FIG. 19. The skull of *Eusthenopteron* from above (A) and below (B). *ch*, Choana; *Dpl*, dental plate; *f*, frontal bone; *fa*, opening for jaw muscle; *fhm*, exit for hyomandibular nerve; *io*, infra-orbital bone; *it*, intertemporal bone; *ju*, jugal bone; *la*, lachrymal bone; *M, mx*, maxilla; *op*, operculum; *p*, parietal bone; *Pl*, palatine bone; *Pm, pmx*, premaxilla; *po*, postorbital bone; *prf*, prefrontal bone; *Ps*, parasphenoid; *Pt*, pterygoid; *ptf*, postfrontal bone; *Qj*, quadratojugal; *Qu*, quadrate; *sm*, lateral rostral bone (septomaxilla); *sq*, squamosal; *st*, supratemporal; *t*, tabular; *Tr*, ectopterygoid; *V*, vomer. From Jarvik.

two large, single, unpaired skull elements. In *Eusthenopteron*, portions of the skull wall in the auditory region remained cartilaginous. In the late Devonian Coelacanthidae, cartilage was also retained in other regions of the skull; bone was laid down separately, in the ethmoid and the sphenoid in the anterior division, in the large paired pro-otics, the unpaired basioccipi-tal and supraoccipital, and sometimes in the paired exoccipitals posteriorly. The same bones (in front of the paired exethmoids) were also retained in. the modern *Latimeria*.

The large and broad palatoquadrate was also completely ossified, at least in the Rhipidistia. In the Coelacanthini the middle section of the palato-quadrate was reduced; anteriorly there was a distinct autopalatine, and posteriorly, two bones, a dorsal metapterygoid and epipterygoid, and ven-trally a quadrate. These same bones are also present in the modern *Lati-meria*, in which even the cartilage in the pterygoid region is interrupted. In

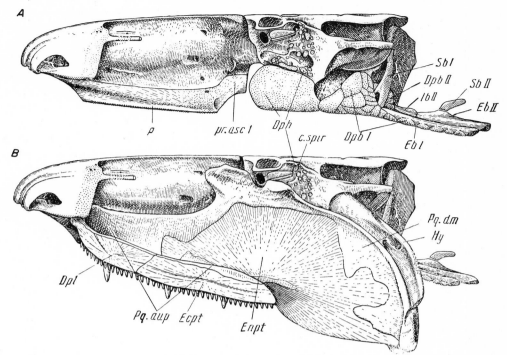

FIG. 20. Braincase of *Eusthenopteron*. Lateral view (A) and showing palatine arch and suspensorium (B). *c.spir*, Spiracular canal; *Dpb*, dental plates of gill arches I and II; *Dph*, dental plate of hyoid arch; *Dpl*, palatine bone; *Eb*, epibranchial; *Ecpt*, ectopterygoid; *Enpt*, entopterygoid; *Hy*, hyomandibular; *IbII*, infrapharyngobranchial; *P*, parasphenoid; *Pq.aup*, *Pq.dm*, anterior and posterior ossifications of palatoquadrate; *pr.asc.1*, ascending process of parasphenoid; *Sb*, suprapharyngobranchials I and II. From Jarvik.

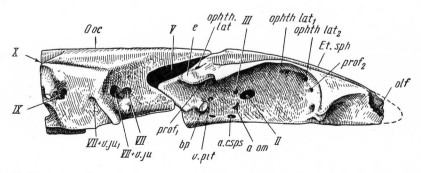

FIG. 21. Braincase of *Nesides* (Devonian). *a.csps*, Exit of internal carotid artery; *a.om*, exit of orbital artery; *bp*, basipterygoid process; *e*, processus antoticus; *Et.sph*, ethmosphenoid; *olf*, olfactory cavity; *Ooc*, otico-occipital; *ophth.lat*, opening for opthalmic nerve VII; *prof₁*, opening for profundus nerve V; *prof₂*, efferent opening for same nerve; *v.pit*, exit for pituitary vein; *II*, *III*, *V*, *VII*, *IX*, *X*, openings for optic, occulomotor, fifth, seventh, ninth, and tenth nerves; *VII+ v.ju*, canal for hyomandibular nerve and lateral head vein. From Stensiö.

the Rhipidistia and in the Palaeozoic Coelacanthidae the palatoquadrate had
a dual connection to the ethmoid region and two connections to the sphenoid
area of the skull—a basal articulation to the processus basipterygoideus of the
skull and, a little higher, a movable connection of the upper end of the
processus antoticus (Figs. 20, 21, and 22) to the skull in front of the exit of
the trigeminal nerve. In the more recent Coelacanthidae (and in *Latimeria*,
Fig. 22) the basipterygoid articulation has disappeared. However, both the
dual connection to the ethmoid region and both connections of the palatoquadrate to the postorbital region of the braincase passed over into the terrestrial vertebrates. The palatoquadrate of crossopterygian fishes was covered
with rows of dermal bones. Anteroventrally there was the dermopalatine, and
behind it, the ectopterygoid and then the very large and broad entopterygoid.
In the lower jaw all the typical bones which were present in the most ancient
Tetrapoda were developed. Meckel's cartilage was ossified posteriorly in
the shape of the articular, and further forward it remained unossified and was
covered by a series of dermal bones, the dentary, and below it, the angular,
preangular, postsplenial, and splenial. On the inner side lay the very large
prearticular (goniale) and, above it, several coronoids. There was a full complement of dermal bones in the braincase and the cheek region of the skull
which, in the main, also passed to the terrestrial vertebrates. Only the structure of the skull roof in the olfactory region was unique. In the most primitive
forms (*Osteolepis* and *Porolepis*) there was a solid rostroethmoidal shield,
and in the later forms (*Eusthenopteron, Holoptychius,* and *Latimeria*) there
were many small nasal, tectal, and rostral bones. Of these only one pair of
nasal bones and a pair of small lateral rostrals (the septomaxillaries) passed

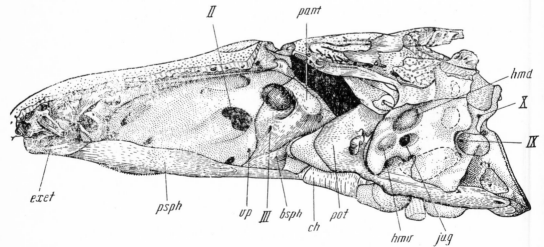

FIG. 22. Braincase of modern *Latimeria*. *bsph*, Basisphenoid; *ch*, notochord; *exet*, ectethmoid;
hmv, hmd, articular facets for ventral and dorsal heads of hyomandibular; *jug*, canal for hyomandibular nerve and lateral head vein; *pant*, processus antoticus; *pot*, otico-occipital (articulation
with ethmosphenoid); *psph*, parasphenoid; *vp*, exit of pituitary vein; *II, III, IX, X*, nerve exits.
From Millot and Anthony.

to the terrestrial vertebrates. There was a joint in the skull roof corresponding to the division of the braincase into two sections with a movable articulation in between (Fig. 20). In the anterior division there were, in addition to the ethmoid shield, the frontal and circumorbital bones, as well as the connected bones of the cheek region (squamosal, preoperculum, quadratojugal, and jugal), and the upper jaw (maxilla and premaxilla). In the posterior division were the remaining bones of the skull roof. The dorsal suture extended transversely between the frontals and parietals and was further connected to an elongated suture between the postorbital and the squamosal on one hand, and the intertemporal and supratemporal on the other hand. This terminated above the operculum lateral to the tabular. The spiracle lay in this suture between the squamosal, intertemporal, and supratemporal. A similar suture was also present in the embolomerous Stegocephalia, between the postorbital and squamosal on the one hand, and the intertemporal and supratemporal on the other hand. It terminated lateral to the tabular at the otic notch. Here we adhere to the long-established homology of the bones and do not accept the interpretation suggested by Westoll (1943b) based on the assumption that the pineal foramen had a fixed position, i.e., that in both crossopterygian fishes and in terrestrial vertebrates it was located between the parietal bones. This is contradicted by a number of facts (Schmalhausen, 1950a), particularly by the arrangement of the canals of the seismosensory organs which, as is well known, are always connected to definite "canalized" bones. The arrangement of the canals in the most ancient terrestrial (Stegocephalia) is exactly the same (Fig. 31) as in crossopterygian fishes. From this one can only conclude that the pineal foramen of crossopterygian fishes was shifted backward in the terrestrial vertebrates from the region of the frontal bones to the region of the parietals (within certain limits such shifts are known both in crossopterygian fishes and in Stegocephalia, in which this opening sometimes occupies an almost intermediate position). Such a shift is associated with an overall development of the hemispheres of the forebrain which causes this division of the brain to move backward. It is interesting that the floor of the skull is underlaid by paired vomers anteriorly, and a median parasphenoid along the base of the anterior division of the braincase. There was a small hypophysial foramen in the posterior part of the parasphenoid. The parasphenoid did not reach under the posterior part of the braincase, of course, owing to the movable articulation with the anterior section. Under the anterior otic region lay a pair of dental plates, however (Fig. 19), which according to Jarvik (1954) are the dental plates of the pharyngohyal, and in both the higher fishes (Holostei-Teleostei) and in the Stegocephalia these were probably fused to the parasphenoid and formed its expanded posterior section with the posterior ascending processes.

The pectoral girdle of crossopterygian fishes was covered with a series of dermal bones which were connected dorsally to the skull roof. The ventral part was covered by the clavicle and an unpaired interclavicle, and on the ossified scapular region lay the large cleithrum which was connected to the skull roof (extrascapula = postparietal and tabular of terrestrial vertebrates) by means of the anocleithrum, supracleithrum, and posttemporal. We find these same bones again in our Stegocephalia (*Eogyrinus* = *Pteroplax*). In *Latimeria*, as in terrestrial vertebrates, the connection of the girdle to the skull roof was lost.

The paired appendages of crossopterygian fishes had an articulated axis with lateral rays which were arranged biserially in Porolepiformes and Coelacanthini, and mainly on the anterior margin of the axis in the Osteolepiformes. The latter, uniseriate type of fin skeleton greatly resembles the pentadactyl limb of the terrestrial vertebrates (Fig. 29). The single basal element articulating with the girdle is undoubtedly homologous with the proximal bone of the limbs of Tetrapoda (the humerus in the anterior limb and the femur in the posterior limb) and both of the succeeding elements are fully comparable to the forearm and foreleg (thus the ulna and tibia correspond to elements of the main axis of the fin of crossopterygian fishes).

As for the structure of the vertebrae, it should first be noted that in many forms a permanent notochord was retained; in others there was complete development of the centra. Details of the structure of the vertebrae are still insufficiently worked out. In some cases, however, considerable similarity to primitive Stegocephalia is found. Thus in *Eusthenopteron* the notochord was enclosed below by large wedgelike hypocentra which contributed to the bases of the neural arches above. Between the latter ossified interdorsals were inserted also. An entirely similar arrangement was present in the vertebrae of the earliest Stegocephalia, the Ichthyostegidae (Fig. 33). The only difference is seen in the shape of the neural arches and spines, and in the articular processes (zygopophyses) which were well developed in *Ichthyostega*, and were present only in the form of vestigial processes in *Eusthenopteron*. In some Osteolepida the vertebral centra were ossified as complete rings surrounding the notochord, quite the same as in certain primitive tetrapods—the Lepospondyli.

The division of the braincase into two interarticulated blocks (Figs. 20 and 21) is characteristic of all crossopterygian fishes (including the modern *Latimeria*) and does not occur in any other group of vertebrate animals. This unique structure is an essential feature of the organization of the crossopterygian fishes and must have had great functional significance in their biology. It has been suggested that the movable joint with attached ligaments served as a shock absorber, protecting the posterior section of the braincase from concussions in seizing large prey. This did not protect the anterior part of the braincase and the anterior section of the brain, however, since shocks would pass from the jaws to the anterior division in particular. Obviously shock-absorbing occurs in the fairly complex connection of the palatoquadrate and skull roof to the braincase since the jolt was received directly by the jaws. On the other hand, the presence of strong subcephalic muscles indicates that active depression of the anterior section of the skull had great importance. This argues against the supposition of a passive role for the intracranial articulation as a simple shock absorber.

In the modern *Latimeria* there are specially elongated subcephalic muscles connecting the two blocks to each other and apparently serving to retract the ethmosphenoid (Millot and Anthony, 1958). Apparently the subcephalic muscles were also present in Palaeozoic Rhipidistia. Millot and Anthony saw an indication of this in the convex shape of the parotic dental plate of *Eusthenopteron;* according to the description of Jarvik (1954) there is no definite antagonist of this muscle in *Latimeria.* However, when the mouth was opened wide (by the action of the m. coracomandibularis) there was a turning of the hyomandibular which pressed forward the palatoquadrate along with the ethmosphenoid. Thus the m. coracomandibularis under certain conditions plays the role of antagonist to the subcephalic muscle. The significance of this action, and consequently of the articulation of the skull itself, nonetheless remains quite uncertain. The very thickness of the subcephalic muscle of *Latimeria* indicates its vital significance, however. This is also indicated by the universal occurrence of a division of the braincase into two blocks movably articulated with each other in crossopterygian fishes.

This organizational peculiarity is probably associated with the mode of respiration associated with predation in these particular forms. The structure of the appendages of the Rhipidistia indicates that these freshwater forms crept along the bottom and could warily work their way into undergrowth; it is doubtful that they could swim rapidly. The body form indicates a mediocre swimmer. The arrangement of the unpaired fins also gives no indication of especially rapid movement, particularly in the more recent forms. *Osteolepis* was probably a relatively good swimmer (Fig. 7). In the more specialized crossopterygians the posterior dorsal and anal fins are shifted backward and lie adjacent to the caudal fin (Fig. 18). The axial part of the fin becomes more and more weak. In *Latimeria* the skeleton of the caudal fin is not well developed. The musculature is differentiated into superficial abductor divisions to the rays and deep muscles serving for folding and expanding the fin. On the whole the caudal fin of *Latimeria* is a quite mobile but undoubtedly very weak organ. The caudal fin was not an especially strong organ in the Palaeozoic Rhipidistia also.

The large jaws and the presence of large raptorial teeth indicate that crossopterygians were powerful predators. Obviously this rapaciousness was not related to the pursuit of prey, but was limited to sudden attack from ambush on suitably available prey. In this case a quiet lying-in-wait, during which the predator did not betray its presence by any movement, was of great importance. The rhythmic opening and closing of the mouth in respiration, however, would cause considerable disturbance in the water. These oscillations were undoubtedly perceived by the seismosensory organs of oncoming fishes at considerable distances in front of the predator, causing the prey to be wary and to withdraw from danger. The predator must have ambushed its prey by literally "holding its breath." This could have been achieved by slow intake of water through the slightly opened oral slit or through the spiracle. In bony fishes the functions of respiration and food intake are usually fulfilled by the same mechanism; thus expansion of the oral cavity must be accompanied by a corresponding extensive opening of the gape. This mechanism was necessary for the crossopterygians also, but only for seizing prey—by strong and rapid opening of the mouth and maximum extension of the oral cavity. In bony fishes these actions were accomplished by abrupt contraction of the elongate hypoglossal musculature (in *Latimeria* the powerful m. coracomandibularis served in this capacity). This same musculature is commonly used for creating the respiratory water flow through the open mouth. For respiration without opening the mouth, other musculature was obviously necessary to alternately expand and contract the lateral walls of the oral cavity.

Expansion of the oral cavity reduced the pressure in it and the consequent intake of water through the slightly opened oral slit, or through the spiracle, may have been accomplished by the action of the following muscles: m. levator palatoquadrati (arcus palatini), m. protractor hyomandibularis, and especially the hypoglossal musculature, m. coracomandibularis and m. coracohyoideus. Contraction of the oral cavity, expelling the water through the branchial apparatus, may have been achieved through the action of the opposing muscles: m. adductor palatoquadrati, m. adductor (retractor) hyomandibularis, and in part also by the m. intermandibularis and m. interhyoideus, but especially the strong m. subcephalicus (in *Latimeria* and probably in all crossopterygian fishes). Increase in pressure in the oral cavity was improved by the existence of oral and spiracular valves for directing the water through the gill slits and outward under the external gill cover. This created a suction action by the operculum and the gular apparatus (Voskoboinikov, 1932). In addition to branchial respiration, a part was probably also played by oropharyngeal respiration, as one might judge from the pronounced development of the olfactory artery (*Megalichthys;* Romer, 1937). The external mechanism was not altered by this. In all the above muscle systems the most important muscle is the m. subcephalicus, by the contraction of which the two units of the braincase are drawn together ventrally and the anterior end of the skull depressed. The palatoquadrate, along with the jaw articulation, should have been turned backward and upward with respect to the anterior unit. This movement was barred, however, by the opposite movement of the hyomandibula. The only remaining possibility was for the palatoquadrate and hyomandibular, together with the jaw articulation, to come together toward the midline of the skull. On the other hand, not only are the above-mentioned muscles (especially m. coracohyoideus) antagonists of the subcephalic muscles, but also the very massive notochord which is compressed by the contraction of the subcephalic muscle and then, through its considerable elasticity, expands again and pushes the two units apart from the ventral side. As a result of this the posterior end of the palatoquadrate was depressed and turned forward; however this again acts against the hyomandibula. As a result the distal ends of the hyomandibula and the palatoquadrate, along with the jaw joint, are turned forward and upward and are thus pushed out laterally. Thus the respiratory movements could be performed by rhythmic contraction of the subcephalic muscles alone.

The division of the braincase into two blocks, the elastic connection between them in the form of the well-developed notochord, and the presence of an elongate subcephalic muscle are the fundamental elements of a mechanism of "concealed" respiration in crossopterygian fishes which have great significance for predators waiting in ambush for their prey. How such an exceptional mechanism originated, one can only guess. Most likely it arose in consequence of a retention of the larval division between the trabecular and parachordal divisions of the skull, as a result, that is, of pedomorphosis.

Thus there was developed in crossopterygian fishes an essentially new respiratory mechanism not dependent upon opening the mouth. The latter served only for seizing prey. The mechanisms for respiration and feeding were elaborated separately, and this had great significance in facilitating the future progress of the transition to terrestrial life. In the Tetrapoda, however, the mobility of the palatoquadrate was lost; the suction mechanism of respiration was operated by the hypoglossal apparatus, and opening the mouth was accomplished by the action of the m. levator hyoideus-m. depressor mandibulae (as in the Dipnoi). Probably this mode prevailed because the free mobility of the skull and palatoquadrate was apparently somewhat limited, as has been noted in *Eusthenopteron*. The presence of a well-developed processus retroarticularis in *Megalichthys* also raises the suspicion that a m. depressor mandibulae was developed, to a lesser degree, in some Rhipidistia.

Dermal respiration may be of some significance to crossopterygian fishes, as is indicated by the existence of a well-developed system of dermal head veins on the dorsal surface of the head (in *Megalichthys*, according to Romer, 1937), and probably in other areas of the body also. The advantage of uninterrupted and completely undetectable dermal respiration is obvious. However, this method of respiration could hardly have been sufficiently effective alone.

In Rhipidistia the concealed respiration mechanism was improved as a consequence of the organization of the olfactory organs. In bony fishes there are two pairs of external nostrils. Of these the anterior pair play the role of inhalational apertures and the posterior pair, outlet apertures. Water currents in the appropriate direction are maintained by the action of ciliated epithelia. This mechanism of water exchange in the olfactory organs is very inefficient and cannot rapidly convey information on the state of the surrounding medium. While the fish is swimming, water currents are accelerated as a result of the creation of differences in pressure in the anterior and posterior nostrils. However, the fish itself is moving so the information is equally delayed. As a consequence of the development of water currents at the front end of the head, water exchange in the olfactory area is accelerated during respiration and while seizing prey. This latter circumstance was of great importance to predators when ambushing their prey.

In concealed respiration through a slightly opened oral slit the function of the olfactory organ was determined to a considerable degree by the distance of the posterior nostrils from the margin of the oral opening. The closer the posterior nostril was to the mouth, the more it was affected by the sucking action of the respiratory movements. A still more rapid suction and propulsion of water through the olfactory organ occurred during feeding, as a rapid opening of the mouth generated a strong water current with which the actual prey was drawn in. In both cases the shift of the posterior nostril to the edge of the mouth meant a more perfect utilization of the olfactory organ. Of greatest advantage, however, was the complete transfer of the posterior nostrils into the oral cavity. This not only afforded opportunity for the maximum utilization of the olfactory organs but also for further perfection of the concealed respiration mechanism. The respiratory water current could be led into the oral cavity not through the slightly opened oral slit, but through the nostrils and respiratory organs. Thus, obviously, the choana arose, which served for the gradual development of olfaction and was simultaneously utilized for concealing the aquatic respiration of the predator while ambushing prey.

It is indisputable that the choana originally had no relation to aerial respiration. The fish can inhale air only at the surface of the water, protruding the anterior end of the head outward. Most rapid inhalation was definitely possible only through the mouth and not through the small nostrils. In reality not only fishes, but also Amphibia, always took in air through the mouth in water (Fig. 28). Moreover, not only larvae of urodele Amphibia, but frequently also larvae of anurans (*Ascaphus;* Noble, 1931, in any case), inhale water through the nostrils and choana. This mechanism of aquatic respiration is regulated by means of valves in the choana. Obviously the origin of the choana in the crossopterygian Rhipidistia was related not to aerial respiration (which exists also in many fishes not having the choana), but to improved utilization of the olfactory organs during concealed aquatic respiration.

Olfactory organs proper were undoubtedly more highly developed in the crossopterygians than in the other bony fishes, the rayfins. They showed some differentiation of the olfactory sac reminiscent of that of terrestrial vertebrates. In the Porolepiformes, aside from the principal chamber, there are also lateral diverticula which communicate posteriorly to the oral cavity through the choana. It is possible that the homolog of Jacobson's organ was here (Jarvik, 1942). In general the olfactory organ of *Porolepis* was very similar to the olfactory organ of modern urodele Amphibia. In the Osteolepiformes (*Eusthenopteron*) the olfactory pouch was still more highly differentiated, especially in its anterior part where two diverticula were located (an upper and a lower), between which there was laterally wedged a median diverticulum also. On the whole the olfactory organ in its differentiation resembles the corresponding organs of anuran Amphibia (Jarvik, 1942). Obviously all this progressive development was stimulated by a more perfect ventilation of the olfactory pouches by the water current passed through the outer nostrils and choanae by periodic respiratory movements of the oral cavity.

In addition to the olfactory organs, development of other sense organs also progressed, and first in order was the system of (lateral line) seismosensory organs. This system consisted of the usual lateral lines of the body and the typical canals in the dermal bones of the skull which were unusual only in the connection of the preopercular canal directly to the postorbital part of the suborbital canal (the same typical canal arrangement also passed to the earliest terrestrial vertebrates, the Stegocephalia). From these canals, even in the most primitive representatives of crossopterygian fishes, extended numerous subsidiary canals which in higher forms were distinguished by abundant branching. In *Eusthenopteron* (Fig. 23) the branching side canals literally permeate the corresponding bones of the skull roof (Jarvik, 1944). This undoubtedly indicates the vast importance that the seismosensory system has in the life of crossopterygian fishes. Together with the olfactory organs it served the ambushing predator in giving immediate information of the

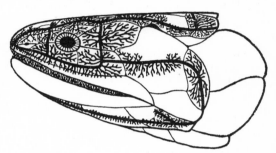

FIG. 23. Skull of *Eusthenopteron* showing lateral line canals and their branches. After Jarvik (1944), from Bystrov.

approach of prey. By contrast, the organs of vision had no great significance for freshwater fishes lying in wait under cover in weeds or among rocks in muddy water. There the crossopterygian fishes had comparatively small eyes and small midbrains.

Also associated with the gradual development of the sense organs was the development of the cerebrum. In the main this was determined by the great importance of the olfactory organs.

The general features of the cerebrum in Rhipidistia (Fig. 24) have been restored from the shape of the cranial cavity, with its canals for nerve exits, in *Megalichthys* (Romer, 1937). With its protracted form, almost without flexure, this brain is very primitive. Of predominant significance is the elongation of the brain. Of the nerves leading out from it the most highly developed were those of the acousticolateralis complex, which was connected to the well-developed auditory organs and the seismosensory system. The inner ear had large volume and complex differentiation. The large sacculus had a posterior diverticulum, corresponding to the lagena, and a small diverticulum apparently indicating the existence of a papilla basilaris. Perhaps there was also a macula neglecta amphibiorum. The dorsal labyrinth was evidently connected to the paired endolymphatic sacs. The cerebellum was very small, as in Amphibia. The midbrain was elongate and narrow, which, like the small size of the eye, indicates the weak development and lesser importance of sight. Anteriorly it passes imperceptibly into the between-brain (diencephalon) from which the habenular ganglia pass directly upward (as in the *Ceratodus*) to the pineal organ.

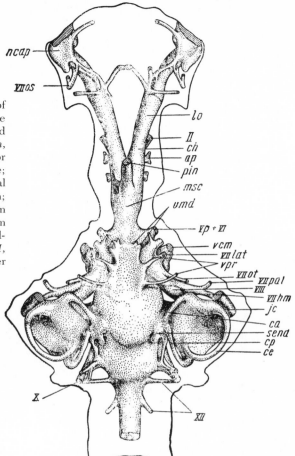

FIG. 24. Cavity of the braincase of *Megalichthys*, dorsal view. *ap*, Palatine artery; *ca*, *ce*, *cp*, anterior, lateral, and posterior semicircular canals of ear; *ch*, hemispheres of forebrain; *jc*, canal for lateral head vein; *lo*, olfactory lobe; *msc*, midbrain; *ncap*, cavity of nasal capsule; *pin*, pineal organ region; *send*, endolymphatic sac; *vcm*, median cerebral vein; *vmd*, veins leading from dorsal surface of head; *vpr*, veins leading from temporal region; *II*, *V*, *VIII*, *X*, *XIII*, cranial nerves. From Romer (1937).

The infundibulum with the hypophysis extends deep anteroventrally. The unique position of the infundibulum and the hypophysis is explained by the position of the notochord, the anterior end of which extends far forward into the anterior division of the braincase (in the ethmosphenoid), attached through the articulation between the two divisions of the cranium.

The forebrain is deeply divided into two widely divergent hemispheres which passed anteriorly into two long olfactory lobes. The hemispheres of the forebrain were weakly developed; they were very primitive, but nevertheless typical hemispheres with a completely divided roof, as in the dipnoan fishes and in terrestrial vertebrates (and consequently profoundly distinct from the forebrain of all other bony fishes, which have only basal ganglia and a thin undivided epithelial roof). Nonetheless it is clear that the forebrain of crossopterygian fishes, like the brain of Amphibia, is a typical olfactory brain.

With regard to the brain structure of *Megalichthys*, Romer (1937) also describes the arrangement of some vessels, as far as this can be judged from the arrangement of the canals in the braincase. Here attention is called to the prominently developed midbrain veins which form at the base of the sinus venosus and are connected laterally from it by a broad canal to the lateral vein of the head. On the other hand Romer noted the existence of a certain system of small veins emerging from the surface of the head inward, in combination with a system of internal vessels [judging from the figure these veins are connected directly through the venous plexus to the endolymphatic sacs (Fig. 24)]. All this, along with the existence of the endolymphatic sacs, is reminiscent of the arrangement of the vessels in Amphibia, in which the dermal veins of the head are connected through the lateral veins and midbrain veins from the branched system of venous vessels to the surface of the endolymphatic sacs. Probably, in the Amphibia, sound vibrations from the aquatic medium are received by the dermal veins of the head and transmitted by this system of canals directly to the endolymphatic sacs, and then through the endolymphatic ducts directly to the auditory macula neglecta amphibiorum, which is constructed precisely like an auditory receptor with membrana tectoria. Such a system of sound transmission is peculiarly specific to the Amphibia and is utilized by them in the aquatic medium (Schmalhausen, 1957b). The existence of the same system in the Rhipidistia is fully in harmony with the above-noted progressive development of the auditory organ, well developed in *Megalichthys*.

All this is well integrated with the presumed way of life of crossopterygian fishes as ambushing predators, for which, in murky fresh water, in a secretive life in undergrowth or among rocks, principal significance (for finding prey) accrued to the olfactory organ and also to the seismosensory system and the auditory organ. Simultaneously, this is a manifestation of the progressive development of the crossopterygian fishes along lines characteristic of terrestrial vertebrates. It was, however, associated only with the adaptations of typical fishes to a particular biological situation in conditions suitable for ambushing prey.

Both the crossopterygians and the earliest terrestrial vertebrates were predators that fed on fishes. In both these and in others there were biserially arranged teeth, relatively small in the outer series (on the premaxillary above, Fig. 25, and on the dentary below) and, in addition, a series of small teeth and separate large raptorial teeth (tusks) in an inner series (on the vomer, palatine, and ectopterygoid above, and at the end of the dentary and on the coronoids below). In both cases the teeth had radially furrowed sculpturing which sometimes attained great complexity, especially in the large tusks. In this regard one can but direct attention to one more peculiarity common to crossopterygian Rhipidistia and all Amphibia, both fossil and modern, and not found elsewhere, i.e., the presence of intermaxillary glands. The position and development of this gland shows some variation (Jarvik, 1942). In Osteolepiformes it was placed under the floor of the ethmoid part of the skull in a shallow depression (fossa apicalis), bounded by the walls of the premaxillary bones and the vomers. Posteriorly it extended into a small pit and into a short intervomerine canal, opening in the palate in front of the anterior end of the parasphenoid (Fig. 25). Evidently the ducts of all the glands opened here. The intermaxillary glands and their ducts in later secondarily aquatic labyrinthodonts occupy a similar position. With regard to the position of the intermaxillary glands the Stegocephalia are allied to the Osteolepiformes. However, in the Stegocephalia the gland was evidently more prominently developed and penetrated through the anterior palatine fenestra into the prenasal space, just as it does in modern anuran Amphibia. In urodele Amphibia the intermaxillary gland is still more developed, it is placed anteriorly between the anterior ends of the vomers and penetrates the anterior palatine fenestra far above and between the olfactory capsules and even as far as the dorsal surface of the head. Here the prominent development of the intermaxillary glands of urodele Amphibia to some degree resembles the crossopterygian Porolepiformes (Jarvik, 1942).

The presence of intermaxillary glands in all Rhipidistia undoubtedly all the more indicates their biological significance. Evidently they played an essential role in the life of these crossopterygians. In the Amphibia the intermaxillary gland secretes mainly mucous which aids in the swallowing of living prey. The latter is no slight matter to them, especially in swallowing their main food—arthropods. In fishes feeding under water this is done more easily. For predators feeding on fishes, swallowing was not an especially difficult task; any fish has a slimy surface increasing its slipperiness. Hence just the reverse problem arises—to hold the fish in the mouth. For this purpose the oral cavity and not only the maxillaries, but also the palatines and part of the branchial apparatus, were well equipped with numerous small teeth. In addition there were also large solitary tusks. The intermaxillary gland in crossopterygian fishes obviously had some function other than that

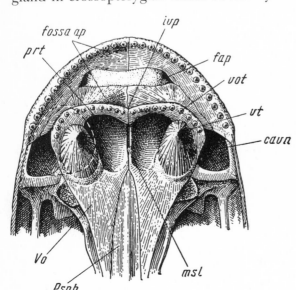

FIG. 25. *Eusthenopteron.* Anterior part of palate with vomers and their tusks. *cavn,* Choana; *fap,* foramen apicale; *fossa ap,* fossa apicalis; *iv,* intervomerine pit; *msl,* intervomerine cleft for duct of intermaxillary glands; *prt,* sockets for the reception of the tusks of the lower jaw; *psph,* parasphenoid; *Vp,* vomer; *vt,* vomerine tusks. From Jarvik (1942).

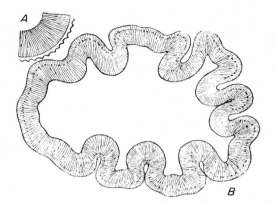

FIG. 26. Transverse thin section of the tusk of *Osteolepis*. Portion of cross section through tip of tusk (*A*) and cross section through base of tusk (*B*). From Bystrov.

characteristic of Amphibia. In the transition to terrestrial life there perhaps arose a gradual change in the function of the intermaxillary glands.

In considering the predatory way of life of crossopterygian fishes the thought involuntarily intrudes that the intermaxillary gland was a poison gland, the secretions of which paralyzed the prey and prevented its escape. For this to be effective it would be necessary to wound the prey. This function was performed by the large solitary tusks. These teeth, covered with enamel, were furnished with a large number of sharp lengthwise ridges, Fig. 26 (Bystrov, 1939). This enabled them to wound the prey and simultaneously facilitated penetration of poison into the wound. In particular, a great role could be played by the anterior tusks on the vomers and on the

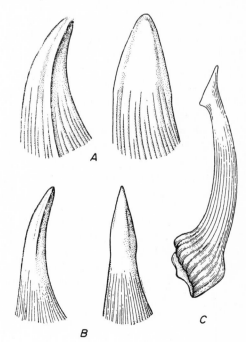

FIG. 27. Tusks of Rhipidistia. *Eusthenopteron*, from side and front (*A*); *Holoptychius*, from side and front (*B*); harpoon-like tusk of *Hamodus* (*C*). From Bystrov.

anterior end of the palatine bones and also by those at the ends of the dentary and the anterior coronoids. Correspondingly it is in this region, between the tusks of the vomers, that the excretory duct of the intermaxillary glands opened (Fig. 25). In addition, to a lesser degree, there was radially folded dentine at the base of the teeth. Poison flowed freely into the wound along the lengthwise furrows between the folds. Simultaneously the folding of the dentine enhanced the firmness of the teeth. The most complex tooth structure was attained in the Porolepiformes, that is, in those crossoptery-gians in which the intermaxillary gland was the most highly developed (Fig. 27). On the other hand, in the Coelacanthiformes there was neither the folded structure of the teeth nor the intermaxillary gland.

In the labyrinthodonts, which fed on fishes, there was also the folding of the teeth as in Rhipidistia, and they attained the same complexity of structure as in the Holoptychiidae. There were also large tusks. At the same time, there was also a well-developed intermaxillary gland which, in pisciv-orous forms, obviously had the same function as in Rhipidistia. Correspond-ingly, in these labyrinthodonts the excretory canal of the intermaxillary glands was located, as in the osteolepid crossopterygians, between the vomers with their tusks (Jarvik, 1942), or opposite the anterior tusks on the dentary.

With the transfer to terrestrial feeding the amount of the secretion and its mucoid character assumed principal importance. The glands continued to develop progressively (especially in the Caudata), but their function altered. At the same time, both the size and structure of the teeth were changed. The prehensile teeth disappeared. Only the relatively small teeth on the maxil-laries, on the vomers, and sometimes on the parasphenoid, which served only for holding prey in the mouth but not for afflicting real injuries (which occurred but slightly when feeding on arthropods), were retained. In all Amphibia there is a greater or lesser capacity to secrete poisonous substances; however, only in the dermal glands, and only as a means of defense, not as weapons for attack.

In all the characteristics of organization examined there has become apparent such a similarity between crossopterygian fishes and lower terres-trial vertebrates that the boundary between them would seem to be quite obliterated. This is all the more remarkable since they lived in different media. However, even this difference was usually not as sharp as it seemed.

7

Structural Prerequisites for the Emergence of Crossopterygians onto Land

Branchial respiration, as far back as the Brachyopterygii, and apparently in the crossopterygian fishes also, was achieved principally by means of the ventral elements of the branchial apparatus (gular type of respiration). The branchial operculum lost its importance and simultaneously the role of the branchial membrane and the gular plates increased. The respiratory movements were localized in the throat region and the floor of the oral cavity (as in the Dipnoi). With this was associated a reduction of the dorsal divisions of the gill arches (epibranchials and pharyngobranchials). Only the lower divisions of the gill arches were retained (hypobranchials and ceratobranchials), which came to bear the external gills in the larvae and in that form passed to the Amphibia.

Crossopterygian fishes had lungs, that is, organs of aerial respiration. The respiratory mechanism only provided gas exchange for animals living in the water, however, and could hardly have been utilized immediately on dry land. The requirements of pulmonary respiration on dry land differ fundamentally from the conditions of pulmonary respiration of fishes living in water. For fishes in water, and also the larvae of Amphibia, aerial respiration is carried out with very little effort. When the fish comes head upward to the surface the water displacement pressure on the abdomen causes air to be expelled from the lungs outward through the pharynx and the oral cavity (Fig. 28). With the mouth open above the water surface, expansion of the oral cavity together with retraction of the visceral apparatus leads to a suction of air into the mouth. The expenditure of energy for this is very slight since the water displacement pressure at the surface is negligible. After this the fish closes its mouth and dives down from the surface. With the fish in this position the water displacement pressure is higher on the oral cavity than on the abdomen. Therefore there should be a free passage of air into the lung through the open pharynx. This is an almost ideal mechanism of aerial respiration in water (Fig. 28).

If this fish should crawl out onto dry land then the situation is altered

51

FIG. 28. The utilization of water pressure in the pulmonary respiration mechanism in fishes.

radically. When the animal rests on the ground the pressure of the whole body is transferred to the abdomen and the floor of the oral cavity. With the fish in this position pulmonary respiration is impossible. Suction of air into the mouth is possible only with difficulty. Inhalation and forcing air into the lungs required even greater energy and could only be accomplished by raising the anterior part of the body (with the lungs) on the anterior appendages. In this event the pressure on the abdominal cavity would be reduced and air could be forced into the lungs from the oral cavity by the action of the hypoglossal and intermaxillary musculature. The expenditure of energy in this was nonetheless relatively high and the fish probably utilized pulmonary respiration only in cases of extreme necessity. In the main, respiration was evidently dermal and oropharyngeal first (as in modern urodele Amphibia). Pulmonary respiration became more economical and was gradually developed in accord with the strengthening of the limbs and elongation of the ribs in the pectoral region.

A certain amount of dermal respiration is possible in many fishes and acquires special significance in fishes crawling out of the water into the air. Gobies in mangrove thickets—*Periophthalmus* and *Boleophthalmus*—definitely breathe through the skin. In these fishes, according to Harms (1934), dermal capillary vessels penetrate directly into the epidermis and sometimes (in *Boleophthalmus*) form special respiratory papillae on it.

It may be assumed that dermal respiration played a by no means negligible role in the life of crossopterygians. Romer (1937) describes the arrangement of vessels connected to the cerebral veins in the wall of the braincase of *Megalichthys*. Attention may be called to the prominent development of the median cerebral vein and to the existence of a system of small veins entering from the surface of the head to join the cerebral vein system. In Amphibia the dermal veins of the head are also joined through lateral veins to the median cerebral vein. One can imagine that in crossopterygian fishes the system of superficial head veins was involved with the dermal respiratory system as in the Amphibia.

Dermal respiration could not have had great significance in fishes living in the water. Its effectiveness would not compare with the normal function of the specialized organs of branchial respiration. If the oxygen content of the water declines, then dermal respiration cannot assist gas exchange as long as the fish stays in the water. In this case relief is only possible by the swallowing of air and the establishment of pulmonary or other internal forms of aerial respiration. Dermal respiration may only be effective through direct contact of the moist skin with atmospheric air, that is (1) by the fish floating in the water so that the back is elevated above the surface (which is possible only with the lungs filled to the maximum), or (2) by the fish crawling out of the water onto the shore. The importance of dermal respiration should increase as the size of the animal decreases, since the relative surface area does not increase in direct proportion to increase of volume. This is evident, for example, in modern Amphibia: the terrestrial Plethodontidae are distinguished by a comparatively small size and are equipped only for dermal and oropharyngeal respiration (they have no lungs). The length of the dermal capillaries in the small *Triturus vulgaris* comprises about 75–80% of the total length of the respiratory capillaries (Czopek, 1957, 1959). The fishes *Periophthalmus* and *Boleophthalmus* which rely on dermal respiration in the air are also small.

It may be suspected that small primitive crossopterygian fishes crawling out of the water could use dermal respiration in humid air without any special adaptation. In larger forms this would require amplification of the dermal capillary net penetrating the epidermis and to a lesser extent supplementation with oropharyngeal respiration. Features of the venous system of the head of *Megalichthys* indicate an especially intensively developed net of dermal vessels, at least on the dorsal surface. Since dermal respiration could be of use only in an aerial medium it may be concluded from the above that not only the small crossopterygian fishes (*Osteolepis* is up to 50 cm long), but also the large ones (*Eusthenopteron* is up to 150 cm long), and even such giants as *Megalichthys* (several meters long), at least pushed their heads out of the water and even crawled with the anterior part of the body on the shore during shortage of oxygen in the water. The structure of the fins of crossopterygian fish also testifies in favor of this conclusion (Figs. 29 and 30).

The skeleton of the paired fins has a many-jointed axis with diverging lateral rays. It is articulated to the girdle by means of a single proximal joint which lends high mobility to the appendage. In the large forms the skeleton was well ossified and was sheathed with a well-differentiated musculature. In a word, it was a strong appendage built like a complex lever. It is clear that it served as an organ of support. However, for movement on the water bottom such a powerful structure is not at all necessary—the cartilaginous skeleton in the appendages of the modern dipnoan fish *Ceratodus* copes with this task excellently. In crawling on the shore, however, the pressure on the appendages is increased many times (in air a fish is approximately 1000 times heavier than in water), and for this function there is a real necessity for both a firm skeleton and strong musculature. In most fishes the posterior (pelvic) fins are very weak. However, *Eusthenopteron*, the skeleton of which is best known, had a fairly well-developed skeleton in the posterior appendages, built on the same plan as in the anterior appendages. In the skeleton of both anterior and posterior margins of the segments of the main axis (Fig. 30). Similar but even more significant processes were also present in the limb skeletons of one of the most primitive representatives of the tetrapods—*Hesperoherpeton* (Fig. 30), which evidently was very close to the crossopterygian fishes. These processes could only have served for muscle attachments. Their development along the posterior margin of the fin skeleton indicates the importance of the postaxial musculature in drawing the appendage backward. This musculature was not yet as highly developed as in terrestrial vertebrates; but comparison with the musculature of the pentadactyl appendage shows that the processes on the basal segment could have served for the proximal attachment of the m. coracobranchialis and m. pectoralis. The pectoral muscle was probably of greatest importance. Lateral to the same process the m. flexor carpi ulnaris originated on analogous processes on the third and fourth joints. By the combined action of these muscles the appendage was pressed against the substrate and drawn backward, thus moving the body forward. The muscles of the dorsal group (m. deltoideus, m. latissimus dorsi and mm. extensores) had a lesser role, assisting mainly in moving the appendage on

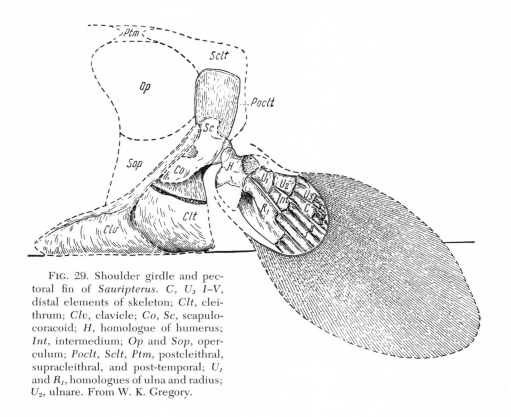

FIG. 29. Shoulder girdle and pectoral fin of *Sauripterus*. C, U_3 I–V, distal elements of skeleton; *Clt*, cleithrum; *Clv*, clavicle; *Co*, *Sc*, scapulocoracoid; H, homologue of humerus; *Int*, intermedium; *Op* and *Sop*, operculum; *Poclt*, *Sclt*, *Ptm*, postcleithral, supracleithral, and post-temporal; U_1 and R_1, homologues of ulna and radius; U_2, ulnare. From W. K. Gregory.

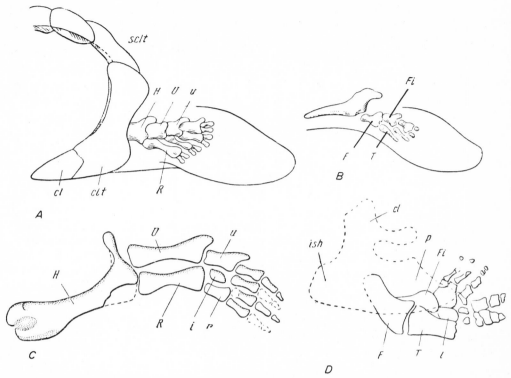

FIG. 30. Limb skeletons. *Eusthenopteron* (A) and (B), anterior and posterior appendages with girdles. From Gregory. (C) Anterior appendage of *Hesperoherpeton* (C) according to Eaton and Stewart (1960). Posterior limb of *Ichthyostega* with pelvic girdle (D) according to Jarvik. *cl*, Clavicle; *clt*, cleithrum; *F*, femur; *Fi* and *T*, tarsal bones; *H*, humerus; *i*, intermedium; *il*, iliac; *ish*, ischium; *p*, pubic region; *R*, radius; *r*, radiale; *sclt*, supracleithral; *U*, ulna; *u*, ulnare.

land. Thus the skeleton structure of the appendages of *Eusthenopteron* indicates a supporting function for crawling from water on to the shore.

Thus we come to the conclusion that crossopterygian fishes could not only emerge from the water into the air, but could also actually crawl out onto the shore. Probably this occurred during shortage of oxygen in the water. They crawled out on to the shore, although only with the anterior part of the body, and used dermal respiration.

8

Devonian Stegocephalia—the Ichthyostegidae

The crossopterygian fishes lived in the Devonian and Carboniferous in the same waters as the Dipnoi. They were quite similar organisms, differing biologically mainly in characteristics associated with feeding. The crossopterygians were heavy predators and the Dipnoi transferred to feeding on vegetation, passively taking in the small animals which had settled there. In the same fresh waters, in the late Devonian there also appeared the first Stegocephalia—the ichthyostegids which inhabited the same ecological zone as the crossopterygian fishes. Then, during the Carboniferous, a gradual displacement of crossopterygian fishes (Rhipidistia) by the Stegocephalia occurred. The last crossopterygians (*Megalichthys*) died out in the early Permian, and the zone of shallow water and freshwater basins was finally left to the amphibians.

The ichthyostegids were actually transitional forms between the crossopterygian fishes and the Amphibia. They still had some features typical of the organization of fishes. Thus in *Ichthyostega* there were rudiments of the gill cover, the preoperculum and suboperculum (Fig. 34). The latter bones are normally found in the mobile part of the gill cover with the operculum. The suboperculum in *Ichthyostega* lies isolated behind the jaws. Clearly it lay in a mobile gill cover which enclosed the internal gills and functioned as a valve, regulating the passage of the respiratory water current. Gill arches have not been found. Evidently they were cartilaginous as in the Osteolepidae.

In the Ichthyostegidae the canals of the seismosensory system of the head passed within the dermal bones of the skull and opened to the surface through external pores just as in crossopterygian fishes (Fig. 31). In all other Stegocephalia the seismosensory organs were arranged in open grooves on the bone surface and were not enclosed in bony canals. Furthermore, in *Ichthyostega* there was a genuine fishlike tail the skeleton of which was entirely similar to that of dipnoan fishes (Fig. 32). The endoskeletal rays corresponded closely with the vertebral spines and obviously reflected their segmentation (in the posterior section of the tail segmented spines as supports of the fin lobes were absent). The caudal skeleton of *Ichthyostega*,

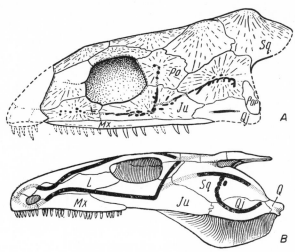

FIG. 31. Skulls of *Icthyostegopsis* (A) and *Palaeogyrinus* (B) showing lateral line system Lateral view. *ju*, Jugal; *L*, lachrymal; *Mx*, maxilla; *Po*, postorbital bone; *Pop*, preoperculum; *Q*, quadrate; *Qj*, quadratojugal; *Sq*, squamosal. From Säve-Söderbergh and Watson.

crossopterygians, and Dipnoi is derived from the axial skeleton (Schmal-hausen, 1913, 1916b) and is of the secondarily symmetrical diphycercal type. The distal part of the skeleton, derived from a fin fold, was covered by *numerous* radii of the dermal skeleton, the lepidotrichia, as in the osteolepids and Dipnoi. The dermis of the ichthyostegids was protected by small fishlike scales. In addition, the somewhat laterally compressed body shape is typical of fishes. In all these characteristics the ichthyostegids were *fishes*, which had probably retained respiration by internal gills, had seismosensory systems within canals, and a mainly fishlike organ of locomotion, a caudal fin with an endo- and exoskeleton. These characteristics were inherited from crossopterygian fishes (as shown by many similarities described later) and were retained only because they continued to live in the water. Ichthyostegids were *primarily* aquatic organisms whose ancestors never left the water medium for a long time.

The similarity to crossopterygian fishes is manifested not only in their general structural plan but in many known details. The structure of the vertebral column is highly similar, consisting in *Ichthyostega,* as in *Eusthenopteron,* of the notochord with enclosing rudimentary centra, the ossified

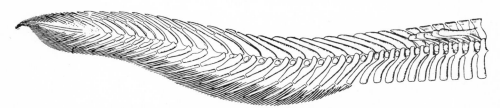

FIG. 32. Caudal skeleton of *Ichthyostega*. From Jarvik.

hypocentra, between which were probably located cartilaginous pleurocentra (Fig. 33). The neural arches with their spines were situated on the hypocentra and between them were placed, in *Ichthyostega* as well as in *Eusthenopteron*, small bony interdorsalia. In the caudal region the hypocentra were directly prolonged into hemal arches and spines. At the posterior margin of the hypocentra the ribs were articulated, the expanded heads of which reached to the bases of the neural arches. The structure of the skull of *Ichthyostega* was approximately the same as in crossopterygian fishes, particularly *Eusthenopteron*. The skull roof was very similar (Fig. 34), differing only in the position of the parietal foramen (cf. Fig. 34), and the fact that the large, broad, ethmoid shield consisted of a smaller number of larger bones than in crossopterygians. The structure of the palate was also similar; it consisted of the same bones as in *Eusthenopteron*. As in crossopterygian fishes, the parasphenoid was narrow and short, underlying only the anterior part of the skull (ethmosphenoid). Traces of the division of the axial skull into two blocks were even retained. From the ventral side a suture between both divisions of the braincase is visible, posterior to the hypophysial pit, located at the level of the movable articulation in crossopterygians (Fig. 32). The structure of the dermal bones

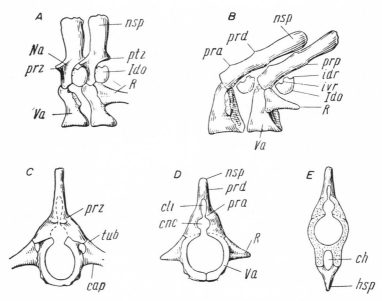

FIG. 33. Vertebrae of *Ichthyostega* and *Eusthenopteron*. Two vertebrae from the base of the caudal region of *Ichthyostega*, lateral view (*A*); the same, anterior view (*C*); two vertebrae from the base of the caudal region of *Eusthenopteron* (*B*); the same, anterior view (*D*); transverse section through caudal vertebra of *Eusthenopteron* (*E*). *cap*, Capitulum of rib; *ch*, hemal canal; *cli*, canal for longitudinal ligament; *cnc*, canal for spinal chord; *hsp*, hemal arch; *Ido*, intervertebral body; *idr* and *ivr*, notches for dorsal and ventral nerve roots; *Na*, neural arch; *nsp*, neural spine; *pra*, *prd*, *prp*, anterior, dorsal, and posterior processes of neural arch; *prz*, *ptz*, anterior and posterior zygapophyses; *R*, rib; *tub*, tuberculum of rib; *Va*, centrum (hypocentrum). From Jarvik.

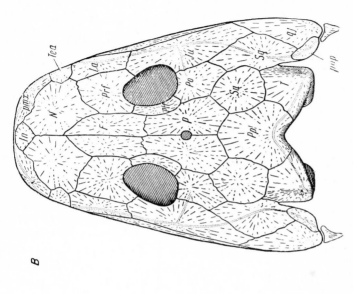

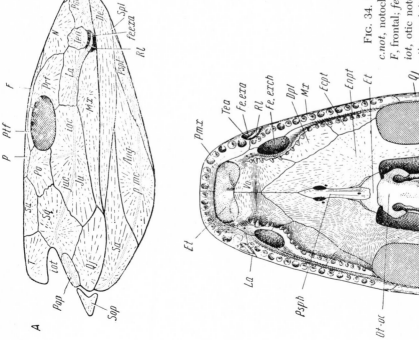

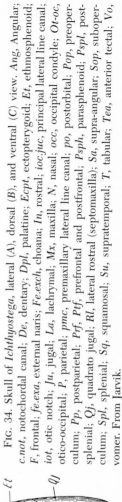

FIG. 34. Skull of *Ichthyostega*, lateral (A), dorsal (B), and ventral (C) view. *Ang*, Angular; *c.not*, notochordal canal; *De*, dentary; *Dpl*, palatine; *Ecpt*, ectopterygoid; *Et*, ethmosphenoid; *F*, frontal; *fe.exa*, external naris; *Fe.exch*, choana; *In*, rostral; *ioc;fuc*, principal lateral line canal; *iot*, otic notch; *Ju*, jugal; *La*, lachrymal; *Mx*, maxilla; *N*, nasal; *occ*, occipital condyle; *Ot-oc*, otico-occipital; *P*, parietal; *pmc*, premaxillary lateral line canal; *po*, postorbital; *Pop*, preoperculum; *Pp*, postparietal; *Prf*, *Ptf*, prefrontal and postfrontal; *Psph*, parasphenoid; *Pspl*, postsplenial; *Qj*, quadrato jugal; *Rl*, lateral rostral (septomaxilla); *Sa*, supra-angular; *Sop*, subopercuulm; *Spl*, splenial; *Sq*, squamosal; *Su*, supratemporal; *T*, tabular; *Tea*, anterior tectal; *Vo*, vomer. From Jarvik.

59

of the lower jaw (exteriorly the dentary, splenial, postsplenial, angular, and supra-angular; interiorly the prearticular and three coronoids) is entirely similar.

Along with all these resemblances emphasizing the close relationship to crossopterygian fishes, however, there were also features which link the ichthyostegids directly to the more recent Stegocephalia. We have already noted the characteristic position of the parietal fenestra in terrestrial vertebrates. Of much greater significance for our discussion, however, are those peculiarities of ichthyostegid organization which indicate progress in the exploitation of the terrestrial habitat. Among such features are the structure of the spinal column and its ribs and the structure of the skeleton of the paired appendages and girdles.

Between the neural arches of successive vertebrae in ichthyostegids there are joints formed by anterior and posterior articulating processes (zygapophyses). These articulations are characteristic features of the vertebral column of all terrestrial vertebrates. They allow bending during movement on dry land. The presence of articulated processes on the neural arches of the vertebrae (Fig. 33) is conclusive proof of the fact that ichthyostegids could successfully move out of the water onto land. Another indication of terrestrial life is the almost vertical position of the vertebral spine, associated with the differentiated spinal musculature. The appendages of ichthyostegids are the pentadactyl limbs of terrestrial vertebrates (Fig. 30). The proximal elements, femur and tibia, of the posterior limb skeleton reach fairly substantial size (in secondarily aquatic Tetrapoda they are always shortened), they have a definite basipodium (tarsus), and typically five articulated digits. The anterior appendages were conspicuously longer than the posterior ones, and the humerus was especially long. There was a sharply pronounced ulnar bend. The skeleton of the digits of the anterior appendages was not preserved. The posterior appendages, judging by their orientation in preserved skeletal remains, by the short phalanges, and by the close association of the elements, are most reminiscent of flippers (Fig. 30). The greater length of the anterior appendages in comparison to the posterior is characteristic of fishes (and secondarily aquatic Tetrapoda). The greater length of the skeletal elements in the anterior appendages indicates their major significance as organs of support. The fact that the distal elements of the skeleton were not preserved is probably due to the presence of the well-developed joints. In a decaying carcass the skeletal part disintegrates earliest at the joints. All this indicates a progressive development of the anterior appendages which played a decisive role in the animals' creeping out of the water onto the shore. The posterior appendages, which are always considerably larger than the anterior ones in wholly terrestrial forms, functioned in *Ichthyostega* more as fins for swimming. In crawling on the shore they served only as secondary organs of support.

The limb girdles of *Ichthyostega* were very similar to the girdles of the lower Stegocephalia. The pectoral girdle already lacked a connection to the skull (which was retained however in lower embolomerous Stegocephalia).

The pelvic girdle was strengthened by musculature, partly through the posterior process (Fig. 30) of the iliac bone (as it was in the primitive labyrinthodonts). The ribs of *Ichthyostega* were greatly expanded in their middle part (Fig. 35). Judging from the position of the dorsal part of the pectoral girdle (scapula) one would imagine that the expansions on the ribs served as surfaces for attachment of a strongly developed system of deeply serrate muscles (mm. serrati profundi). These muscles attached the pectoral girdle to the body and in *Ichthyostega* must have played a major role in aiding the anterior appendages in dragging the body (when crawling on the shore).

This all indicates a considerable advance, in comparison to crossopterygians, in adaptation to locomotion on a solid substrate out of the water. In comparison with the later terrestrial Stegocephalia the appendages, especially the posterior ones, were still weak however. Also, the characteristics first noted, especially in the skeleton of the caudal fin, are an indication that ichthyostegids lived not only on land but also in the water. One can be certain that they bred and also fed in the water. They were, in Jarvik's apt expression, "four-footed fishes." They lived in the water and frequently crept out on the shore. They did this not only during oxygen shortage in the water, but probably in the dry season also, especially at night. The cool and humid air at night facilitated dermal respiration and thus constituted a very favorable environment since at this time there were still no potential enemies on dry land for these primordial terrestrial vertebrates.

In speaking of the organization of ichthyostegids, one must point out that for all the primitiveness of these earliest Stegocephalia their known representatives were nonetheless more advanced in some respects of their evolution than were some Stegocephalia of the early Carboniferous. In the primitive embolomeres (*Eogyrinus*), the typical connection of the pectoral girdle to the skull roof by a complete series of dermal bones (clavicle, cleithrum, anocleithrum, supracleithrum, and posttemporal) was still

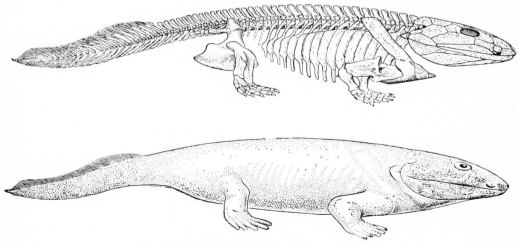

FIG. 35. *Ichthyostega*. Restoration from Jarvik.

retained. While characteristic of bony fishes (including crossopterygians), this connection had already been eliminated in ichthyostegids (as far as is currently known). Apparently the structure of the pectoral girdle was also more primitive in *Eogyrinus*. Furthermore, in the skull roof of these embolomerous forms (Anthracosauria) the parietal region of the skull roof (parietals, intertemporals, supratemporals, and tabulars) was separated from the cheek region (squamosal) by a cleft. This cleft terminated posteriorly at the otic notch. A similar cleft, in which the spiracle was located, was present in crossopterygian fishes. In all more recent Stegocephalia the squamosal was united to the intertemporal and supratemporal by a firm suture. A similar firm connection was also present in the known ichthyostegids.

To the intermediate forms, still very close to crossopterygian fishes, should be added the recently described *Hesperoherpeton* (Lower Carboniferous) (Eaton and Stewart, 1960). Although in skull structure it was an uniquely specialized form with relatively very large orbits and a reduced number of bones (especially in the postorbital region), in some respects it still retained features of the organization of crossopterygian fishes. Like the latter, this animal evidently could crawl forth on the shore. In the skull the ethmosphenoid remained cartilaginous, but there was a distinct movable articulation with the otico-ocipital (this is evident in the articular surface at its anterior end). The pectoral girdle was connected to the tabular of the skull roof. There was a single ossification in the girdle, the scapulocoracoid, as in crossopterygians and Stegocephalia. The appendages were tetradactyl, very similar to the appendages of *Eusthenopteron,* especially in the existence of processes on the posterior margin of the humerus, ulna, and ulnare (Fig. 30). The proximal bones, however, were much longer as in the Tetrapoda. In the carpus there were only the proximal elements (radiale, intermedium, and ulnare), as in *Eusthenopteron.* There were metacarpals, however, and two phalanges in the digits. The hyomandibula is especially interesting (Fig. 36). It had two heads as in the crossopterygian fishes and the distal end was connected to the quadrate. The dorsal head was very large, the ventral small. These heads fitted into pits in the lateral wall of the otic capsule. The lower pit was small but deep. In addition there was a flat process on the hyomandibula, inclined toward the otic notch. Evidently the hyomandibula, typical in form but without nerve foramina, functioned here as an auditory ossicle, the columella. The vertebrae had an almost embolo-

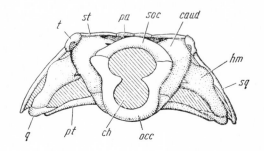

Fig. 36. Skull of *Hesperoherpeton;* posterior view, showing position of hyomandibular. *caud,* Otic capsule; *ch,* notochordal canal (canal for spinal chord immediately above it); *hm,* hyomandibula; *occ,* occipital bone; *pa,* parietal; *pt,* pterygoid; *q,* quadrate; *soc,* supraoccipital; *sq,* squamosal; *st,* supratemporal; *t,* tabular. From Eaton and Stewart.

merous structure, although the pleurocentra were smaller than the hypocentra (they were wholly ossified, however). It is especially interesting that the zygapophyses were relatively very weakly developed. This indicates that *Hesperoherpeton* was still a basically aquatic animal, i.e., also a "four-footed fish." In contrast to the ichthyostegids, *Hesperoherpeton* does not lie in the series of forms leading to the Stegocephalia. It is a member of an early divergent branch of crossopterygian fishes which also made an attempt to invade the terrestrial environment, but which left no descendants.

9

Fundamental Processes in the Transition from Aquatic to Terrestrial–Aerial Life

We know that auxiliary organs of respiration, larval external gills and lungs, were acquired in the fishes as long ago as adaptations to seasonal variation in water conditions. With high temperature and complete absence of oxygen in the water, pulmonary respiration would have been insufficient to satisfy the requirements of fishes for gas exchange. In this case some assistance could have been rendered by cutaneous respiration in the case of fishes swimming at the water surface or, if only partially, crawling on the shore. In this case respiration was accomplished without utilization of the branchial apparatus. In the aerial medium, oropharyngeal respiration could also have been established, the mechanism of which required participation of the hypoglossal apparatus; it did not require the mouth to be opened, however, since the air was inhaled through the nostrils and choanae. In the Stegocephalia, skin respiration undoubtedly played a major role. This is indicated by the existence of a well-developed network of dermal capillaries. Elements of these capillaries were enclosed in the superficial dermal bones during their growth (Fig. 37) and can be seen in microsections (Bystrov, 1947).

In large Stegocephalia, however, dermal respiration could not provide adequate gas exchange. It is certain that oropharyngeal respiration was of great significance in these animals. This mechanism could only be developed from the branchial respiration of fishes, however, when the hypoglossal apparatus was detached from the jaws. Aerial respiration on dry land is carried on with the mouth closed. The air is inhaled into the oral cavity through the nostrils during the expansion caused by the backward and downward movement of the hypoglossal-branchial apparatus. Then in the reverse, forward, movement of the hypoglossal apparatus the air is compressed and propelled outward through the same nostrils. Expiration also involves contraction of the interhyoid and intermandibular musculature. This mechanism of respiration did not require the existence of any valves. The air passed freely in each direction in turn. In the larvae of urodele Amphibia there is a valve in the choana which automatically shuts when the pressure in the oral cavity rises.

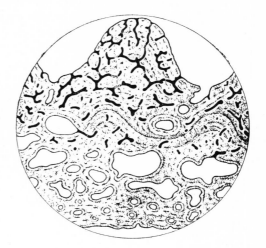

FIG. 37. Thin section through a dermal bone of *Benthosuchus*. Canals of dermal vessel shaded. From Bystrov.

It serves to regulate the water flow during branchial respiration, forcing its exit through the nostrils. This valve is eliminated during metamorphosis. It is very likely that such a valve was also present in crossopterygian fishes. However, it probably disappeared in the transition to terrestrial life.

More difficulties arose in the utilization of pulmonary respiration by fishes that had emerged onto land. In forcing air in and out of the lungs it was necessary to overcome the pressure of the entire body weight on the abdominal cavity (Schmalhausen, 1957a). It was possible to reduce this pressure by slightly raising the body, or at least the anterior part of the body, above the surface of the ground. This required considerable development of the limbs, especially the anterior ones. The simplest mechanism of pulmonary respiration was the mechanism used in oropharyngeal respiration, developed from the branchial respiration mechanism. This, however, required development of new valves in the nostrils, not merely passive ones as in the choanae, but active ones, the action of which was controlled by a special musculature. Such valves were also developed in the nostrils of Amphibia. They close the nostrils in order that the pressure in the oral cavity may be raised to drive air through the pharynx into the lungs. In all Amphibia there was thus developed a combined mechanism of oropharyngeal and pulmonary respiration. The intermandibular muscle, which by its contraction compresses the air in the oral cavity, plays the principal role in this mechanism. The effectiveness of the intermandibular pumping, i.e., the volume of driven air, increases with increase of the distance between the rami of the lower jaws. In Amphibia this is attained by a wider spreading of the quadrate bones to which the lower jaws are articulated. As a result the amphibian skull as a whole acquires distinctive breadth and flatness. It should be pointed out that the widest skulls characterize these terrestrial Amphibia with the most highly developed pulmonary respiration (the anurans, especially toads and peepers). In fossil Stegocephalia a gradual flattening of the skull may be traced in the transition from primitive Stegocephalia with fairly high skulls of the piscine type to the more recent Stegocephalia and the modern form in anuran Amphibia (Fig. 38).

The transition to terrestrial aerial oropharyngeal and pulmonary respiration was therefore accompanied from the very first by a complete separation of the functions of feeding and respiration in separate mechanisms of the jaws and of the hypoglossal gill apparatus (which are combined in fishes). This gave an opportunity for more perfect specialization of both functions. The apparatus for seizing food was then strengthened in crossopterygian fishes, which were powerful predators. The bones of the upper jaw, maxillae and premaxillae, were firmly connected to the skull roof bones. The palatal arch, the palatoquadrate, was attached not only anteriorly by median and lateral articulations of the palate in the olfactory region as in other bony fishes, but also in the central part (Fig. 39). The latter attachment was made at two points, at the base of the skull by the basipterygoid articulation (a primitive characteristic), and in the postorbital region by the articulation between the processus ascendens and processus antoticus of the skull (a new joint). The existence of these articulations allowed only a very limited degree of movement,

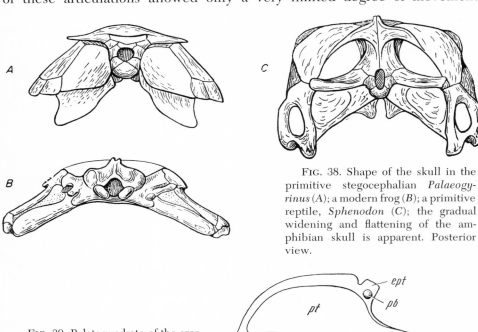

FIG. 38. Shape of the skull in the primitive stegocephalian *Palaeogyrinus* (A); a modern frog (B); a primitive reptile, *Sphenodon* (C); the gradual widening and flattening of the amphibian skull is apparent. Posterior view.

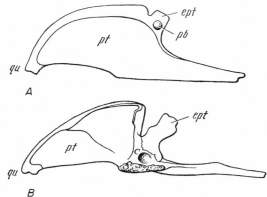

FIG. 39. Palatoquadrate of the crossopterygian fish *Eusthenopteron* (A) and the stegocephalian *Benthosuchus* (B). *ept*, Epipterygoid; *pb*, basal process; *pt*, pterygoid. From Bystrov and Efremov (1940).

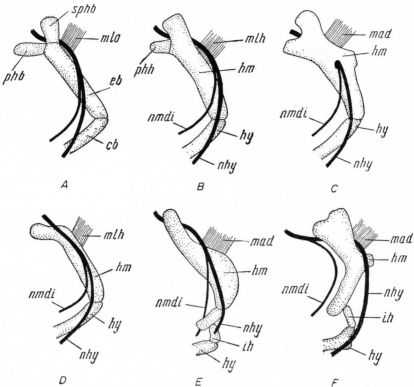

FIG. 40. Schemes of relationship of the hyomandibular and its nerve in fishes. Gill arch of sturgeon (A); hypothetical original position of hyoid arch (B); hyoid arch of crossopterygian fish (C); hyoid arch of elasmobranch fish (D); hyoid arch of sturgeon (E); hyoid arch of Brachiopterygii (F). cb, Ceratobranchial; eb, epibranchial; hm, hyomandibula; hy, hyoid (ceratohyal); ih, inter-hyal; mad, adductor muscle of hyomandibular; mla, m. levator arci branchialis; mlh, m. levator hyoides; nhy, hyoid nerve VII; nmdi, internal mandibular nerve VII; phb, pharyngobranchial; phh, pharyngohyal; sphb, suprapharyngobranchial.

determined by the requirements of gill respiration (expansion and contraction of the oral cavity by lateral movements of the palatine arch). The freeing of the feeding mechanism from the respiratory function led to a further attachment of the jaw in its posterior part by the processus oticus palatoquadrati. Thus the hyomandibula, which in crossopterygian fishes gave auxiliary support to the jaw, finally lost its importance as a suspensor (Fig. 40).

By the division of the visceral apparatus into the jaw apparatus and the respiratory apparatus, the hyomandibula was left in an intermediate position and lost its functional connection with both the food-taking mechanism and the breathing mechanism. Therefore it could assume a new function, which was predicated by its connection to the gill operculum and by its articulation to the otic capsule of the skull. This was connected with the fact that when the animal went into the air an air-filled cavity was left under the gill operculum. An enclosed air chamber was formed with a movable membrane which in-

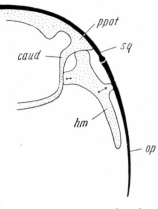

FIG. 41. Relationships of hyomandibula in crossopterygian fishes. *caud,* Otic capsule; *hm,* hyomandibular; *op,* operculum; *ppot,* processus paroticus of otic capsule; *sq,* squamosal. Reception of water vibrations indicated by arrows.

evitably responded to vibrations of the sound waves striking it. These vibrations passed through the hyomandibula directly to the otic capsule. The hyomandibula in crossopterygian fishes was attached to the skull at two points, laterally on the otic crest (crista parotica) and medially to the base of the otic capsule (Fig. 40). The lateral articulation was the firmer and can be regarded as a point of leverage in transmission from the operculum to the base of the otic capsule. The long arm of the lever is measured as the distance from the place of articulation of the operculum to the point of support on the otic crest (Fig. 41). The short arm of the lever is measured as the distance from the point of support to the medial attachment at the base of the otic capsule. Thus the vibrations of the operculum were transmitted in a changed form with decreased amplitude and increased pressure to the otic capsule. The thinness of the walls of the otic capsule at the point of the basal articulation of the hyomandibula allowed a more perfect transmission of sound. According to Watson (1926b), in the primitive Stegocephalia (*Eogyrinus* and *Palaeogyrinus*) there was a pit here. In all later forms a fenestra covered by a resilient membrane was developed in place of the pit. In this case the sound vibrations were transmitted through the hyomandibula, now the auditory ossicle, directly from one membrane to another, and thus from a membrane having a large surface (operculum or tympanic membrane) to a membrane of small surface (the fenestra ovalis membrane). Transmission was accomplished by this means with considerable increase of the force of the vibrations received. All these modifications gave considerable impetus to the progressive development of the auditory organ, which is one of the most important sense organs in terrestrial vertebrates. Only in higher crossopterygians and the terrestrial vertebrates were specialized auditory receptors differentiated (the papilla basilaris and the papilla neglecta amphibiorum) from a common receptor, the lagena.

In crossopterygian fishes the dominant sense organs were the seismosensory organs and the olfactory organ. With emergence onto land the former lost its significance, and the latter had to be reconstructed in line with the replacement of the aquatic medium by an aerial medium. The olfactory organ was well developed as far back as the Brachiopterygii. It attained still higher development in crossopterygian fishes. This was undoubtedly conditioned by the acquisition of a new, more perfect and well-controlled mechanism of water flow in the olfactory organ. In the ancestors of crossopterygian fishes both pairs of nostrils were located not on the dorsal part of the head but on the sides. Therefore, they were affected by water currents created by the respiratory movements. The posterior nostrils were located at the very edge of the mouth. Opening of the mouth and drawing-in of water caused a difference of pressure in the olfactory organs; the water entered through the anterior nostril and emerged through the posterior. The closer the posterior nostril to the mouth the more intensively was the water inducted through the olfactory organ. The difference in pressure was increased, and the water flow reached its highest rate when the posterior nostril moved into the oral cavity. In the Dipnoi the movement stopped halfway, so to speak; the posterior nostril, like the anterior one, lay under the upper lip but did not penetrate the palate region. It was not yet a choana. In the Coelacanthidae choanae were absent altogether.[1] Only in the Rhipidistia did true choanae originate, located on the palate on the inner side opposite the maxillary bones (properly, between the premaxilla and maxilla), as a result of a shift of the posterior nostrils. Their origin was not correlated with the respiratory mechanism. The movement of the nostrils and the formation of choanae was correlated with an increased importance of the olfactory organ, and formed an important step in its progressive development (Schmalhausen, 1958d). In the lower Rhipidistia there were even three pairs of nostrils (Fig. 42) since, evidently, the posterior pair had not completely shifted inward and at the edge of the oral opening they had divided into two nostrils of which the lower was transformed into a choana, and the upper made a connection with a branch of the suborbital

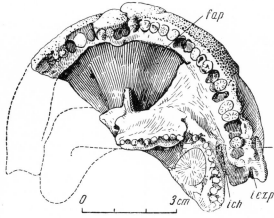

FIG. 42. The three nostrils in the crossopterygian fish *Panderichthys*. *fap*, Apical pit; *fe.exa*, anterior nostril; *ich*, choana; *iexp*, posterior external nostril. From Vorobjeva-Blokhina.

[1] Apparently they had vanished epigenetically.

canal of the seismosensory organs and gave rise, in terrestrial vertebrates, to the nasolachrymal duct (Schmalhausen, 1958d). The olfactory sac itself also underwent a gradual differentiation (Jarvik, 1942). Particularly, even in *Porolepis*, differentiation of an orbital chamber and a lateral recess (recessus lateralis) evidently occurred. In *Eusthenopteron* the nasal cavity was much more complex. Anteriorly it was subdivided into upper, middle, and lower recesses. Posteriorly the main cavity merged into a choanal tube. In this tube was a ventromedial notch, which perhaps corresponded to Jacobson's organ (situated as in the *Anura*). It is certain that one of the important adaptations to life on land was the development of various glands for maintaining the olfactory epithelia in a moist state. The aerial medium gave greater possibilities of distant perception of different odors (particles borne in the air).

Together with differentiation of the olfactory organs the olfactory division of the brain was gradually developed. Of the bony fishes only in crossopterygians and Dipnoi were cerebral hemispheres developed which were extended anteriorly into the olfactory lobes. In the Crossopterygii (*Megalichthys;* Romer, 1937) they were narrow and long (Fig. 24). In primitive Stegocephalia (*Edops* and *Eryops*) they were shorter and broader, but nevertheless smaller than in modern Amphibia (Romer and Edinger, 1942). The development of the forebrain in lower terrestrial vertebrates on the whole was correlated with the development of the olfactory organs.

The organs of vision were weakly developed in crossopterygians. The life of a predator lying in wait in ambush required development of the seismosensory system and the olfactory organs to a high degree. In plant undergrowth, among rocks, and in stagnant waters, vision could not have major importance. Correspondingly the eyes were small, and the midbrain was also small.

In the transition to the aerial medium there had to be major alterations in eye structure. In fishes the main light-refracting body is the crystalline lens of the eye. It is of spherical shape and of very high refractive index (higher than optical glass). On the other hand there was no light diffraction at the boundary of the cornea and the water (index of diffraction 1). In the aerial medium all this had to be altered. In the air, diffraction at the corneal surface took on major significance. Therefore it became more convex. On the other hand the crystalline lens was now of less importance; it was flatter and served mainly for accommodation. The latter is achieved by movements of the crystalline lens by means of muscles (m. protractor lentis) drawing it forward (toward the cornea). Fishes living in the water are extremely short-sighted. Therefore, their eyes first had to be adapted to the new conditions. In modern terrestrial Amphibia they are normally adjusted for distances. For vision at short distances accommodation is employed.

The main adaptation for life in the terrestrial-aerial medium, however, was protection of the cornea from desiccation, its maintainance in a humid state by means of special glands. It was also protected by movement of the eyelids. A large Harderian gland is located in the orbit in Amphibia, and along the lower lid, a lachrymal gland. In addition, a definite role in eye protection is played by a muscle drawing the eye into the orbit, m. retractor bulbi, which is derived from the m. rectus externus. Its opposite is the m. levator bulbi, a derivative of the jaw musculature.

The retina of the eye of Amphibia contains relatively coarse elements, especially in urodele Amphibia. Therefore their acuteness of vision cannot be outstanding. Probably the same was true in crossopterygian fishes also.

So we see that adaptation of the organs of vision to the aerial medium was not simple, and undoubtedly required a long time during which the animal could have emerged on land only periodically. The transparency of the aerial medium, however, which permitted practically unlimited distance of vision, was especially favorable for further progressive development of the organ of vision.

Among the leading processes of evolutionary change in the transition from the aquatic to the terrestrial-aerial medium, transformation in the locomotory organs (Fig. 30) must also be included.

Fish may crawl on dry land by means of the usual "swimming" movements. In this action the paired fins take no active part. They may, however, serve as auxiliary points of support. With the development of a jointed skeleton and differentiated musculature, the paired fins played a more and more significant role in the fishes' creeping onto the shore. More prolonged crawling on the land required, however, a reconstruction not only of the appendages but also of the vertebral column and the lateral body muscles.

Swimming in water and walking on land are based on different mechanical principles. In swimming in the water by means of lateral flexures the elasticity of the main skeletal axis, the notochord or spinal column, is of major importance.

The vertebral column of fishes is a highly flexible rod, the elastic strength of which is used in the movement of the body by serial wavelike undulations along the axis (front to back). In this there is considerable economy of muscular effect. Almost all the muscular energy in the movements of fishes is expended in overcoming the frontal water resistance. The better swimmers have a very flexible vertebral column made up of well-developed vertebrae firmly connected by a complex system of elastic ligaments. Special processes of the vertebrae sometimes take part in reinforcing the ligamentous connections of the spine. The uniformity of the medium (water) in which the fish moves requires a regular rhythm of muscular contractions, fully coordinated to an even succession of elastic waves running along the spinal column. On land, while it is using the original normal swimming flections of the body, the animal moves over an uneven substrate. It is obliged to avoid all obstacles. The regular rhythm of wavelike undulations not only loses significance, but also is obstructed by the resistance of the irregularities of the substrate. The elastic capacity of the skeletal axis can not be utilized, and even if it could, it would work in opposition to the active bending of the body. Even in creeping along a water bed, eel-like fishes increase the flexibility of the spine, and at the same time an increase in the amplitude of the wavelike undulations and a lessening of their frequency occurs. In terrestrial vertebrates there is a further increase in amplitude and a decrease in frequency of the body undulations. Moreover, the regularity of the rhythm and the height of the amplitude are lost, due to the above-mentioned unevenness of the substrate on which the animal is moving. Therefore the axial skeleton of terrestrial vertebrates attains maximum flexibility, much greater even than in eel-like fishes, within certain limits. This is accomplished by a weakening of the connections between successive vertebrae and in the characteristic development of movable articulations both between the centra of the vertebrae and between the neural arches. Since the centrum of the vertebra often consists of cartilage and the connecting intervertebral cartilage which is not preserved in the fossil state, the firmness of the connections between the vertebral bodies of fossil Amphibia is difficult to judge. The neural arches are always well ossified, however, and the nature of the articulations between them is easily established. In all terrestrial vertebrates, beginning with the Stegocephalia, there were well-developed articular processes (zygapophyses) by means of which easily movable (although limited) connections between the successive vertebrae were established. Only in the more primitive Stegocephalia, the Devonian ichthyostegids, were the articular processes of the neural arch of the vertebrae somewhat weaker than in recent forms (Fig. 33).

Change in the conditions of locomotion in terrestrial vertebrates also required a reconstruction of the trunk musculature. In fishes the lateral trunk muscles are divided by horizontal partitions into approximately equal dorsal (epaxial) and ventral (hypaxial) divisions at the level of the vertebral column. This is logical since in maintaining position in the water the swimming movements of the body require uniform effort of the muscles lying above and below the main axis. On land the situation is altered due to the force of the weight on the ventral surface of the body. Reduction of the trunk musculature of the abdominal section increases the pressure on the limbs and makes possible the utilization of frictional support during locomotion.

Meanwhile the reduction of the musculature of the abdominal region reduces the pressure of the abdomen on the ground and, consequently, lessens the friction of the ventral body surface on the substrate during locomotion (crawling). Only by strong development of the abdominal (hypaxial) musculature can this friction be lessened and then entirely eliminated, by raising the abdomen above the soil level on the limbs (transition to walking). Therefore, in all terrestrial vertebrates the hypaxial musculature predominates. Laterally it comes into close contact with the ribs. The regular rhythm of the swimming motions of a fish also requires a uniform segmentation of the lateral muscles. In terrestrial vertebrates the complexity of the body movements is associated with differentiation of this musculature into a great number of separate muscles attached to various parts of the spinal column.

Movement on land, at first very awkward, required an increase in the mobility of the head with its sense organs. Therefore the anterior part of the vertebral column in terrestrial vertebrates was developed into a more mobile neck, connected by a movable articulation to the occipital region of the skull.

This in turn was associated with a progressive differentiation of the spinal musculature of this region.

In fishes the position of the head is fixed by a connection of the skull to the bones of the pectoral girdle. In terrestrial vertebrates this connection is eliminated. Only in some primitive Stegocephalia (*Eogyrinus*, Fig. 43) did there persist a connection of the pectoral girdle to the skull roof by the dermal bones characteristic of fishes, the supracleithrum and posttemporal (Fig. 44). In other terrestrial vertebrates these bones are reduced and the head becomes mobile.

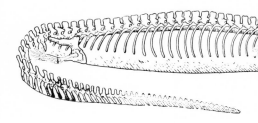

FIG. 43. Skeleton of *Eogyrinus*, an embolomerous stegocephalian from the Lower Carboniferous. From Watson (1962b) and Gregory.

FIG. 44. Skull and pectoral girdle of *Eogyrinus*. *cl*, Clavicle; *ct*, cleithrum; *ic*, interclavicle; *pt*, post-temporal; *sc*, scapula; *sct*, supracleithral. From Bystrov.

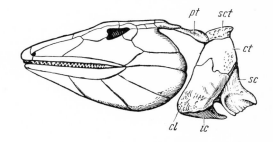

At the same time the pectoral girdle also acquires mobility. This mobility is used in improving the movements of the appendages in locomotion. This, however, requires some development of the trunk musculature of the pectoral girdle region. Thus the differentiation of muscles of the pectoral girdle [secondary (limb) musculature] from the lateral body muscles arose. This musculature was also a new acquisition of terrestrial vertebrates. As a result of the attachment of the musculature to the primordial skeleton of the pectoral girdle, the scapular and the coracoid, these parts were gradually developed, and the dermal bones predominating in the anterior girdle of fishes began to lose their significance (in Stegocephalia and the earlier reptiles they are still very substantial).

In fishes the posterior girdle is represented by a small plate. The necessity for a firmer support for the posterior appendages which fulfill the basic task of "pushing" in movements on land, led to expansion of the pelvic girdle. In particular, the dorsal (iliac) processes of the girdle were expanded. The original loose pelvic girdle became attached, as did the pectoral girdle, by means of the lateral trunk muscles which joined it to the ribs. In more primitive Stegocephalia (*Eogyrinus*, *Cricotus*, and *Pholidogaster*) the iliac element

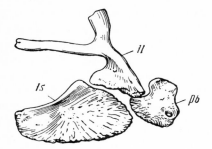

FIG. 45. Pelvic girdle of a primitive stegocephalian. *Il*, iliac; *Is*, ischium; *Pb*, pubis. From Steen.

of the pelvis lay free (among the muscles) on the ribs of the nearest vertebrae (Fig. 45).

In all recent forms direct connections of the iliac bones to one or two "sacral" ribs were established. Thus the pelvic girdle acquired a firm support on the vertebral column. This simultaneously limited its mobility, however, particularly in forms in which an attachment to two pairs of ribs was established. In Amphibia the iliac bones were attached, in some degree movably,

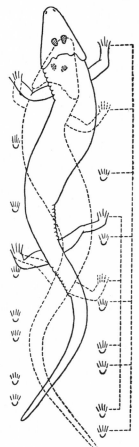

FIG. 46. Movement (essentially rotatory) of a primitive stegocephalian (*Eogyrinus*) on dry land. After Watson.

to one pair of sacral ribs. This mobility was often utilized in the animal's movement (especially in the Anura). The free appendages originally served as simple points of support for the animal while advancing over the land by means of such lateral body undulation as were utilized when swimming in the water (Fig. 46). By differentiation of the musculature and elongation of the skeletal elements, these supporting organs were gradually transformed into complex levers with a more and more active role in locomotion. The anterior limb moves forward with the opposite flexure of the anterior part of the body, i.e., on the convex side. The posterior limb is drawn forward at the concave side of the body. As shown in the diagram (Fig. 46), the coordinated action of the body flexures and the movement of the limbs leads to a considerable increase of the stride. The effort is sequential, the anterior limbs raising and pulling the body, and the posterior limbs pushing it forward (at first with definite assistance from the tail). The difference in the work of the anterior and posterior limbs is shown in their structure. In the anterior limbs the elbow is turned backward and the forearm extended forward; in the posterior limbs the knee is directed forward and the tarsus is extended backward. In movement on land the posterior limbs were of principal significance. This circumstance, with the distinctive function of the limbs as organs of support, led to abrupt structural differences in the pentadactyl limbs as contrasted to the fins of fishes.

The fish fin functions as a single elastic blade in which vibrations pass from the base to the periphery. In bony fishes the musculature is attached solely to the bases of the branched and very stiff dermal fin rays. The endoskeleton serves only as a support for the dermal skeleton and does not enter into the fin lobe. In crossopterygian fishes the situation was somewhat different. The endoskeleton was articulated and entered, along with the musculature, into the formation of the lobe of the fin. This was undoubtedly related to the new function as supporting organs in creeping along the water floor. The skeletal structure of paired appendages was sometimes astonishingly similar (Fig. 30) to the structure of the limbs of the terrestrial vertebrates.

Whatever the extent of this similarity between the fin of the fish and the limb of the terrestrial vertebrate, however, there remains a fundamental difference. The fin functions as a more or less flexible but nonetheless simple elastic blade; therefore there are no real articulations (diarthroses) between the parts of its skeleton. The limb of the terrestrial vertebrate is a system of levers; it consists of a series of segments linked by articulations. Only in secondarily acquired aquatic life are the skeletal elements reconnected by syndesmoses and synchondroses, and the pentadactyl appendage transformed into an elastic plate, a flipper (as in seals). In fishes crawling on the water bed the anterior appendages play the main role, as they do in swimming. Correspondingly, the pectoral fins in the crossopterygian fishes were more strongly developed that the pelvics. In terrestrial vertebrates the main work is done by the posterior appendages which acquire firmer support (at the sacrum) and become extremely powerful. Adaptation to life on land is accompanied by an elongation of the levers, the main bones, of the skeleton, expecially in the posterior limbs (only upon return to life in water are the skeletal elements of the limbs again reduced and the importance of the posterior appendages minimized).

Incidentally, the structure of the appendages, with wide and short proximal divisions of the skeleton, shows the primitiveness of the Stegocephalia. In the ichthyostegids, moreover, the posterior appendages are even weaker than the anterior ones (Fig. 35). Apparently the articulations in the posterior appendages were also not yet fully formed.

I O

The Structure of the Tetrapod Skull and the Homology of Its Elements

The two divisions of the skull of crossopterygian fishes, the ethmosphenoid and the otico-occipital, usually movably articulated, are sometimes joined to each other more closely. In *Eusthenopteron* the connection was very close and probably scarcely movable. In terrestrial vertebrates the two sections are fused to each other. In *Ichthyostega*, however, the suture between the sphenoid and otico-occipital sections of the skull is still visible on the ventral side of the braincase. In crossopterygian fishes the gap between the two divisions formed the aperture for the exit of the anterior part of the trigeminal nerve, n. profundus V. The pit of the hypophysis is located in the posterior part of the anterior division; above it, on the side of the skull, is the processus basipterygoideus, and still higher is the processus antoticus. In addition to the olfactory organ, the eye and the pineal organ are located in the anterior division. In various crossopterygians the relative positions of the dermal bones of the skull roof and the pineal opening vary with the position of the eye and the pineal organ. In *Osteolepis* the orbits lie on the same level with the pineal opening, in *Eusthenopteron* the pineal orifice lies a little behind the orbit and in *Eusthenodon* well behind. In *Osteolepis* the pineal opening lies between the anterior parts of the frontal bones, and in *Eusthenodon* between the posterior parts (Fig. 47). The variability in position of both the orbit and the pineal orifice has significance in respect to the comparison of the skull roof of terrestrial vertebrates with the skull of crossopterygian fishes.

In the general similarity of the skull roof of Stegocephalia to that of the crossopterygian fishes which are obviously closest to the forms that gave rise to terrestrial vertebrates (Osteolepidae), there is one important difference relating to the position of the parietal opening. In all fishes the parietal opening is located between the frontal bones, and in terrestrial vertebrates (Stegocephalia and reptiles) it is located between the parietals. This difference is so obvious and constant that it has stimulated an examination of the whole question of the homologization of the main bones of the skull roof (Westoll, 1943b).

77

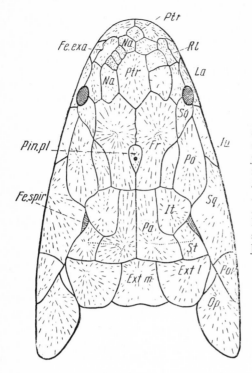

FIG. 47. Skull of *Eusthenodon*, from above. *Extm*, *Extl*, Extrascapulars (postparietal, tabular); *fe.exa*, nostril; *fe.spir*, cleft for spiracle; *Fr*, frontal *It*, intertemporal; *Ju*, jugal; *La*, lachrymal; *Na*, nasal; *Op*, operculum; *Pa*, parietal; *Pin.pl*, pineal plate; *Po*, postorbital; *Pop*, preoperculum; *Ptr*, rostrals; *Rl*, lateral rostral; *So*, supraorbital; *Sq*, squamosal; *St*, supratemporal. From Jarvik.

According to the concept of Westoll, the frontal bones of fishes are homologous to the parietal bones of terrestrial vertebrates and, correspondingly, the nasals to the frontals, the parietal and supratemporal bones to the posttemporal and tabular bones of Stegocephalia. The nomenclature of a number of other bones of the skull roof is similarly modified.

The new homologization of the bones of the skull is based on certain assumptions. It is presumed that in the transition from fishes to terrestrial vertebrates there arose, first, a considerable modification of the relationships of the preorbital and postorbital regions of the skull: the first was much expanded and the latter reduced, with corresponding reduction in the size of some bones and the complete disappearance of others. Second, there was a shift of the nasal bones of the fishes from the olfactory region to the orbital region, and the frontal bones were excluded from this region. It is presumed that in these modifications the original position of the parietal foramen in relation to the frontal bones of fishes was retained. However, the relationship between the orbits and the cranial bones was altered. The orbits, lying in the anterior part of the skull in fishes lateral to the "parietal" bones (that is, the frontals of previous nomenclature), were moved backward in terrestrial vertebrates to the middle of the skull, but as a result of this shift they are found anterior to the parietal bones, in the frontal region. This in itself is improbable, since it presumes an active expansion of the bones of the olfactory region backward into the interorbital region. Furthermore, as will be seen later, this is linked also with the assumption of a shift of certain lateral line canals from one bone to another. Such an assumption does not accord with modern knowledge, and therefore the whole structure of the Westoll theory requires a critical reexamination.

1. The transition from fishes to terrestrial vertebrates was actually associated with some modification of the skull roof proportions. The olfactory region of the skull was expanded and the postparietal region reduced. In certain cases, however, various modifications of this relationship occurred. In various Stegocephalia there is seen not only an expansion of the preorbital region (as in *Cyclotosaurus*, for example) which was sometimes drawn out into a long snout (*Platyops*), but also an expansion of the postorbital region of the skull anterior to the parietal foramen (*Trematosaurus* and especially *Metoposaurus*), or behind it, in the postparietal region (*Batrachiderpeton*). Sometimes there was an abrupt reduction of the olfactory region (*Diceratosaurus, Diplocaulus*). Such secondary transformations lead to almost complete restoration of typical piscine proportions in skull structure (*Dolichopareias disjectes*, Fig. 48). In all these modifications, however, the typical relationship between the skull bones, the orbits, and especially the canals of the lateral lines remain unchanged. Considerable variations in position of the orbits and in the relative development of the areas of the cranial roof are also seen in bony fishes. They are present in various members of the crossopterygian fishes in particular. The position of the orbit at the anterior end of the head in *Osteolepis* cannot be regarded as typical. The skull structure of *Eusthenopteron* probably represents a structure derived from the ancestors of terrestrial vertebrates to a great extent. Notwithstanding all the differences in relative development of skull parts, however, the general correlation here between the bones and sense organs is very constant. Therefore the sharp modifications of these relationships in the transition from crossopterygian fishes to terrestrial vertebrates postulated by Westoll are incorrect.

2. The variation of the relative sizes of the preorbital and postorbital regions of the skull of which Westoll speaks actually reflects a shift of the orbits. In the Osteolepida the latter lie at the anterior end of the head, and in the Stegocephalia farther back at the middle or even in the posterior half of the cranial roof.

The shift of the orbits is associated with an unequal expansion of the bones of the preorbital and postorbital regions. Occasionally unequal bone growth appears in individual development. Age differences are then manifested in the position of the orbit. Thus in young *Benthosuchus sushkini* (Bystrov and Efremov, 1940) the orbits are located at about the middle of the skull; in the adult they are located in posterior half. This shift of the orbits is related to expansion of the bones of the preorbital region (prefrontals), and the repression of growth of the postorbital ones (postorbitals and postfrontals). Still sharper differences are seen in the growth of the bones of the preorbital and postorbital regions in *Cyclotosaurus* in which the orbits are set even farther back than in *Benthosuchus*. The increased growth in length of the bones of the preorbital region is shown not only in the form and size of these bones

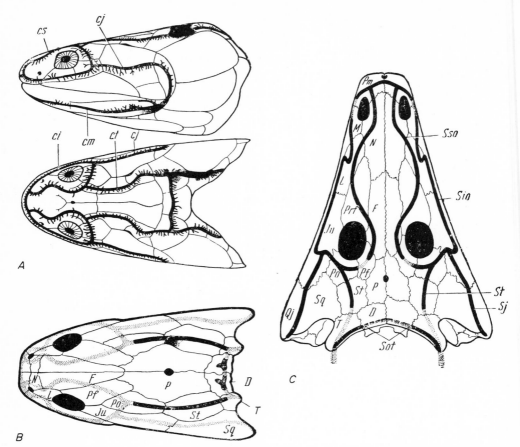

FIG. 48. Seismosensory canals in the skull roof of *Osteolepis* (A), *Dolicho-pareias* (B), and *Benthosuchus* (C). *ci, so,* Suborbital canal; *cs, Sso,* supraorbital canal; *cj, cm, sj,* preopercular canal; *ct, st,* temporal bone; *D,* post-temporal canal; *F,* frontal bone; *Ju,* jugal bone; *L,* lachrymal bone; *M,* maxilla; *N,* nasal bone; *P,* parietal bone; *Pf* and *Prf,* postfrontal and pre-frontal bones; *Pm,* premaxilla; *Po,* postorbital bone; *Qj,* quadratojugal bone; *Sot,* occipital commissure; *Sq,* squamosal bone; *St,* supratemporal bone; *T,* tabular bone., From Bystrov (1935).

but also in their sculpturing—in the elongated pits (cf. Bystrov, 1935). In this process the anterior parts of the frontal bones, which are thus borne far anterior of the orbits, are also involved. In the opposite case of a shift of the orbits to the anterior part of the head there is an expansion of the postorbital bones (cf. *Metoposaurus, Batrachosuchus,* and especially *Dolichopareias,* Fig. 48). This unequal growth sometimes includes the frontal bones which are therefore moved far beyond the orbits.

From the above it is clear that there is a connection between movement of the orbits and unequal development of the bones of the skull roof. Without the latter the former could not occur. The frontal bones also take part in this process although they are involved only through the agency of the adjacent circumorbital bones. We should regard these as correlated modifications, occurring during the shift of the orbits in the skull roof. Correspondingly we should recognize that the shift of the orbits is determined only insignificantly by the trend of growth of the frontal bones with the existence of only an indirect relationship between them.

According to Westoll's theory, the orbits moved backward through the movement of the frontal ("parietal") bones, and therefore moved from the area of the "parietal" bones (in fishes) to the area of the frontal bones (in Stegocephalia).

Meanwhile the position of the eye, rather than the relative positions of the skull bones, was obviously of decisive biological significance. Indeed the shift of the eye was a predominantly biological process. The movement of the orbit was accompanied first by unequal growth of the circumorbital bones. The frontal bones could not determine this process; they could only follow it. The frontal bones could be dissociated from the shift of the orbits, but could not obstruct their forward advance.

This is clearly seen in a comparison of the skull roof structure of different Stegocephalia. When there is an abrupt shift of the orbits into the posterior part of the skull they are located in the region of the posterior ends of the frontal bones (*Benthosuchus* and *Cyclotosaurus*). In their movement they pass beyond the frontal bones. In the case of a secondary shift of the orbits to the anterior end of the skull they are found in the region of the anterior ends of the frontal bones (*Batrachosuchus* and *Dolichopareias*). In this movement, consequently, the orbits move in front of the frontal bones and do not withdraw from them as they would according to the Westoll theory.

From the foregoing it follows that the shift of the orbits, which accompanied the transition from crossopterygian fishes to terrestrial vertebrates, could not have led to their transposition from the region of the "parietal" bones to the frontal region. The relationship could only have been altered in the opposite direction. And in fact, while the generally accepted homologization of the bones is maintained, we see that in the Osteolepida and other primitive fishes the orbits are frequently located in the region of the anterior ends of the frontal bones (as in some Stegocephalia with a similar position of the eyes, cf. *Dolichopareias*), and in Stegocephalia they are located in the middle or the posterior part of the frontal bones. The backward shift of the orbits is accompanied by their approach toward the parietal bones. The facts consequently speak in favor of the generally established homology of the skull roof bones.

3. The validity of the generally accepted homology is proved still more convincingly by consideration of the correlation of the dermal bones of the skull with the canals of the lateral line organs (Fig. 48).

As is well known, in fishes these canals have a quite distinctive arrangement; the main canal of the lateral line of the trunk extends anteriorly on the dorsal surface of the head as the temporal, postorbital, and supraorbital canals. To these are connected, behind the orbits, the suborbital canals surrounding the orbits from below. In addition, in the temporal region of the main canal, the preopercular canal branches downward and forward. However, in crossopterygian and dipnoan fishes this canal branches off not from the orbital canal but from the suborbital. It is interesting that in the Stegocephalia the arrangement of the lateral line canals was the same as in crossopterygian and dipnoan fishes.

All these canals are found to be associated with particular bones of the skull, and bones bearing canals of the lateral line are very stable (Allis, 1935, 1936). This is explained by the history of the bony skull. As shown by Pehrson (1922) for *Amia calva* and later for *Polypterus* (Pehrson, 1947) and by Severtsov (1926) for *Acipenser, Amia,* and *Lepidosteus,* the dermal bones bearing lateral line canals arise in close association with the latter and sometimes are even closely associated with the individual sensory papillae of these canals. The bones are laid down by aggregations of osteoblasts lying directly under the lateral line canals. The bony material appears in the form of deposits, forming furrows and then complete tubes around the canals. Later, from the bases of the tubes, lamellated extensions arise expanding in various directions and forming the dermal bones of the skull. Thus, along the lines of the main canals on the dorsal surface of the head, from one to three pairs of primordia are initiated, from which one pair of nasal bones of the adult fish are developed; from one to three pairs of primordia merge into one pair of frontal bones (more precisely—lateral frontals), one pair of interparietals, one pair of temporals (intertemporals and supratemporals), and usually one pair of postparietals (postparietalia s. extra scapularia). All these bones (like the other bones of the lateral line) are distinguished by great stability which is determined by the organizational association with the lateral line canals. The known exceptions only affirm this rule. Thus in *Polypterus* the central canal passes over the "parietal" bone which does not occur in other fishes. It has been determined in adult *Polypterus* that these are not real parietal bones. As in other fishes, they are developed in the larvae without relation to the canals of the lateral line and then are eliminated. They are supplanted by the expanding pairs of temporal bones (intertemporals and supratemporals) which are normally canal-bearing.

Of the Stegocephalia, only in the family Ichthyostegidae do these canals pass within the dermal bones of the skull. In other Stegocephalia there are only grooves on the surface of the corresponding bones in which canals of the lateral lines are located. These grooves had the same arrangement as the lateral line canals in crossopterygian fishes and apparently they passed over the same bones.

One might definitely presume (as does Westoll) that a close association of the canals with skull bones, with respect to their superficial arrangement, is lost in the Stegocephalia.

However, the work of Bystrov (1935) shows that this is not true. It appears that the lateral line furrows pass unchanged over the same bones as in the fishes. Furthermore, and this fact is especially important, they always transect the centers of ossification of the corresponding bones. As demonstrated by the distribution and shape of the pits of the surface sculpture of the bones, and also by their deeper structure (in the arrangement of dermal canals), this is true in those cases in which the furrows of the lateral line seem only to touch the margin of a particular bone. Thus, for example, in the Stegocephalia the supraorbital canal passes along the outer edge of the frontal bone only to a small extent. The center of ossification is located just here, however, right at the upper rim of the orbit (in modern Amphibia the frontal bones are also expanded from anlagen on the side of the skull roof to the orbital region along the median line). The apparent exceptions to the case, in which the lateral line grooves seem to avoid the bones completely and pass along the sutures between adjacent bones, are also explained by the special expansion of certain bones. Thus in *Benthosuchus*, according to Bystrov, the preopercular lateral line canal is not located directly on the quadratojugal bone but passes along the suture between this bone and the squamosal. The fact is, however, that the quadratojugal is greatly expanded dorsally and here covers the downwardly expanding margin of the squamosal. The squamosal has extended below forward and laterally, covering the upper part of the quadrojugal as far as the groove of the canal lying on it.

The association of the lateral line canals with the cranial bones in the Stegocephalia is consequently found to be very close (Fig. 48). Therefore the presumption of a transfer of some canals from one bone to another, as implied in the hypothesis of Westoll, must be regarded as completely unfounded. This close alliance, according to Bystrov, is shown not only by the position of the canals on the anlagen of the bones in the larvae but also by the arrangement of the corresponding nerves under the dermal bones of the skull. The nerve branches supplying the sense organs in the lateral lines of the head pass through the dermal bones in special canals. Replacement of these canals is shown to be almost impossible. The frontal bones in both fishes and Stegocephalia typically bear the supraorbital canals, and the parietal bones develop independently of this canal in both fishes and stegocephalians. Therefore one cannot homologize the frontal bones of fishes with the parietal bones of terrestrial vertebrates. The postorbital canals in fishes and in Stegocephalia lie on the intertemporal and supratemporal bones and consequently bypass the parietal bones laterally. While the supraorbital canal actually passes on the parietal bone in the Ichthyostegalia, this is obviously the result of expansion of the intertemporal bones (this is also probably a function of the shape and position of the lateral portions of the parietal bones).

Furthermore, in fishes as in some Stegocephalia, in the occipital region of the skull there is a transverse canal passing along the postparietal bones (extrascapular, supratemporal, tabular, and postparietal). Obviously these bones are homologous (Fig. 48). Nevertheless the Westoll hypothesis presumes that the extrascapular of fishes has vanished and the tabular and postparietal of Stegocephalia are homologous with the supratemporal and parietal bones of fishes. This makes their connection to the transverse occipital canal, which is quite clear in some Stegocephalia [*Benthosuchus*, *Trematosaurus*, *Keraterpeton*, according to Bystrov (1935); *Dolichopareias*, according to Watson (1926a) and others] quite incomprehensible.

We should recognize the validity of the established nomenclature of the bones of terrestrial vertebrates and further affirm their similarity to the bones of the skull of crossopterygian fishes. The sole indisputable difference (aside from the reduction of the gill operculum) is the previously noted pineal foramen.

4. In fishes the pineal foramen lies between the frontal bones. However, it may be shifted one way or the other. According to Berg (1939) it is sometimes located at the boundary between the frontal and parietal bones in sturgeons. In terrestrial vertebrates it lies between the parietal bones. In some reptiles, however, it is located, as in some fishes, at the boundary between the frontals and the parietals or even at the posterior end of the frontal bones (*Conolophus*). On the other hand, as Berg shows, the pineal foramen may also be shifted to the posterior end of the parietal bones (Nothosauridae). In gymnophionan larvae (*Hypogeophis*, Marcus *et al.*, 1936), the pineal foramen is sometimes located in an unpaired ossicle lying between the frontals and parietals. Furthermore, in modern anuran Amphibia there are rudimentary parietal eyes located in the region of the boundary of the frontal bones and the nasals. In *Xenopus* the pineal orifice is even described as being between the frontal bones (Winterhalter, 1931). Evidently one must admit the possibility not only of a backward shift of the pineal body to the area of the parietals but also the reverse movement (as in Anura). Berg (1939) subjected the question of the position of the pineal orifice to a critical review, and came to the conclusion that "notwithstanding the fact that in the Osteolepides the pineal foramen is placed between the frontalia, and in the Stegocephalia between the parietalia, this fact does not oppose the homologizing of the bones involved."

The pineal foramen lies between the orbits in fishes, and posterior to the orbits in terrestrial vertebrates. The transition from crossopterygian fishes to terrestrial vertebrates was undoubtedly accompanied by a more pronounced shift of the pineal foramen than the displacements seen in fishes or in terrestrial vertebrates. This movement is seen in the crossopterygians. Thus, in the primitive crossopterygian *Osteolepis* the pineal foramen is located between the anterior part of the frontal bones in the preorbital region and in *Eusthenopteron*, which is more advanced, and undoubtedly more closely related to terrestrial vertebrates, it is behind the orbits, between the posterior parts of the frontal bones. In the Stegocephalia it is always placed behind the orbits although it is sometimes in the anterior part of the parietal bones (*Diceratosaurus* and *Stegops*) or at the boundary between the frontals and parietals just behind the orbits (*Platyrhinops*).

The existence of an age-dependent shift of the parietal foramen can also be established. Thus in the young *Benthosuchus sushkini* described by Bystrov and Efremov, the parietal foramen is located in the postorbital region, between the front ends of the parietal bones, directly behind a small unpaired ossification similar to the os pineale s. epiphysale of some fishes. In the adult *Benthosuchus*, and especially in larger adult specimens, the parietal foramen lies much farther behind the orbits, midway between the parietals (Bystrov and Efremov, 1940). In the young of some fishes, for example the sturgeons, *Amia*, and *Lepidosteus*, the epiphysis takes the form of a small eye, lying in a foramen with a special epiphysial cover of the chondrocranium, just under the skin in the orbital region of the head. A similar relationship occurs in *Polypterus*, and also in dipnoan fishes. In the larvae of the modern *Protopterus* the epiphysis takes the form of a well-developed eye with sensitized cells with rodlike bases directed inward to a cavity. The neural tracts may be traced from the eye to the habenular ganglia and to the posterior commissure. This eye is located behind the orbits. In all cases it is on a short stalk located directly over the roof of the midbrain or directly in front of it. Undoubtedly the parietal eye was sessile in the Stegocephalia and located in the same region of the brain. This is consequent upon the topographical correlation between the parietal foramen and that region of the skull base in which the hypophysis is located. First Efremov (1933) and then Bystrov (1935) called attention to the fact that the parietal foramen in Stegocephalia occupies a definite position in relation to the braincase and the skull floor during all changes of the general shape of the skull. The vertical projection of the parietal foramen falls at the point of origin of the ensiform process from the parasphenoid body. Directly behind this point, over the expanded parasphenoid, the basipterygoid process of the skull base and the hypophyseal pit was located. Westoll also called attention to the relationship; he noted a pattern in the relative position of these elements. This topographical relationship serves as proof of the fact that the parietal eye in crossopterygian fishes, as in the Stegocephalia, was on a short stalk, i.e., was situated in the midbrain region, or directly in front of it (but not far in front, as in modern Anura). It follows from this that the shift of the parietal organ in the ancestors of terrestrial vertebrates was connected with a change of the position of the midbrain.

With the development of the olfactory organs, the olfactory lobes, and the hemispheres of the cerebrum, the midbrain was reduced in relative size and shifted backward, being located in the adult animal behind the orbits along with the pineal organ. The shift of the parietal foramen is consequently determined only by the shift of the midbrain and the pineal organ associated with it. This is completely true only when this organ is on a short stalk (and we have shown that this was true in the Stegocephalia).

A possible shift of the pineal foramen in crossopterygian fishes was restricted by the division of the skull into two divisions. The pineal organ, connected to the midbrain, could not pass beyond the borders of the anterior division (ethmosphenoid) and the frontal bones covering it, and consequently under no condition could the pineal foramen be transferred backward into the region of the parietal bones (covering the otico-occipital). Such a shift became possible only after fusion of the two divisions to each other as occurred in the Tetrapoda. The orbits may be shifted, however, in terrestrial vertebrates or fishes; the frontal bones always belong to the orbital region of the skull, and the parietals to the otic region. All this testifies, consequently, in favor of the long established homology of the cranial roofing bones and definitely indicates a transfer of the pineal foramen from the frontal bone region backward to the parietal area.

5. We must still cite some data on the arrangement of the skull roof bones in the Crossopterygii and Tetrapoda. In Crossopterygii, in accordance with the division of the braincase into two parts, the skull roof is also divided into two movable interconnected parts. The division between the anterior and posterior divisions passes across the skull roof between the frontal and parietal bones (Fig. 49). Laterally from this transverse suture a prolonged suture passes obliquely backward between the parietal shield and cheek region of the skull. The latter is immovably connected to the lateral part of the skull and its anterior division. To the otico-occipital is connected only the central parietal shield, consisting of the parietals in the middle, the intertemporals and supratemporals on the sides (through them pass the main canals of the seismosensory organs), and the "extrascapulars" (with the transverse canal of the seismosensory organs) posteriorly (cf. Fig. 48, *Osteolepis*). The cleft between the parietal shield and the cheek bones (squamosal and postorbital) ends posteriorly at the upper edge of the operculum. In the middle of it the spiracle opens. In all terrestrial vertebrates the transverse cleft between the frontal and parietal bones has been replaced by a firm suture. However, in the embolomerous Stegocephalia (Anthracosauria) there was a typical parietal shield consisting of parietals in the middle, intertemporals, and supratemporals (with the main canals of the seismosensory organs) on the sides, and the tab-

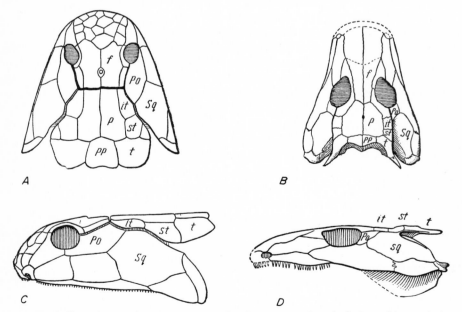

FIG. 49. Skull roof of *Diplopterax* (*A, C*) and *Palaeogyrinus* (*B, D*). *f*, Frontal bone; *it*, interparietal bone; *P*, parietal; *Po*, postorbital; *pp*, postparietal; *Sq*, squamosal; *St*, supratemporal; *t*, tabular. From Watson (1926b).

ulars and postparietals (undoubtedly homologues of the "extrascapulars") posteriorly. Along the later, in some Stegocephalia, passed the same tranverse lateral line canal. Between this shield and the bones of the cheek region, squamosal and postorbital, there was, in Anthracosauria, a quite definite cleft passing backward to the otic notch (Fig. 49).

The existence of this cleft in the Stegocephalia (Fig. 49) is undoubtedly a remnant of the movable articulation of crossopterygian fishes, rendering the homology of this whole complex of bones completely irrefutable. To this should be added the fact that in those cases in which the connection of the pectoral girdle to the skull was retained (as in *Eogyrinus*), it was located between the posttemporal and the tabular. Consequently the "lateral extrascapular" of crossopterygian fishes, to which the posttemporal is attached, is also the homolog of the tabular of the Stegocephalia.

As was stated before, a very important criterion in the homologization of the skull roof bones is the system of lateral line canals which are always connected with precisely identified bones.

There is no such criterion for homologization of the dermal bones of the floor of the skull and the palatal region. However, the general arrangement of the bones in the Stegocephalia and the crossopterygian fishes is so similar that no doubt can be raised. An interesting problem is the question of the origin of the parasphenoid of Amphibia (as well as of higher fishes). In crossopterygian fishes it underlies only the anterior division of the skull (ethmosphenoid), and in the Amphibia (and in higher fishes) it underlies the entire base of the skull. In crossopterygian fishes (*Eusthenopteron*) there are, however, a pair of toothed plates located under the otic region of the skull. Jarvik (1954) regards these plates as the anterior pair of upper pharyngeal tooth plates and assigns their origin to the upper internal division of the hyoid arch (infrapharyngohyal). Whether or not the latter suggestion is true it is difficult to tell. The hypothesis of Jarvik, however, that by fusion of these plates the parasphenoid of the terrestrial vertebrates acquired its posterior expanded division, is highly probable. In the urodele Amphibia the parasphenoid is divided into two anlagen, anterior and posterior, of which the posterior anlage is occasionally paired, or traces of this are found (Lebedkina, 1960, 1963). The posterior ascending processes of the parasphenoid found in both fishes and in amphibian larvae are developed on the posterior anlage, and in the crossopterygian group are represented by small tooth plates on the sides of the otic region (under the spiracular canal).

The dermal bones of the lower jaw in lower Stegocephalia and crossopterygian fishes have a very similar arrangement and are undoubtedly homologous.

The problem of the homology of the internal ossifications of the skull, that is, the enchondral bones, is rather different. Usually they have the same nomenclature in terrestrial vertebrates as is used for the corresponding regions of the fish skull. However, a sufficient basis for this is lacking. In crossopterygian fishes the braincase was ossified in the form of two complete bones, the ethmosphenoid and the otico-occipital. In lower Stegocephalia, an integrated ossified brain case (*Palaeogyrinus*; Watson, 1926b) was formed by their fusion. Even in the otico-occipital region of most Carboniferous Stegocephalia the bone is divided into a small number of typical skull bones. In later forms part of the braincase remained cartilaginous, and certain bones were also divided off in the olfactory-orbital region. The similarity in their arrangement in Amphibia and in some fishes (e.g., the paired orbitosphenoids of *Polypterus* and the Caudata) is due to convergence. On the other hand, it is very likely that the braincase of early Stegocephalia, and also both blocks of the skull of crossopterygian fishes, were developed from several typical ossification centers which, by reduction of the bony skull, gave rise to the individual elements. In such cases individual bones could have been formed in *Polypterus* and the Actinopterygii analogous to the skull bones of terrestrial vertebrates as the result of parallel process of reduction of the ossified braincase.

The similarity of the replacement bones of the visceral apparatus also rests better on analogy than on homology. Among these are the autopalatine, epipterygoid, metapterygoid, and quadrate in the upper jaw and the mentomandibular and articular in the lower jaw.

I I

The Stegocephalia of the Carboniferous and the Adaptive Radiations of the First Terrestrial Vertebrates

All the more primitive Stegocephalia, not only the Devonian ichthyo-stegids, but also the Lower Carboniferous labyrinthodonts and the lepospon-dylous forms, were aquatic animals. They lived, fed, and reproduced in water (Romer, 1958). Like the ichthyostegids they crept out on shore, but did not make any definite migrations on land. Nevertheless, even in these ancient forms there were marked ecological divergences which later progressively deepened and led to the formation of the main branches of terrestrial verte-brates, the rhachitomous labyrinthodonts, the embolomeres, and the lepo-spondylous Amphibia. The first includes a vast number of extinct forms and gave rise to the Anura, the second were the source of the many forms of rep-tiles, and the third continued in the form of modern Apoda and the urodele Amphibia.

All these Amphibia lived in the water. The labyrinthodonts fed on fish, and the lepospondylous Amphibia obviously fed mainly on invertebrates, worms, crustacea, and arthropod larvae. Correspondingly they lived in different waters; the labyrinthodonts lived in rivers and lakes and the lepospondylous Amphibia lived in shallow standing waters. This ecological divergence left its mark on their morphology. This is expressed in the skull structure (bat-rachomorphic and reptiliomorphic) and especially in the structure of the backbone. There was a simultaneous development of the appendages, the organs of hearing, and the respiratory mechanism. The most pronounced divergence, however, was in the structure of the vertebral column (Fig. 50). Most Stegocephalia (labyrinthodonts) retained the way of life of their ich-thyostegid and crossopterygian fish ancestors. It was the way of life of a fish-eating predator. Correspondingly, in the vertebral column, the principal organ of locomotion, essentially the same structure was retained. The elastic notochord formed the central axis with the overlying elements of the centra which more often than not were ossified. The vertebrae consisted of ossified

89

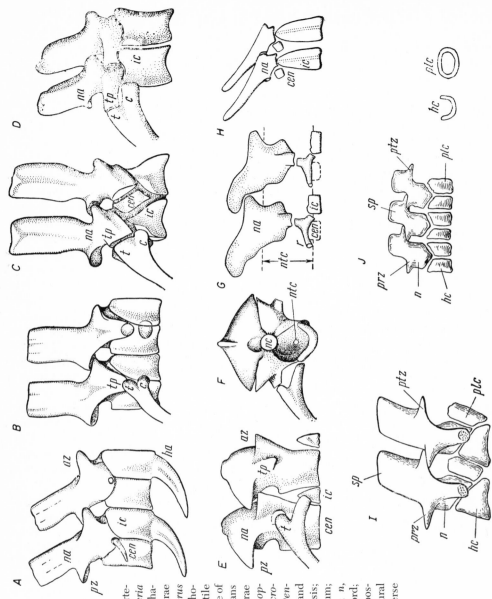

FIG. 50. Caudal and thoracic vertebrae of the embolomere *Archeria* (A, B); thoracic vertebrae of the rhachitome *Eryops* (C); thoracic vertebrae of the stereospondyle *Mastodonsaurus* (D); lateral and anterior views of thoracic vertebrae of the primitive reptile *Seymouria* (E, F); thoracic vertebrae of the hypothetical ancestors of anurans *Amphibamus* (B); thoracic vertebrae of the crossopterygian fish *Eusthenopteron* (H); thoracic vertebrae of *Micropholis* (I); thoracic vertebrae of *Dendryazousa* (J). From Romer, Kuhn, and Steen. *az*, Anterior zygapophysis; *c*, capitulum; *c*, *plc*, pleurocentrum; *ha*, hemal arch; *ic*, intercentrum; *n*, neural arch; *nc*, canal for spinal chord; *ntc*, notochordal canal; *pz*, *ptz*, posterior zygapophysis; *r*, rib; *sp*, neural spine; *t*, tuberculum; *tp*, transverse process (diapophysis).

anterior hypocentra and posterior pleurocentra. The bases of the neural arches were wedged between them. In connection with the powerful development of the vertebrae, the lateral muscles and the neural spines were well developed. In the rhachitomous labyrinthodonts, in accord with their progressive adaptation to locomotion on land, the elements of the vertebral column became more ossified; they drew together and thus the whole column acquired greater solidity without any special reconstruction (as in *Eryops* and *Cacops*). This mode of evolution, however, was not developed further since it did not provide either sufficient firmness within the segments (since the centrum of the vertebra was made up of separate parts) or the required flexibility between the segments (since no definite articulations were developed between the centra). In only one line of rhachitomous Stegocephalia did there arise a reconstruction of the vertebral column; the whole centrum of the vertebra was developed from an expansion of the base of the neural arch which supplanted the other elements of the vertebrae. This line led to the development of anuran Amphibia.

Otherwise adaptation to terrestrial life arose in other branches of the more ancient Stegocephalia. In one branch of primitive labyrinthodonts the hypocentra and pleurocentra attained equal development and enclosed the notochord as hemivertebral rings. In each segment of the trunk region the anterior ring, the hypocentrum, gave support for the capitulum of a rib, and in the caudal region it was continued into a hemal arch. Both types of vertebral structure in labyrinthodonts, the rhachitomous and the embolomerous, readily displace each other. The original one is obviously the primordial rhachitomous type characteristic of the batrachomorphic forms. Embolomerous vertebrae are characteristic of reptiliomorphic Stegocephalia and are one of the characteristics leading to their divergence. The limbs, weak in the ancestral forms, were gradually strengthened during the transition to life on land. We find quite another type of structure in the lepospondylous group of Amphibia evidently connected to their quite different way of life. Indeed their small overall size indicates another type of adaptation sharply differing from that of the large predators, the labyrinthodonts.

The backbone shows fully ossified centra in the form of biconvex cylinders. Evidently they were formed by early fusion of the hypocentra and pleurocentra to the base of the neural arch. The fairly long centrum of the vertebra indicates the width of the muscular segments and consequently the greater length of the muscle fibers and their slower contraction. The low neural arch and the negligible neural spine indicate the weak development of the spinal (epaxial) musculature which takes the main role in swimming. Lepospondylous Amphibia, while they lived in the water, could not have been good swimmers and could not have hunted for fishes. Apparently they lived in standing waters and fed on invertebrates, worms, crustaceans, and arthropod larvae. The definite development of articular processes indicates the flexibility of the vertebral column, a good adaptation for crawling on land. Evidently the lepospondylous Amphibia were pioneers in invading wet land and in feeding on arthropods. In the main they were swamp dwellers. Many of them went over to serpentine locomotion and lost their limbs. Occasionally they became transformed into burrowing animals. Many of them returned to permanent life in the water, giving rise to two types of adaptations to that life, eel-like forms and forms with a flattened trunk and a flat broad head. The limbs in all lepospondylous Amphibia were weak, and in many cases were reduced. One of the most essential acquisitions of terrestrial vertebrates are the organs of sound reception. In the labyrinthodonts a system of hearing in the air was developed. This system was apparently developed simultaneously and somewhat differently in batrachomorphs and reptiliomorphs. In the first the tympanic cavity and tympanic membrane were developed in a dorsal position, in the otic notch at the site of the former operculum. In the second group the corresponding parts were developed more ventrally, perhaps at the base of the operculum (suboperculum). This led also to differences in the relationship of the auditory ossicle to the hypoglossal nerve (cf. Fig. 40). In lepospondylous Amphibia the system of aerial hearing was reduced and transformed into a system for sound reception from the land. The history of this transformation is revealed only in the ontogenesis of urodele Amphibia (Schmalhausen, 1956a,b). Palaeontology gives no indication of the origin of the sound receiving apparatus and does not reveal the origin of the vertebrae and the early general history of the lepospondylous Amphibia. In the early Carboniferous, typical members of all three main branches of the Stegocephalia, the rhachitomous and embolomerous labyrinthodonts, and lepospondylous Amphibia, were already present.

The divergences in organization of the older Stegocephalia were continued in other organs also, in particular the breathing mechanism, and this in turn was expressed in the structure of the skull and the pectoral framework. Crossopterygian fishes when crawling on land undoubtedly utilized dermal respiration. In the Stegocephalia this system of dermal respiration was particularly well developed. However, dermal respiration supplemented oropharyngeal and then pulmonary respiration, the force mechanism of which is an adaptation of the gill respiration mechanism. In the smaller Stegocephalia with relatively large body surfaces the main role was always played by cutaneous respiration. Oropharyngeal respiration was only of secondary significance and the pulmonary system was used mainly while living in the water. The same situation was retained in modern urodele Amphibia as in the lepospondylous Stegocephalia.

In the larger Stegocephalia cutaneous respiration was insufficient. Correspondingly, in the labyrinthodonts oropharyngeal and pulmonary respiration were gradually developed. In both cases the intermandibular muscles served as the main respiratory muscles which contracted rhythmically and pulled air into the oral cavity and either expelled it through the nostrils or forced it into the lungs (through the open pharyngeal slit). The effectiveness of the force pump depended therefore on the superficial mandibular muscles and, consequently, upon the distance between the rami of the lower jaws (Schmalhausen, 1957d). The latter depended in turn on the position of the palatoquadrate. With gradual development of oropharyngeal and pulmonary respiration in Amphibia the palatoquadrate was expanded and passed from a vertical to a horizontal position. Correspondingly the whole head became widened and flattened (Fig. 38). In the later rhachitomous labyrinthodonts the relatively large head lost its flat shape. In Triassic stereospondylous forms this flattening of the head reached even greater proportions, but evidently was associated with the benthic life of these aquatic giants.

The evolution of the reptiliomorphic Stegocephalia, in which very long ribs enclosing the abdominal cavity were retained, proceeded differently. With gradual development of the limbs, lifting the body above the ground, there could be developed a suction mechanism of pulmonary respiration which supplanted all previous mechanisms (dermal, oropharyngeal, and force-pulmonary respiration). A movable thorax was developed and with the decline of the importance of cutaneous respiration, the keratinous layer of the skin was gradually strengthened. This increased the possibilities of emergence into dryer land environments. The respiration mechanism and its effectiveness now no longer depended on the width of the intermandibular muscles and in some reptiliomorphic Stegocephalia not only did the flattened skull form not occur, but on the contrary, the skull became even taller, as in Fig. 38 (Schmalhausen, 1957d). All these divergent characteristics are noted even in the more primitive Carboniferous Stegocephalia and this undoubtedly was a very early divergence.

Rhachitomous Stegocephalia in the main retained the way of life of their ancestors, that of fish-eating predators. They frequented only the shore zones of rivers and permanent bodies of water.

The embolomerous Stegocephalia, also originally fish-eating predators, invaded land very slowly and gradually gave rise to the reptiles.

The lepospondylous Amphibia lived in swampy, occasionally drying-out waters, and fed on invertebrates. They were undoubtedly pioneers in the occupation of a wet land environment and in feeding on arthropods. Having occupied this ecological zone they survived in it to the present in the form of their comparatively little-modified offspring, the wormlike Caecilia and the urodele Amphibia.

I 2

The Labyrinthodonts and the Evolution of the Riparian Amphibia

The ichthyostegids (*Ichthyostega, Ichthyostegopsis,* and *Acanthostega*) are actually transitional forms between the crossopterygian fishes and Stegocephalia. Such a similarity in the skull roof structure of certain stegocephalians and the ichthyostegids has been found that they are now included into one suborder—Ichthyostegalia. The skull roof in the Lower Carboniferous *Otocratia* and in the ichthyostegids is especially similar, both in general shape and in structure. There are fairly large postparietals and the orbits are separated from the frontals lying between them by the prefrontals and postfrontals. There is a fairly large supratemporal and no intertemporal. A unique feature is a fenestra between the squamosal and tabular at the usual location of the otic notch. Romer (1945) assigns to the Ichthyostegalia the more recent Upper Carboniferous *Colosteus* (Fig. 51) and *Erpetosaurus*. In general form and in the structure of the skull roof these Stegocephalia are similar to the ichthyostegids. They have fairly large postparietals and supratemporals; also, the intertemporals are absent and the orbits are separated from the frontals by the enclosed prefrontals and postfrontals. In addition, in all these forms the nostrils lie very low, in the immediate vicinity of the mouth. There is also a movable basipterygoid articulation. However, in addition to these primitive characteristics there is a large interpterygoid fenestra at the side of the parasphenoid in *Colosteus* and *Erpetosaurus*, a feature typical of the more recent Stegocephalia. Of the latter, many (e.g., *Edops*, Fig. 52) also resemble the ichthyostegids, and this circumstance, as well as the structure of vertebral column consisting of independent elements with predominant hypocentra, leads one to regard the ichthyostegids as primitive rhachitomous labyrinthodonts. All the above forms were obviously mainly aquatic animals. In the ichthyostegids the seismosensory organs are still arranged in canals within the skull bones (as in fishes), while in *Colosteus* they lay in grooves on the surface of the skull. In the vertebral column of *Erpetosaurus* the hypocentra and pleurocentra are about equally developed and have the shape of thin ossified half-rings surrounding the notochord laterally. In external aspect the vertebral column resembles the embolomerous type.

94

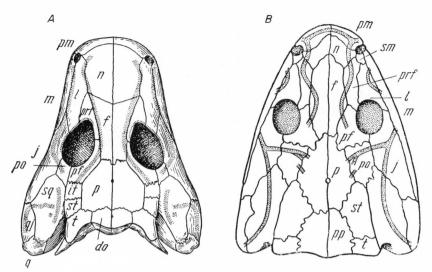

FIG. 51. Skull of the embolomere *Palaeogyrinus* (A), from Watson; and skull of the primitive rhachitome *Colosteus* (B). From Romer (1945). *do*, Postparietal; *f*, frontal; *J*, jugal; *l*, lachrymal; *it*, intertemporal; *m*, maxilla; *n*, nasal; *p*, parietal; *pf* and *prf*, postfrontal and prefrontal; *pm*, premaxilla; *po*, postorbital; *pp*, postparietal; *q*, quadrate; *qj*, quadratojugal; *sm*, septomaxilla; *sq*, squamosal; *st*, supratemporal; *t*, tabular.

Among the earlier Carboniferous labyrinthodonts there were also a small group of very primitive forms with embolomerous vertebral structure (*Megalocephalus*, *Loxomma*, and *Baphetes*), in which the hypocentra and pleurocentra acquired about equal development to form two centra in each segment. This is probably correlated with the elongation of the body of these batrachomorphic Stegocephalia. Otherwise, they retained a very primitive skull

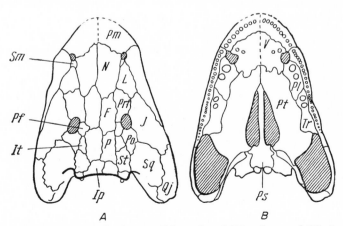

FIG. 52. Skull of the primitive rhachitome *Edops*, dorsal (A) and ventral (B) views. *F*, Frontal; *Ip*, postparietal; *It*, intertemporal; *J*, jugal; *L*, lachrymal; *N*, nasal; *P*, parietal; *Rf*, postfrontal; *Pl*, palatine; *Pm*, premaxilla; *Prf*, prefrontal; *Ps*, parasphenoid; *Pt*, pterygoid; *Qj*, quadratojugal; *Sq*, squamosal; *St*, supratemporal; *Tr*, ectopterygoid; *V*, vomer. From Romer.

structure with a complete set of roofing bones, including the rostral elements (internasals) seen in ichthyostegids (and Osteolepida), and sometimes also the intertemporal which was lost in the icthyostegids. The palate was complete, without the interpterygoid fenestra, as in ichthyostegids. There was a movable basipterygoid articulation. The nostrils were placed farther down, at the very edge of the mouth. A unique feature of the skull was the long orbit in the anterior part of which some glands were probably located. The grooves for the seismosensory organs, retained in the skull roof, indicate an aquatic life, and the powerful tusks indicate a predatory mode of life (Fig. 53). This line of Stegocephalia did not achieve further development.

A large number of diversified Carboniferous labyrinthodonts with rhachitomous vertebral structure are closely allied with the ichthyostegids. In a number of these forms a gradual adaptation to terrestrial life begins, manifested in the loss of the grooves for the seismosensory organs and in the gradual development of the limbs and backbone. There were almost no fully terrestrial forms among them, however. Their evolution is expressed in adaptive radiations of riparian Amphibia that spent their whole life bound to water basins.

These Stegocephalia are very diversified, but can be divided into two main groups of biological forms. On the one hand there is a group of rather large crocodilelike predators with long snouts, and on the other hand there are numerous small forms with shorter heads.

In the background of these groups are primitive Carboniferous Stegocephalia, similar in general to the Ichthyostegalia (*Edops*, Fig. 52, and *Gaudrya*). From here a line of large fish-eating predators leads to a return to fully aquatic life (*Archegosaurus, Platyops, Trematosaurus, Tertrema, Aphaneramma, Lyrocephalus, Peltostega,* and others). These Permian and Lower Triassic Stegocephalia retained the full set of bones in the skull roof (without intertemporals). There was a large interpterygoid fenestra in the palate. A basipterygoid articulation is seen in the suture between the pterygoid and parasphenoid. The long snout and powerful tusklike teeth indicate a predatory life and aggressive pursuit of prey (fishes). In all these forms there were

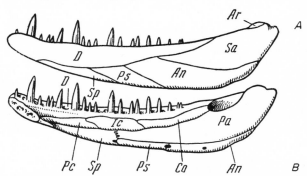

FIG. 53. Jaw of the primitive rhachitome *Megalocephalus*, external (*A*) and internal (*B*) views. *An*, Angular; *Ar*, articular; *Co*, coronoid; *D*, dentary; *Ic*, intercoronoid; *Pa*, prearticular (goniale); *Pc*, precoronoid; *Ps*, postsplenial; *S*, surangular; *Sp*, splenial. From Watson.

well-developed grooves for the seismosensory organs. Some of them (*Aphaner-amma* and others) are found in the marine deposits of Spitzbergen. A maritime life has been attributed to them, however, there is little likelihood of this. Most likely the carcasses drifted down from rivers into the sea.

In the course of evolution there were many parallel branches of large fish-eating predators. Predominant development of the hypocentra and reduction of the pleurocentra led through neorhachitomous to stereospondylous vertebral structure. Beginning with fairly primitive Permian forms (*Rhine-suchus*) their evolution was also manifested in gradual adaptation to completely aquatic life. In place of the basipterygoid articulation a suture is found between the pterygoids and the parasphenoid. The interpterygoid fenestra is large. The skull is flattened, with well-developed grooves for the seismosensory organs. A typical representative of the neorhachitomous forms is *Benthosuchus*, described in detail by Bystrov and Efremov (1940).

In more recent forms [*Capitosaurus, Cyclotosaurus,* and *Mastodonsaurus* (the head of the latter up to 1 meter long)] not only the skull but the trunk was also widened. The orbits were brought near each other in the roof of the skull. In every characteristic the stereospondylous Stegocephalia were benthic animals which did not pursue prey but lay in wait for it. The huge heavy head, which with the short trunk and small appendages completely excluded the possibility of locomotion on land (*Metoposaurus*), at the same time did not permit rapid swimming although strong tails had been developed. The gradual broadening and shortening of the head led to quite aberrant forms (*Batrachosuchus, Plagiosaurus, Gerrothorax*); of these *Gerrothorax* was a neotenic form with external gills.

During the Permian all these Stegocephalia changed over to life in water, not remaining on land in competition with more active reptiles. In the Triassic the large Stegocephalia were represented only by such secondarily aquatic forms. By the close of this period, however, they had all become extinct, evidently as a result of competition from fishes and reptiles.

The Paleozoic Stegocephalia living at the boundary of the two media, which associated with water not only for reproduction but also for feeding, gradually changed over to foraging on land. Among the many small rhachitomous Stegocephalia manifesting a more or less definite adaptation to terrestrial life there occurred, however, a secondarily derived return to purely aquatic life. Such an aquatic form, for example, was *Trimerorhachis*, which had excellently developed grooves for the seismosensory system. To such forms may also be added *Dvinosaurus* (Fig. 54), which retained the external gills into the adult stage, that is, they were neotenic forms. On the other hand, many definitely terrestrial rhachitomous forms are known. From such terrestrial forms in the Permian period, during the increasing aggressiveness of predatory reptiles, special biological types of marine Stegocephalia developed. A later but characteristic representative of this type, for example, is the Lower Triassic *Micropholis* (Fig. 55). As an adaptation to locomotion on land there is seen a completely ossified vertebral column retaining, however, a typical rhachitomous structure and considerably strengthened limbs. The trunk and

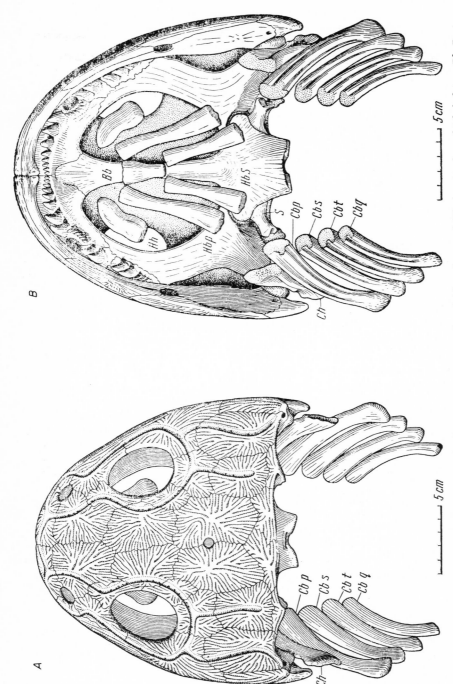

Fɪɢ. 54. Skull of the Permian neotenic rhachitome *Dvinosaurus*, dorsal (A) and ventral (B) showing branchial skeleton. *Bb*, Basi-branchial; *Cbp*, *Cbs*, *Cbt*, *Cbq*, ceratobranchials 1–4; *Ch*, ceratohyal; *Hbp*, *Hbs*, hypobranchials 1–2; *Hh*, hypohyal; *s*, stapes. From Bystrov.

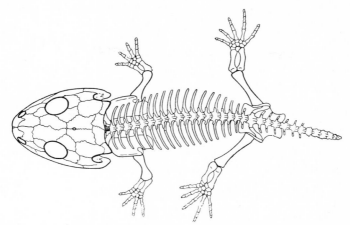

FIG. 55. Skeleton of the late coastal rhachitome *Micropholis* (Triassic). From Watson.

especially the tail are much shortened. The skull is of very primitive composition, but lightened in structure with very large interpterygoid fenestrae.
The basipterygoid articulation was retained. A similar type is found in the
terrestrial marine *Trematops* (Lower Permian), which also showed well-
developed limbs and a short tail. Not all terrestrial Stegocephalia were distinguished by small or medium size. Thus, the Permian *Eryops* (Fig. 56) was a
huge crocodiliform animal with a massive skull. The body and tail were also
relatively short. The limbs and their girdles were very strongly developed and
completely ossified (Fig. 57). Such an awkward animal certainly could not
keep up with fishes. Nevertheless it was a powerful predator. Evidently
Eryops fed on small and less mobile Amphibia on land. In support of this
is the appearance in other Amphibia (e.g., Zatrachydae) of defensive adaptations. The mode of feeding was probably the same in Permian predatory
reptiles also. *Eryops* was not able to survive in competition with reptiles.
A series of forms is known closely approaching *Eryops* and characterized
by an even more highly developed adaptation to terrestrial life. Of these,
for example, *Dissorophus* and *Cacops* (Fig. 58) are small, evidently terrestrial
animals, with solid vertebrae, short tails, and very strong limbs, but with

FIG. 56. The Permian rhachitome *Eryops*. Restoration from Colbert (1955).

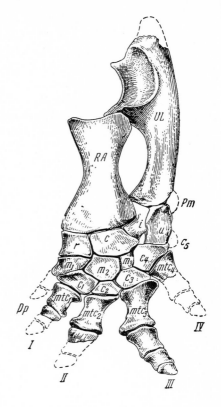

FIG. 57. Forelimb of *Eryops*. *c*,
Proximal centrale; c_1, c_5, distal carpals; *i*, intermedium; m_1–m_3, medial
carpals; mtc_2–mtc_4, metacarpals; *Pm*,
postminimus; *Pp*, prepollex; *r*, radial;
RA, radius; *u*, ulnare; *UL*, ulna; *I–IV*,
digits. From Miner.

an appearance somewhat reminiscent of frogs. On the back was a protective
armor of dermal bones resting on the neural spines. In all these cases the
vertebrae were very fully ossified but retained a typical rhachitomous structure. This line of development may be called "nonadaptive specialization" according to V. Kovalevskii, or "wrongly directed adaptation" (fehlgeschlagene
Anpassung = misadaptation) of Abel (1929). The strengthening of the backbone came about through more complete ossification of its elements and their
closer union, without any particular reconstruction. In this there was obtained
neither sufficient firmness within the segments, nor sufficient movability
between the skeletal segments. All these forms arose rapidly, flourished,

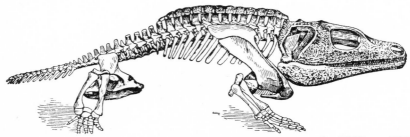

FIG. 58. Skeleton of the Permian rhachitome *Cacops*. From Romer, after Williston (1909).

and as quickly became extinct, leaving no descendants. A more progressive type of vertebral structure was developed at various times on the basis of the vertebral column of the most primitive members of the rhachitomous labyrinthodonts. The requisite reconstruction of the backbone was accomplished here by various means.

In some terrestrial labyrinthodonts the hypocentra and pleurocentra became equally developed and alternated regularly along the backbone so that the latter acquired the embolomerous structure. This occurred in a small group of Carboniferous labyrinthodonts—the Dendrerpetontidae. *Dendrerpeton* (Fig. 59) were lizardlike animals of moderate size (the skull was about 8 cm long), covered with scales, and had strong limbs with long toes. They were found in sandstone inside hollow *Sigillaria* trunks along with remains of insects. Apparently they fell into the hollow trunks of broken-down *Sigillaria* in pursuit of insects and were then unable to jump out of these traps. During floods, mud and sand were washed in and buried them along with their prey. The hypocentra, similar to those which are found in the rhachitomous spine, enclosed the notochord below and laterally. They were not joined together on the dorsal side. In the closely related *Dendryazousa* they were reduced dorsally. As in the embolomerous column, however, the pleurocentra took the form of complete rings enclosing the notochord on all sides. The neural arches were massive basally with saddle-shaped transverse processes covering the notochord between the hypocentra and pleurocentra. There were stout zygapophyses and short neural spines. In the pectoral girdle there was a short interclavicular bone; the clavicle was also expanded ventrally. The cleithrum extended as a shaft along the scapular bone and continued as a broad plate covered by the suprascapular cartilage. The scapula

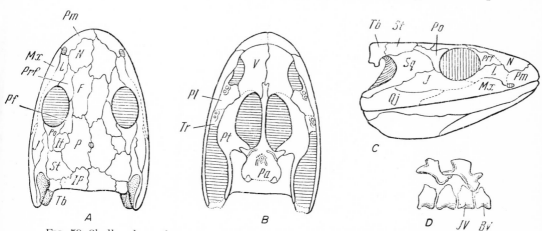

FIG. 59. Skull and vertebrae of the primitive embolomere *Dendrerpeton*; dorsal view of skull (*A*), ventral view of skull (*B*), lateral view of skull (*C*), and two vertebrae (*D*). *BV*, Hypocentrum; *F*, frontal; *Ip*, interparietal (postparietal); *It*, intertemporal; *JV*, pleurocentrum; *J*, jugal; *L*, lachrymal; *Mx*, maxilla, *N*, nasal; *P*, parietal; *Pa*, parasphenoid; *Pf*, postfrontal; *Pl*, palatine; *Pm*, premaxilla; *Po*, postorbital; *St*, supratemporal; *Tb*, tabular; *Tr*, ectopterygoid (transversa), *V*, vomer. From Steen.

was short and broad in the shoulder joint area. The humerus, very broad in its distal part, had a large entepicondylar foramen. The forearm was long. The long phalanges indicate that the digits were long. The ilium, wide in the acetabular part, had a narrow downwardly inclined process as in *Ichthyostega, Eogyrinus,* and in some primitive reptilomorphs. The ischium and pubis were ossified but not suturally fused. The thigh bone was straight and massive. There were five digits in the posterior limbs. The skull of *Dendrerpeton* was very primitive in its composition (Fig. 59). It was fairly high, as in the ichthyostegids, and relatively narrow as in *Acanthostega.* In the exoccipitals there were small foramina for the occipital nerves (XII). The upper occipital region was not ossified. There was a single unpaired occipital condyle formed mostly from the basioccipital (with a negligible part of the exoccipitals). In the skull roof there was a predominant development of the parietals, frontals, and nasals. The latter were short and broad. The fairly large orbits were located in the middle of the skull and were separated from the frontal bones by the enclosing prefrontals and postfrontals. There was not only a supratemporal but also an intertemporal. The small nostrils lay ventrally on the margin of the mouth. The lachrymal was elongated. The squamosal enclosed a deep otic notch. The small tabular bounded only a small part of this notch on the medial side. There were broad postparietals which separated the tabulars from the parietals (the latitabular type of structure characteristic of batrachomorphs). The choanae were large but also widely separated, and lay at the inner edge of the mouth. The interpterygoid fenestra was small. The parasphenoid was expanded posteriorly and bore a small patch of teeth. In general the palatal structure was also primitive. However, the palatine and especially the pterygoids were small. Each bore only a pair of teeth. The vomer was very large. There was an epipterygoid. The basipterygoid processes on the basisphenoid were well developed and had movable articulations to the palatoquadrate. Above the quadrate, on the margin of the squamosal, there was a depression along the posterior crest of the pterygoid in which the cartilaginous process of the stapes probably lay (cf. Urodela), as in *Dvinosaurus* also. The stapes itself was ossified. It was expanded at both ends.

Throughout this there is manifested the primitiveness of the Dendrerpetontidae, which combine characteristics similar to the Ichthyostegalia, to the primitive rhachitomes, and even to the reptiliomorphs (having embolomerous vertebrae with a tendency to reduction of the hypocentra, posterior processes on the ilia, and the presence of the intertemporal). In some respects they are close to *Eugyrinus,* and they are also apparently close to the Microsauria in which (*Hylonomus*) posterior processes are also found on the ilia. They probably take their ultimate origin from some Devonian forms.

From the rhachitomous stegocephalians to the Dendrerpetontidae there are also similar, later, somewhat aberrant forms, such as *Acanthostoma* and *Stegops.* In *Acanthostoma* the column is reminiscent of the embolomeres but the pleurocentra are paired and do not take the form of a complete ring, although laterally they cover the full height of the notochord. In *Stegops* the spinal column also resembles the embolomeres; both its elements, the hypocentra and pleurocentra, take the form of paired half-rings of thin bone.

Of considerable interest to us with regard to our theme is a group of larger forms showing another trend in vertebral reconstruction associated with a gradual adaptation to terrestrial life. Their early representatives are related to the most primitive rhachitomous labyrinthodonts, *Edops, Gaudrya,* and *Dendrerpeton.* In these forms the skull roof retained a full complement of bones, including the intertemporal; the palate had an even smaller interpterygoid fenestra. There were well-developed basipterygoid articulations and a single occipital condyle in the formation of which both the basioccipital and the exoccipitals took part. In the ancestral forms there were also grooves for the seismosensory system. Evidently they were semiaquatic animals with a typical rhachitomous vertebral column. In later evolution the skull roof was lightened, the interpterygoid fenestra enlarged, the occipital condyle widened, the vertebrae ossified more fully, and the limbs gradually strengthened. In all of this, adaptation to a riparian life is manifested, apparently correlated with a transition to feeding on arthropods on land. To this group belong the species of *Branchiosaurus,* in which there was early established the predominant development of the neural arch in the column. The skull was flat and relatively broad. The postparietals and tabulars were relatively small. There were large orbits and large interpterygoid fenestrae. The pterygoids were triramose and the parasphenoid was much expanded posteriorly. Since external gills occurred in some Branchiosauria, according to Romer (1945) they are larval forms of various rhachitomous labyrinthodonts similar to *Eryops.* Nevertheless their similarity to the later described forms, *Eugyrinus* and *Amphibamus,* indicates that they are clearly allied species whose evolution followed a very similar course (in parallel). Owing to the incomplete elucidation of the position of the Branchiosauria we set them aside and pass on to consideration of material the position of which is more definite.

We begin with a description of an interesting primitive Carboniferous representative of these forms, *Eugyrinus* (Fig. 60), studied in detail by Watson (1940). It was just a small animal (the skull was about 2 cm long) whose body was completely covered with scales. The vertebral column was evi-

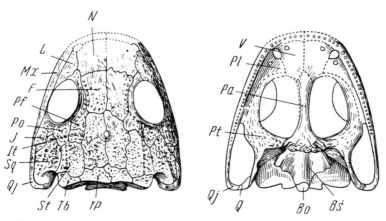

FIG. 60. Skull of the small primitive rhachitome *Eugyrinus. Bo,* Basioccipital; *Bs,* basisphenoid; *Ip,* postparietal; *Q,* quadrate. Other abbreviations as in Fig. 59. From Watson.

dently rhachitomous with, however, some indications of remodelling: the basiventrals remained persistently cartilaginous, and the neural arches ossified early and their bases expanded downward over the notochord surface and bore transverse processes. The short ribs were expanded at both ends and were articulated by a single head to the transverse process. The scapula was massive. In the pelvic girdle the ischium and ilium were ossified. The latter bone, widened in the acetabular area, had the dorsal fork projecting backward.

The rather broad skull had very primitive composition. There was a third occipital condyle present on the basioccipital and both exoccipitals. The upper occipital region was not ossified. In the skull roof the parietals, frontals, and broad nasals predominated. The small prefrontals and postfrontals bounded the inner sides of the fairly large orbits. It had a rather large supratemporal and a small intertemporal. The postparietals were small but wide.

The tabulars were small. The lachrymal was long. The quadratojugal contacted the margin of the quadrate posteriorly. There was a basipterygoid articulation. The parasphenoid was very wide posteriorly with small teeth in the central area. The interpterygoid fenestra was moderately large. The pterygoids were triramose, and the epipterygoids were raised above them. The posterior fork of the pterygoid ascended along the quadrate and joined the squamosal, bounded by the posterior wall of the large otic capsule. Otic notches were present. There were the usual bones in the lower jow, the dentary, splenial, postsplenial, angular, supraangular, a coronoid with teeth, and a very large goniale (prearticular). In one skeleton, small insects were found which indicates feeding on arthropods.

Aside from some lesser known forms, another, still smaller, animal very closely allied to *Eugyrinus* was *Amphibamus* (*Miobatrachus*, Fig. 61), the skull length of which was less than 1½ cm (probably not a fully adult animal). The abdomen was covered with scales. The vertebral column was still rhachitomous, however, the hypocentra were very small and covered only the underside of the notochord. The pleurocentra, also small, lay lateral to the notochord between the hypocentra. The main elements of the backbone were the well-developed neural arches which were prolonged ventrally over the sides of the notochord enclosing it for half of its height. Large transverse processes were located here. The neural spines were small. The ribs were bicipital and straight. In the tail the hemal arches were continuous with the hypocentra. The presacral vertebrae totaled 18 to 20 (26 in *Eugyrinus*). There were two vertebrae in the sacrum. The tail was very short. The scapulocoracoid was massive, and there were clavicles and a cleithrum. The ilium projected backward dorsally; the acetabular area was broad; the ischium was ossified; the humerus and ulnar bones were elongated.

The skull (Fig. 62) in general was similar to the skull of *Eugyrinus*, however, it was somewhat solidified. The postparietals were very small. The tabulars were evidently fused to the supratemporals. The intertemporal had disappeared. The orbits were large. The squamosal bordered the broad otic notch anteriorly. The occipital condyle was simple. There was a basipterygoid articulation and above it was located the epipterygoid. The pterygoid

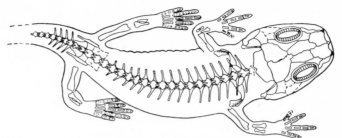

FIG. 61. Skeleton of the small froglike stegocephalian *Miobatrachus* (*Amphibamus*). From Watson.

FIG. 62. Skull of *Amphibamus. doc*, Postparietal; *f*, frontal; *j*, jugal; *l*, lachrymal; *mx*, maxilla; *n*, nasal; *p*, parietal; *pf*, prefrontal; *ptf*, postfrontal; *qj*, quadratojugal; *sq*, squamosal; *st*, supratemporal; *stp*, stapes. From Watson and Gregory.

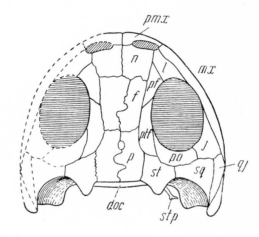

was triramose. The parasphenoid was separated off by a very small interpterygoid fenestra. The vomer was large and lateral to it lay the large choanae which were bordered by the palatine bones posteriorly. A stapes was present. The lower jaw had a retroarticular process.

In this line of development of small Carboniferous Stegocephalia the adaptation to terrestrial life was accompanied by a lightening of the skeleton and in particular of the skull (by the interpterygoid fenestrae, and the elimination of certain bones) and the pectoral girdle (by reduction of the dermal bones), some shortening of the trunk (especially of the tail), increase in the length of the appendages, and reconstruction of the vertebral column in which the bases of the neural arches displaced the other elements of the rhachitomous vertebrae. The sense organs were developed gradually, especially the eyes and the auditory organs, as was evident by the large orbits and the size of the otic capsules.

We have called special attention to the members of this group since they turned out to be the sole progressive branch of rhachitomous labyrinthodonts which in the corresponding reconstruction of the vertebral column led to new forms. The latter found a firm place in nature, flourished biologically, and at the present time are represented by the vast diversity of forms of anuran Amphibia (Salientia).

13

The Origin and Evolution of
Anuran Amphibia

Until recently the history of the origin of anuran Amphibia seemed a complete enigma. Fossil remains were known only from the late Mesozoic and belonged to fully advanced Anura which were readily placed among the members of modern families. However, the discovery of a very similar form—*Protobatrachus*—in the Lower Triassic of Madagascar (Piveteau, 1937) set off a search for much earlier anuran ancestors in the depths of the Paleozoic. From the Permian there are known various froglike forms with abbreviated trunks, short tails, and elongate appendages, as in *Eryops* and especially *Cacops* (Fig. 58). However, they possessed the typical rhachitomous vertebrae without any indications of modification. Likewise, in their skull structure there are no indications which would lead one to regard them as ancestors of anuran Amphibia. At present, due to the labors of Watson (1940), the story of the origin of the latter has been clarified to some extent. In the preceding chapter we described in detail those forms which apparently gave rise to anuran Amphibia. They were small rhachitomous Stegocephalia (*Eugyrinus* and *Amphibamus*) in which the vertebral column was reconstructed by the advanced development of the neural arches on the notochord replacing the elements of the rhachitomous vertebrae, hypocentra, and pleurocentra (Fig. 50).

Both of these forms still have a relatively long body and perhaps more readily resemble a large-headed salamander than a frog. Nevertheless the tendency to reduction of the number of vertebrae is there: in *Eugyrinus* there were 26 presacral vertebrae; in *Amphibamus*, 18 to 20; in *Protobatrachus*, 13 to 14; in modern Salientia, 5 to 9. In *Amphibamus* the tail was very short. In *Protobatrachus* there were still distinct caudal vertebrae, and in modern Anura they have been fused into one terminal bone—the urostyle. The shortening of the trunk and the elongation of the appendages were the consequence of adaptation to a new form of locomotion by saltation. Why was a reconstruction of the mechanism of locomotion needed? It seems to me that this

106

is explained by the conditions of life of riparian Amphibia in the Permian, when there were already large predatory reptiles. In respect to small Stegocephalia such predators were probably *Eryops,* which perhaps in turn were pursued by larger reptiles. One means of protection was the dermal ossifications on the back (*Cacops,* Fig. 58) and stout vertebral spines (*Platyhystrix*). Of still more significance were the sense organs; their progressive development is documented especially in increase in sizes of the orbits and the tympanic membrane (*Cacops*). The sense organs signaled the approach of danger. However, the need was for quick and effective reaction to signals of danger. If, as we suggest, these Amphibia remained on the shores of the water all the time, then the natural reaction to danger would have been just a quick jump into the water. Probably *Cacops* and even *Eryops* escaped in this way. A less specialized example of such genera was *Micropholis,* a small stegocephalian in which the body was much shortened, with an almost rudimentary tail but with typical rhachitomous vertebrae. The appendages and their girdles were relatively very strong. It was this particular biological type which evidently lay at the base of the anuran Amphibia. It was a particular biological type, however, and not an ancestral form. Morpholgically it was quite distinct; the vertebral column was typically rhachitomous, in that and in other respects it was not especially similar to the anurans. *Micropholis* was found in the Lower Triassic and consequently it was a contemporary of *Protobatrachus.*

Apparently this biological type was highly prevalent in Permian times, a fact that was reflected in the organization of the Triassic Stegocephalia. Many coastal Stegocephalia of this type, which at first merely took refuge in water, transferred to a totally aquatic life and with it retained the short trunk and tail which did not at all fulfill the requirements of an active aquatic animal. They could survive only as slightly mobile passive benthic predators. Among these were many stereospondylous labyrinthodonts such as *Metopias,* and especially the Brachyopidae group (e.g., *Gerrothorax*).

In the group of forms which evidently gave rise to anuran Amphibia (*Eugyrinus–Amphibamus*) in Permian times (the fossils of which were not preserved) the formation of the same biological type of short-bodied, long-legged forms which are clearly marked in *Amphibamus* probably occurred. In coastal life they were obliged to escape from predators by quickly leaping into the water and perhaps burrowing into the muddy ground in the waters until danger had passed. This was prompted by the gradual development of the organs of sight and hearing, and also by strong appendages all the more adapted for jumping into the water. This same adaptation led to the lightening and flattening of the skull structure.

Concretely these modifications consisted of the following: a reconstruction of the vertebral column was accomplished along the lines observed in *Eugyrinus–Amphibamus.* Having extended around the notochord, the bases of the neural arches were united underneath the notochord so that the centrum of the vertebrae is found to consist of only one element (the fused basis of the neural arches), the "notocentral" backbone (as in *Protobatrachus*).

Between the centra the pleurocentra were probably retained in the form of the intervertebral cartilage. In the caudal division of the backbone, still composed of individual vertebrae in *Protobatrachus*, they later fused forming a single bone—the urostyle. The short straight ribs had become unicipital (even in *Eugyrinus*) and then reduced. They were present in *Protobatrachus* and are retained in the modern Discoglossidae. In the limbs, all the longer bones are still more elongated, especially in the posterior appendages. Both the bones of the forearm and also both foreleg bones, separate in *Protobatrachus*, are fused in modern Salientia into one unit. In the posterior limbs not only the thigh and tibial bones, but also the two proximal bones of the tarsus which thus formed just one supplemental lever, are much elongated. Corresponding to the strengthening of the limbs, their support in the limb girdles was also reinforced. In the pectoral girdle the scapula and the separate coracoid were ossified, and the clavicle became more narrow as did also the cleithrum lying at the edge of the cartilaginous suprascapula. The interclavicular bone disappeared. In the pelvic girdle, the ischia and ilia were ossified. In *Protobatrachus* the long ascending processes of the ilia were directed forward and not backward, as in *Eugyrinus* and *Amphibamus*. This was undoubtedly correlated with saltation. The impetus in springing was passed from the posterior limbs to the vertebral column anterior to the center of gravity of the animal (in extending the appendages backward) and thus the body maintained a fully stabilized position in its movement through the air. Correspondingly the iliac bones were very elongated, and the sacrum was also moved forward. In *Protobatrachus* 2 to 3 sacral vertebrae succeeded 13 to 14 trunk vertebrae. In modern anura 1 to 2 sacral vertebrae (2 sacral in *Pelobates, Pipa,* and *Humenochirus*) follow 5 to 9 trunk vertebrae; the ascending forks of the iliac bones are extended straight forward and attain considerable length.

Modifications in the skull essentially narrow down to enlargement of the orbits and, correspondingly, of the interpterygoid fenestra and enlargement of the otic capsules. This process began back in *Eugyrinus–Amphibamus* and was accompanied by a gradual lightening of the skull and a decrease of the number of bones in its roof. This, like the elimination of the cover of scales, which in *Eugyrinus* were present over the whole body and in *Amphibamus* on the abdomen, led to a marked reduction of weight and consequently to an increase in the animal's mobility.

In *Eugyrinus* there was still the full complement of bones characteristic of the primitive Stegocephalia. In the arrangement of bones *Protobatrachus* still resembled *Amphibamus*, however, the number of bones in it was reduced, resembling modern Salientia. Instead of separate frontal and parietal bones there are fused frontoparietals. Posteriorly they are expanded, covering the otic capsules, and laterally they extend to the squamosals. Of the orbital elements, only the prefrontal was retained in *Protobatrachus*; the postfrontal disappeared. The postparietals and tabulars, which are reduced in the series *Eugyrinus–Amphibamus*, have altogether disappeared in *Protobatrachus*. The squamosal encloses the archlike otic notch anteriorly and extends to the quadrate and the posterior fork of the pterygoid (as in *Amphibamus*). The parasphenoid, very broad posteriorly, extends anteriorly in a long and narrow processus cultriformis (as in *Amphibamus*). At the medial tip of the pterygoid is a depression where the cartilaginous basal process of the palatoquadrate evidently lay, which participated in the basipterygoid articulation with the base of the skull. The palatine borders the choana posteriorly (Fig. 163) in the form of a narrow transverse band, as in modern Anura.

Besides the bony pro-otic, there was also a distinct opisthotic. Between them lay the large foramen ovale. There was an ossified stapes. The otic capsules were large, as in *Amphibamus*. The sphenethmoid was located over the anterior part of the parasphenoid. In the occipital region only the exoccipitals were ossified, they bore a pair of occipital condyles (instead of three as in the *Eugyrinus–Amphibamus* series), as in modern Salientia (Fig. 163).

On the whole, notwithstanding the small amount of paleontological material, the excellence of its preservation affords the conclustion that in *Eugyrinus, Amphibamus* (*Miobatrachus*), and *Protobatrachus* we have an excellent morphological series. The organization of *Protobatrachus* is the logical conclusion of those transformations which were noted above in *Eugyrinus* and *Amphibamus*. Thus a series of phylogenetic stages leading from typical rhachitomous Stegocephalia to modern anuran Amphibia is restored. It is true that in this series *Protobatrachus* stands much closer to modern forms, especially to *Ascaphus*) than to the earlier labyrinthodonts. In this series there occurred a gradual development of the sense organs (sight and hearing), a shortened and reconstructed vertebral column, and strongly developed appendages, especially the posterior. The appendages and the pelvic girdle, like the skeleton as a whole, were adapted to saltatory locomotion. With this was correlated the lightening of the skull and the reduction of certain bones, especially in the skull roof. The shape of the skull, short and broad, as well as the wide mouth, is obviously adapted to feeding on arthropods. We know that even *Eugyrinus* fed on insects. Perhaps this is partly correlated with the elaboration of the jumping ability. The main role in the capture of arthropods was transferred to the tongue, and in connection with this the dental system was reduced.

The anuran Amphibia were already fully formed as a biological type at the start of the Mesozoic (*Probatrachus* was in the Lower Triassic). At the present time it is undoubtedly a proliferating group of animals. Only extremely sparse remains are known from the Mesozoic, however. At this time they were evidently very far from flourishing (in the quantitive sense); otherwise they would have been found far more often in the continental deposits of the Mesozoic. The transitional forms which should have lived in the Permian period are essentially unknown. The numbers of these forms were apparently negligible which can probably be explained by a high mortality rate as well as life in conditions preventing the burial of their carcasses.

In Permian times there were already many predatory reptiles (*Limnoscelis, Captorhinus,* and many Therapsida) which could feed on small reptiles, but in particular there were terrestrial forms of Stegocephalia which through their inferior mobility became easy prey for these predators. Only small forms leading secretive lives hidden under rocks or burrowed into forest litter or loose soil (*Microsauria*), and also riparian forms with well-developed sense organs which, at the approach of predators, leaped quickly into the water and hid in waterweed or muddy soil, could escape this destruction. Thus in the Permian only the saltatory forms of Stegocephalia (*Eryops* and *Cacops*) became abundant. It is true that there were predatory Stegocephalia in the waters (*Archegosaurus, Trematosaurus, Platyops, Tertrema,* and others); they, however, were well-developed piscivorous forms and their complex snouts show that they pursued and seized their prey "on the run." Hidden on the water bed, the riparian Stegocephalia probably scurried away from these predators. Larger and heavier coastal Stegocephalia (*Eryops*-type) were not always able to scurry into the water in time and they often became prey of reptiles. Therefore they gradually changed over to life in the water and gave rise to benthic forms with flattened bodies—the Stereospondyli—which achieved wide distribution in the Triassic as predators. Inheritance of the short body and short tail from coastal forms did not obstruct active catching of fish. However, small coastal Stegocephalia escaping from reptiles on the shore by jumping into the water fell directly into the enormous mouths of these benthic predators. The position of the small riparian Stegocephalia became critical. The sole mode of withdrawal led along stream banks through channels where the less mobile benthic labyrinthodonts could ascend only with difficulty.

What had happened in the Silurian when fishes with osseous skeletons fled from pursuit by Gigantostraca was repeated. The small riparian Stegocephalia were obliged to ascend streams along channels where those less active predators could not follow them (Romer, 1933). Thus amphibians were transplanted to the headwaters of streams, in mountainous localities where they could always be concealed in water and where there was much cover (under rocks, in mosses), on land inaccessible to predatory reptiles. During the Mesozoic, anuran Amphibia only maintained their existence in such mountain reserves where they were to some extent protected. Only after the extinction of the large reptiles did these Amphibia emerge into a wider living arena; at present they are flourishing in their characteristic ecological situations.

This hypothesis is in excellent accord with the extreme rarity of known fossil remains of anuran Amphibia all during the Mesozoic (in mountainous localities erosion and not sedimentary phenomena predominate and therefore burial conditions are extremely unfavorable). In support of the hypothesis there is also the unique organization of anuran larvae which is evidently the result of adaptation to life in running waters but not in standing waters.

The larvae of Stegocephalia were very similar to the larvae of modern urodele Amphibia (and also to the larvae of crossopterygians and Dipnoi) and probably had the same large external gills. This is evident in remains of *Tungussogyrinus,* Branchiosauria (larval forms of labyrinthodonts), *Gerrothorax,* and, as one would conclude by the form of the gill arches, *Dvinosaurus.* The latter is a neotenic form of the primitive rhachitomes to which

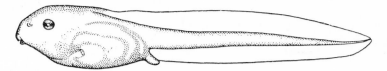

FIG. 63. Typical larva of an anuran amphibian (tadpole).

Eugyrinus also belongs. Undoubtedly the larval forms of early Anura had the same organization as larvae of modern urodele Amphibia. However, in modern Anura they differ markedly in their external aspect. First of all, one's attention is taken by the existence of a sucker right from the time of the young larva's hatching from the egg envelope. The sucker takes the form of a paired or horseshoe-shaped glandular organ lying behind the mouth on the ventral surface of the head. It is utilized in the attachment of the young larva to the egg envelope from which it has hatched, and to plants and other underwater objects (in young larvae of urodele Amphibia there are also organs of attachment—balancers—which can serve only for attachment to aquatic plants). At the time of the start of active feeding, lips are developed on the edges of the oral opening, supported by the larval jaws ("labial" cartilages) differentiated above from the cornua of the trabeculae and below from the front ends of the Meckel's cartilage, on which horny teeth are developed. The oral apparatus takes the form of a funnel, sometimes very broad, by which the larva may also be supported on the substrate. This apparatus, armed with keratinous teeth, serves for sucking in and macerating plant material (and also tissues of dead animals) on which anuran larvae feed.

The larva (or tadpole) of anurans (Fig. 63), is of a highly unique general body form. It is slightly streamlined and does not have any protruding parts.

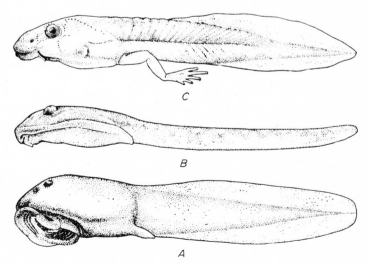

FIG. 64. Oral funnel and sucker in larvae of mountain anurans: *Ascaphus* (A), *Borborocetes* (B), and *Astylosternus* (C). From Noble (1927).

The gills are entirely covered by opercular folds, as are the developing ante-rior appendages. The posterior appendages are developed late and do not protrude since they lie between the expanded body ("the head") and the tail. The streamlined form of the body is not the result of adaptation for rapid swimming; anuran larvae cannot swim rapidly. Noble (1927) notes the ease with which larvae of members of the most diverse families of anuran Amphibia become adapted to life in mountain streams (Fig. 64). The matter comes down to the fact of the enlargement of the oral funnel serving as an organ of attach-ment (or to the development of a special sucker), to some narrowing of the body, and reduction of the dorsal and caudal fins. It shows that the larvae of anurans as a whole are adapted to life in running water. The presence of a sucker in young larvae, and the abundance of anurans in mountainous lo-calities is definitely related to this. In addition, the existence among moun-tain and high montane forms of the most primitive representatives (*Ascaphus* in the family Liopelmidae, *Alytes* and others of the family Discoglossidae, *Megalophrys* of the family Pelobatidae and others) is characteristic of anurans. This compels us to recognize that anuran Amphibia were originally limited in their life and reproduction to streams with a constant flow, confined mainly to mountainous areas. If this is true, then our hypothesis sheds light on the unique gill respiration in the larvae of anurans.

In anuran larvae external gills of the same type present in urodele Amphibia (which were also present in larvae of labyrinthodonts) are developed first. Thereafter, however, with development of opercular folds covering the bases of the external gills, the latter were reduced, and farther ventrally under the folds new "internal" gills were developed which were homologous neither to the gills of urodele Amphibia nor to fish gills. They only resemble the abortive gill filaments sometimes seen at the base of outer gills of urodele Amphibia (Schmalhausen, 1955b). What is the explanation of this strange re-placement of organs of uniform functions? Why could not the external gills of the larvae (the result of the transformation from the internal gills of fishes; Schmalhausen, 1954) be transformed into internal gills with opercular folds covering them? It seems to me that this can be answered by the following hypothesis.

In mountain brooks with a rapid current and cold water rich in oxygen, the outer gills of the larvae of urodele amphibia are always reduced in size and their structure is simplified (in larvae of *Ranodon, Onychodactylus, Dicamp-todon,* and others).

In high montane conditions the significance of dermal respiration is in-creased and in many Amphibia the lungs are markedly or completely reduced (in anurans—*Ascaphus,* in urodeles—*Salamandra atra, Ranodon, Onycho-dactylus,* and *Rhyacotriton*). Probably primitive anurans lived in mountain-ous areas and bred in mountain brooks. In these conditions external gills increased the danger from the drag of the water current and their size was sharply reduced. The role of gas exchange organ passed over to the skin and the mucous membrane of the oral cavity. The mouth or sucker of the larva scraped off with the jaws and drew in algae from rock surfaces or underwater vegetation; therefore, the mouth could not serve for drawing in water. The respiratory water current was probably drawn into the oral cavity through the nostrils as in the larvae of *Ascaphus* (Noble, 1927). Thence the water was driven outward through the gill slits beneath the opercular folds. The external gills were reduced. With the abundantly vascularized walls of the oral cavity, the pharynx, and gill slits, this adequately provided for the oxygen requirement in mountain brook conditions. With the spread of Anura downward along the stream channels the oxygen requirement was increased and this requirement was met by development of folds of mucous membrane in the gill slit region. This complex of folds gave rise to the "internal" gill of anuran larvae. The reduction of the external gills and the streamlined form of the larvae of anuran Amphibia we consequently explain as being due to the life forms originated in mountain brooks. This in itself is explained by the existence of suckers in young larvae, and probably by the mode of feeding and the structure of the oral apparatus. The adaptation to life in mountain brooks led to quite different types of adaptation in the larvae in Urodela and Anura. This was correlated to the difference in feeding. The larvae of Urodela feed on ostracods and larvae dwelling in the benthos. In mountain brook conditions life is under the rocks or between rocks, but not in the current. The larvae of Anura transferred to vegetable food; they fed mainly on algae. In mountain brook conditions these plants live on rocks. Since algae grow in light, they cover the upper surface of rocks, freely washed in the rapid current. For larvae of Urodela it was enough to cling by the toes in order to keep between the rocks; for Anura larvae special organs of attachment (the oral funnel) and maximum streamlining of form were necessary (Figs. 63 and 64).

The transition to vegetable feeding by the larvae of anurans is probably explained by the scarcity of plankton in mountain streams. The larvae originally fed on ostracods scattered about in algae covering the rocks on the brook bottom, and then went on to swallowing algae along with ostracods and other animal matter. Finally the anuran larvae took to scraping algae from the rocks and generally changed over to feeding on aquatic vegetation.

This transition to vegetable food could have played the deciding role in the evolution of anurans. The larvae of anurans were spared from competition for food with larvae of urodele Amphibia, and in transition to waters inhabited by fishes also escaped from the competition of the larvae and young of fishes. This made possible the much wider dispersal of anuran Amphibia in comparison with the urodeles when, at the close of the Mesozoic, favorable conditions for a new prosperity of Amphibia in general developed.

The particular organization of the larvae and the abrupt expansion not only in habitat but in feeding between the larval and adult forms was complicated, however, by the process of metamorphosis which is correlated in anurans with a cessation of feeding and by very complex processes of reconstruction of the whole organization.

The modern distribution of Anura supports our hypothesis of montane origin. Many modern Anura live in mountainous localities, but an especially interesting fact is that these are obviously the most primitive representatives.

The foremost among these are some members of the most primitive family Liopelmidae: *Ascaphus* breeds in cold, swift mountain brooks of northwestern America (egg, 4.5 mm in diameter), *Liopelma* in New Zealand lays eggs (5 mm in diameter) on land. The primitive family Discoglossidae has members in montane localities—*Discoglossus pictus, Alytes obstetricans,* and some species of *Bombina.* Only our *Bombina bombina* is characteristic of the lowlands. Among the members of the Pelobatidae there are many mountain forms also (e.g., our *Pelodytes caucasicus*) and their most primitive member *Megalophrys* breeds in mountain brooks. Many typical anurans are widely dispersed in lowlands, as are our frogs and toads. In all these forms the eggs are small and the development is rapid (especially in toads) and this undoubtedly is correlated to development in small drying-out water bodies.

Modern anurans breed mainly in small standing waters or overgrown channels with slow currents. Many such waters dry up in summer and this causes loss of all the larvae that have not reached the stage of metamorphosis. High mortality of larvae leads to natural selection toward high fertility. The increase in numbers of eggs naturally is accompanied by a reduction in egg size.

Since by middle or late summer, with the drying up of waters, only those larvae perish which did not succeed in reaching the stage of metamorphosis, i.e., were arrested in their development, there is natural selection of the individuals with more rapid development. Hastened development, however, always brings about simplification of development. Therefore, in the embryonic and larval development of Amphibia it is not easy to find traces of any characteristics of the organization of ancestral forms. Thus, for example, although modern Amphibia undoubtedly arose from the Stegocephalia (and farther back from crossopterygian fishes) having a very large number of dermal bones in the skull roof and also some dermal bones in the pectoral girdle, almost no traces of this were retained in the larvae.

Modern anurans form a large group of fairly diversified forms inhabiting all the continents, and are especially prevalent in the southern hemisphere. The morphological differences between the various forms are very slight.

The embryonic and larval development of anurans documents the main stages of the historical transformations of their skeleton. In modern anurans the centra of the vertebrae are developed from the bases of the neural arches, the primordia of which early merge into paired bands of cartilage on the upper surface of the notochord. Under the notochord metameric cartilaginous anlagen are also developed. These, however, are unpaired and merge into one elongate hypochordal strand. These anlagen clearly correspond to hypocentrae. Ossification of the vertebrae begins on the neural arches and covers the notochord above epichondrally. In some anurans, however, the ossification includes the whole notochord, forming the perichordal centrum. Between the ossified centrae intervertebral cartilages remain, probably homologous to the pleurocentra. All this agrees well with the paleontological data.

The short unicipital ribs in most anurans (excepting Pipidae and Discoglossidae) are fused into single units with the transverse processes.

In the skull of anuran larvae there are well-marked connections between the braincase and the palatoquadrate cartilage owing to adaptation to the unique vegetable nutrition. In the development of the bony skull there is an evident fusion of the anlagen of the frontal and parietal bones, and in addition to these there are found anlagen of some bones inherited from more primitive ancestors—the supratemporal, jugal, praefrontal, and lachrymal (Lebedkina).

In the pectoral girdle both dermal bones, the clavicula and the cleithrum, which are closely connected to the underlying cartilages, the procoracoid and the suprascapular (Schmalhausen, 1917a), are still developed.

In the appendages there are developed rudiments of both bones of the forearm and both bones of the thigh, which are later fused into one bone in each division. The wrist is composed embryonically of a large number of the usual elements which are thereafter fused into larger complexes. In the tarsus the two proximal anlagen of the tibia and fibia which form the accessory saltation leverage are greatly elongated. The distal elements are decidedly reduced.

In modern anuran Amphibia the sense organs, the organs of olfaction, vision, and hearing, are highly developed. Sound transmission from the air is also highly perfected. The auditory ossicles of anuran Amphibia consist of a simple columella, transmitting by pistonlike action. It consists of a cartilagenous basal plate lying in the membrane of the fenestra ovalis, a middle shaftlike osseous part, and a distal cartilaginous part (extracolumella) standing at an angle to the shaft and ascending to the tympanic membrane. The cartilaginous part is also joined by a dorsal process to the cranium wall (the fulcrum of the lever). The columella collects oscillations which are definitely smaller at the base of the ossicle than at the distal end. Nevertheless the surface of the membrane of the fenestra ovalis is considerably smaller than the surface of the tympanic membrane.

The transformation of vibrations is the result of the adoption here of a mechanical system of dual leverage sound transmission. The auditory ossicle transmits not the sound vibration itself, but the tympanic membrane vibration.

Such reception and transmission of sound vibrations in the aerial medium is the most perfect mechanism for sound transmission and is accompanied by the least loss of energy. The latter is inevitable during passage into the liquid-filled canals of the inner ear; however, it is compensated for by the larger surface of the tympanic membrane and the leverage-accented pressure during transmission along the auditory ossicle. Opposing this action there are only the internal friction (which is minimized by the development of an articulation between the divisions of the columella) and the inertia of the system. However, this unfavorable inertia is reduced to a minimum by maximum reduction of the weight of the auditory ossicle.

In anuran Amphibia there is excellent development of both auditory receptors, the macula acustica basilaris and the macula neglecta amphibiorum. The latter probably functions (for the animal dwelling in water) through the medium of sacculus endolymphaticus (Schmalhausen, 1957b).

I4

Lepospondylous Stegocephalia and Their Relationship to the Labyrinthodonts

In the case of the anuran Amphibia we saw how great the possibilities were for reorganization of the basic rhachitomous vertebral column of the Stegocephalia. It was easy to analyze the nature of the reorganization because of the existence of fossil materials in which were recorded all the principal stages of the transformation, the progressive development and envelopment of the notochord by the bases of the neural arches, and also the gradual reduction of the main elements of rhachitomous vertebrae—the hypocentra and pleurocentra. In this case the emphasis is entirely on the ossified elements which alone are preserved in fossil material. The pleurocentra were reduced as bony elements but probably were retained in the form of intervertebral cartilages. The main types of structure of the vertebral column of fossil labyrinthodonts—embolomerous, rhachitomous, and stereospondylous—passed through a series of successive intermediate stages. The notochordal type of vertebral column of the urodele Amphibia is the result of the transformation of the rhachitomous type.

There remains, however, a group of Stegocephalia occurring in the Lower Carboniferous with sharply different vertebral structure—lepospondylous or pseudocentral vertebrae. The paleontological history of the origin of these vertebrae is quite puzzling.

Nevertheless comparison of existing material with embryological data obtained in the study of the development of modern urodele Amphibia allows certain conclusions to be drawn.

Of special value is Watson's (1926a) description of the vertebrae of *Adelogyrinus*. The centrum of the vertebrae of *Adelogyrinus* is cylindrical and biconvex. It has a flat bony surface which passes internally into a system of thin crossbeams or plates. On the dorsal side there is a pair of roughened depressions for the neural arch. Laterally there is a pair of deep pits extending almost to the canal for the notochord. These pits are arranged so that in the dorsal midline they divide the centrum surface into three equal parts. The

116

neural arches form a single bone which is connected to the dorsal depression on the centrum by a suture. There are well-developed zygapophyses and short depressed vertebral spines. The bases of the neural arches bear stout lateral transverse processes (diapophyses).

From this the following conclusions may be drawn. The ossified centrum was developed in the form of a cylinder either at the surface of the perichordal cartilage (perichondrally), or in the perichordal connective tissue as a membrane bone. From the surface of the ossified cylinder ossified crosspieces were developed which expanded within the perichordal cartilage (as in *Lepidosteus*) or within the perichordal connective tissue (as in *Amia*). In either instance the centrum of the vertebra was developed as a single unit. The lateral processes of the hemal arch (hypocentra) did not ossify and deep pits were retained at the site of the former cartilage. It is very likely that the hypocentra themselves remained cartilaginous. On the other hand, the bases of the neural arches were ossified at their connection to the centra of the vertebrae and with them formed one uninterrupted unit. However, at the foot of the upper arches independent ossification occurred, and they remained connected to their basal part and to the centrum of the vertebra at the suture (essentially as in some fishes, in *Sphenodon*, and in some lizards).

In comparison with the development of vertebrae of urodele Amphibia the following may then be presumed. In all terrestrial vertebrates there occurs a trans-segmentation of the sclerotomes; the front half of each sclerotome enters into the structure of the preceding vertebra, and the posterior half into the structure of the succeeding one. Such trans-segmentation also occurs in urodele Amphibia but only in the later stages of development. The sclerotomes give rise to skeletogenous mesenchyme which forms paired condensations on the sides of the notochord; these are the anlagen of the perichordal cartilage. In addition, paired intersegmental thickenings are formed on the dorsal side of the notochord, the anlagen of the neural arches, and in the caudal region there are similar anlagen of the hemal arches. The origin and formation of the vertebral arches cannot be established with complete certainty; however, they apparently develop mainly from the posterior half of the sclerotomes.

The paired anlagen of the perichordal cartilage are expanded around the notochord and form complete rings. During their chondrification there is seen a median zone of newer cartilage which divides the perichordal ring into two rings, the anterior belonging to the preceding vertebra, and the posterior entering into the structure of succeeding vertebra. Thus the *cartilaginous* anlagen of the vertebra centrum in each segment consist of two rings, which in my opinion are fully comparable to the half-vertebrae of the embolomerous vertebral column. Developing from this the perichondral ossification of the bases of the neural arches thence spreads rapidly downward over the surface of the notochord and over the surface of the perichordal rings. This ossification links both of the perichordal rings together. The zone of new cartilage dividing the centra of the vertebrae is the growth zone of both the cartilaginous centra and the ossified cylinders covering them. During meta-

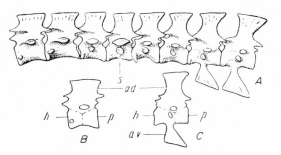

FIG. 65. Vertebral column of the nectridian *Urocordylus* (A), thoracic (B), and caudal vertebra (C). *ad*, Neural arch; *av*, hemal arch; *h*, hypocentrum; *p*, pleurocentrum; *s*, sacral vertebra. from Bystrov, after Steen.

morphosis the intervertebral articulation is developed in it. In the Stegocephalia, this articulation always lies between the pleurocentrum in front and the hypocentrum behind. Therefore in each vertebra the anterior perichordal ring is homologous to the hypocentrum, and the posterior to the pleurocentrum.

It may be presumed that the process of formation of adelospondylous vertebra took place in an analogous manner. The hypocentra and pleurocentra formed a cartilage base on which the perichordal ossification from the neural arch bases spreads out enclosing both cartilage and notochord within the boundaries of each vertebra (i.e., between the successive myotomes). Whether it originated prior to the merging of the two cartilage half-rings or whether they were joined only when the osseous centrum was developed (as in Urodela in which the median part of the bony cylinder lies directly on the notochord) is not as critical. Evidently the unique adelospondylous vertebrae consist only of *early fused elements* from ossifications developed from the bases of the neural arches (Fig. 65). This ossification began very early, even at those stages when the main elements of the vertebrae—the hypocentra and pleurocentra—were cartilaginous. In addition, the existence of two centers of ossification in the neural arches, in their bases and farther distally in their stems (as in *Sphenodon et al.*) was also distinctive.

To the adelospondylous Stegocephalia belong two very primitive forms from the oldest strata of the Lower Carboniferous—*Adelogyrinus* and *Dolichopareias*. By the structure of vertebrae, the later (Upper Carboniferous and Lower Permian) Microsauria also belong among them. The parapophyses were ossified and set at the front edge of the centrum, but they did not protrude; often they were merely articular regions for the capitula of the ribs at the front edge of the centrum, or were even intervertebral. The diapophyses were well developed and were located on the front part of the neural arches. Lepospondylous vertebrae are distinguished from adelospondylous vertebrae only in that the whole neural arch forms a single unit with the centrum of the vertebra, i.e., the suture dividing them has vanished. The parapophyses form the normal conspicuous protuberances in the middle part or forepart of the vertebral centrum; the ribs are bicipital. The diapophyses in the middle part of the foot of the nerual arch are fairly long. The skulls of even the primitive Adelospondyli (*Adelogyrinus* and *Dolichopareias*), moreover, differ somewhat in the skull structures; not only are there no intertemporals, but often no distinct tabulars. In place of this there are very large supratemporals (which probably include the tabulars). There is no otic notch. These same peculiarities are also retained in the Microsauria (however, a small tabular is present in *Gymnarthrus* and *Pantylus*). They serve to distinguish them both from older reptilomorphs (*Anthracosauria*) and from primitive reptiles (*Seymouria et al.*).

The parasphenoid of the Microsauria runs forward to the vomers and divides the small interpterygoidal fenestra. The processus cultriformis is sometimes broad. The expanded posterior part extends to the fenestra ovalis. The stapes has a very broad base and small shaft.

The lower Adelospondyli were small aquatic animals—in *Dolichopareias* there were well-developed grooves for the seismosensory organs. The same was true in the more primitive Microsauria (*Microbrachis*). Later Microsauria were apparently totally terrestrial animals.

Typical Lepospondyli were represented in the Carboniferous and Lower Permian by aquatic animals of moderate size having a long swimming tail (*Nectridia*). The vertebral spines were broad and connected to each other (Fig. 65). Besides the usual zygapophyses there were supplemental zygosphenes and zygantrae. The skull in the more primitive Nectridia had the usual stegocephalian organization, however, its shape was very peculiar; the tabulars, and sometimes the squamosals also, extended laterally and backward forming large processes covering the external gills (Fig. 66). The inter-

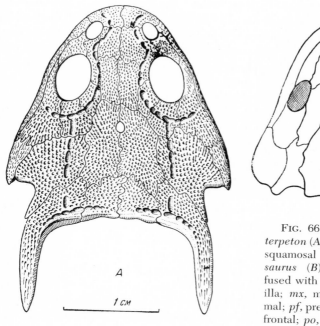

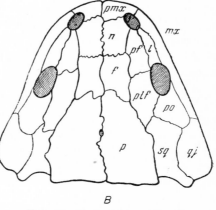

FIG. 66. Skull of Nectridia: *Keraterpeton* (A), supratemporal fused with squamosal (from Bystrov), *Scincosaurus* (B), postparietal apparently fused with the parietal. *pmx*, Premaxilla; *mx*, maxilla; *n*, nasal; *l*, lachrymal; *pf*, prefrontal; *f*, frontal; *ptf*, postfrontal; *po*, postorbital; *p*, parietal; *sq*, squamosal; *qj*, quadratojugal. From Huene.

pterygoid fenestra was small or totally absent. The orbits were small. In *Scincosaurus* there were no skull crests, there being neither tabulars nor postparietals. Both the skulls and the appendages approximated modern Urodela in structure. However, the tail was typical nectridian—with distally expanded veretebral spines. To the Nectridia also belong some eel-like forms—Aistopoda—which have a narrow skull and a very long trunk. All the Nectridia were probably benthic animals and evidently became extinct, leaving no descendants. Some authors link modern urodele Amphibia with the Nectridia, but it seems certain that they are simply more primitive forms, so far of unknown ancestry, of which there are no known highly specialized members.

THE PROBLEM OF THE POSITION OF THE MICROSAURIA

The Microsauria were originally described as reptiles; they were assigned to the reptiles by Goodrich (1930). Recently most authors have assigned them to the Amphibia. A critical review of this matter is that of Romer (1950a). However, Huene (1956) cited the Microsauria as members of the reptiles, mainly on the grounds of the composition of their vertebral column (the existence of distinct hemal arches in two members). In view of this we are obliged to examine more closely the essential features characterizing the microsaurs. Very small size and the elongate salamandriform shape of the body could have occurred also in the reptiles. More important is the organization of the spinal column. The entirely cylindrical, fairly long, biconvex centrum of the vertebrae in the trunk region is not divided into independent intercentra. Apparently there were no hemal arches in the caudal region. The neural arches are fairly high and narrow (not convex as in the primitive reptiles). The vertebral spines are scarcely developed (Fig. 67). The first vertebrae do not show any modification resembling the atlas and axis of the reptiles. On the contrary, the first vertebra has an odontoid process (Fig. 68) and is quite simi-

A   B   C

FIG. 67. Lepospondylous vertebrae: *Hylonomous* (A), *Lysorophus* (B), and *Crossotelos* (Nectridia) (C). From Watson.

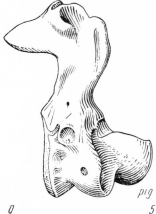

FIG. 68. First vertebra of the microsaur *Cardiocephalus; pig,* tuberculum interglenoidale. From J. P. Gregory *et al.*

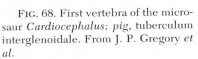

lar to the first vertebra of modern Urodela (J. P. Gregory *et al.*, 1956). This circumstance is of great significance. The ribs are bicipital. The capitulum is articulated to a small parapophysis or to a facet on the anterior edge of the centrum. The interclavicular bone consists of a very broad plate and a short, narrow, posteriorly directed shaft. The appendages are relatively short and weak. The whole body was covered with scales, rounded on the dorsal side and elongated on the ventral side (in reptiles they aquire the structure of abdominal ribs). The scales have a very characteristic radial striation. The skull (Fig. 69) has an elongate postorbital section (in reptiles it is shortened). There are no otic notches. The skull roof in general is very primitive, however, the tabular is absent, the supratemporal is very large, and the postparietals are usually well developed (in reptiles the reduction of the tabular is accompanied by the simultaneous reduction of the postparietals and supratemporals). The palate is primitive, with narrow interpterygoid fenestrae; the parasphenoid is broad posteriorly with a long processus cultriformis. There was a movable basipterygoid articulation. The occipital condyle was simple, but expanded laterally forming paired extensions (as in the labyrinthodonts). From the sum of these characters we must assign the microsaurs to the Amphibia. Of decisive importance in this is the composition of the vertebral column (absence of intercentra in the trunk region) and especially the similarity of the first cervical vertebrae to those of the Urodela (Figs. 68 and 156) in sharp contrast to the reptiles. The skull roof and the covering of rounded scales are quite characteristic and do not occur in that form in reptiles.

As to the relation of the Microsauria to the labyrinthodonts, there are a sufficient number of characteristics indicating an alliance with them, although not very close. This involves the most primitive representatives of the batrachomorphs—the icthyostegalian *Ichthyostega*, *Acanthostega*, *Otocratia*, *Colosteus*, and *Erpetosaurus*. In the latter, however, there were large interpterygoid fenestrae (which were not present in Microsauria). Microsauria are somewhat similar to the Loxommoidea also, e.g., *Baphetes*. They are even more similar to the primitive Rhachitomi, e.g., *Trimerorhachis* (in which, however, there are also large interpterygoid fenestra) and *Eugyrinus*. The latter is interesting because it perhaps shows some proximity to the original forms of the two branches of modern Amphibia—the Salientia and Caudata, which would account for the many parallel courses of their evolution. Nevertheless of the primordial Rhachitomi, the closest to the Microsauria are the abovementioned Dendrerpetonidae (Fig. 59). The centra of the vertebrae had an embolomerous structure with the pleurocentra in the form of complete rings). The bases of the neural arches encloses the notochord and bore transverse processes and stout zygapophyses. The vertebral spines were very low. The ilium had a long posterior process. The skull was very primitive with small interpterygoid fenestrae. The palatine and pterygoid were small. The parasphenoid was broad posteriorly; the processus cultriformis extended to the vomers. The vomers were large. There was a well-developed basipterygoid articulation. The postorbital part of the skull roof was relatively long,

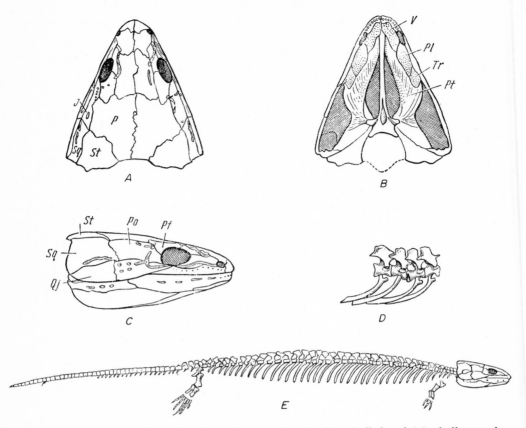

FIG. 69. A microsaur from the Carboniferous, *Microbrachis;* skull dorsal (A), skull ventral (B), skull lateral (C), four thoracic vertebrae (D), restoration of whole skeleton (E). *J,* Jugal; *P,* parietal; *Pf,* postfrontal; *Pl,* palatine; *Po,* postorbital; *Pt,* pterygoid; *Qj,* quadratojugal; *Sq,* squamosal; *St,* supratemporal; *Tr,* ectopterygoid; *V,* vomer. From Steen.

but the postparietals and especially the tabulars were small. As in the Microsauria also, the nasals, frontals, and parietals predominated in the skull roof. The lachrymals were long, extending from the orbits to the nostrils. There were unpaired occipital condyles on the basioccipital, but with some participation of the exoccipitals. The supraoccipital was not ossified. There was also a general similarity in the shape of the skull, which was rather high and convex with orbits of moderate size (Fig. 59).

If, as we suggest, adelospondylous and lepospondylous vertebrae were developed as the result of the fusion of the elements of embolomerous vertebrae, i.e., of hypocentra and pleurocentra, with a considerable proportion of the bases of the neural arches, then the vertebral structure of the Dendrerpetontidae could have been ancestral to that of Microsauria. Certainly, *Dendrerpeton* could not be the actual ancestral form, in fact it was contemporaneous with the microsaurs. However, it quite possibly indicates the common ancestry of these forms. It remains only to be added that it is quite likely that the Microsauria underwent very rapid evolution in the early Carboniferous, while the Dendrerpetontidae proved to be a more conservative branch.

The modern Urodela belong to the lepospondylous forms. At present there can be no doubt that lepospondylous vertebrae were derived from the adelo-spondylous type as a result of simple fusion of the neural arches. The developmental history of the vertebral column of Urodela gives obvious proof of this.

I5

The Microsauria and the
Origin of the Apoda

The Microsaurs were very small animals (skull length from several milli-meters to several centimeters; only *Pantylus* is larger—length of skull, 8–10 cm) of elongate salamandriform shape, sometimes very long, with small appendages. The posterior appendages were pentadactyl, the anterior ones were usually tridactyl. Some of them (Gymnarthridae) led a burrowing way of life, as is evident in the shape of the well-ossified skull (Fig. 70), in the forward-directed quadrate bones, narrow mouth, well-developed posterior process of the lower jaw, absence of vertebral spines, and horizontal zyga-pophyses. These features also characterize the Apoda and other burrowing vertebrates (J. P. Gregory *et al.*, 1956). The relatively large orbits, however, were hardly consistent with an underground existence. Probably all Micro-sauria led a secretive way of life, hiding by day under rocks and burrowing in moss and in forest litter. Only the more elongate forms, as for example *Car-diocephalus*, were more specialized burrowing animals.

The Microsauria had large teeth that could macerate fairly hard food, vegetable or animal; possibly they could also break up the shells of molluscs (*Pantylus*). Perhaps they were to some extent predators which fed mainly on worms, arthropods and even small vertebrates (*Euryodus*, skull length, 33 mm).

In *Cardiocephalus* there were very small limbs and the long body was completely covered with rounded scales (Fig. 71). It is not difficult to con-ceive of a complete reduction of the appendages by further adaptation to a burrowing life. In this connection there naturally arises the question of the origin of modern Apoda (fossil remains of which are unknown).

The organization of the Apoda shows fairly great similarity to that of the Microsauria. The structure of the vertebrae and the position of the transverse processes in the forepart of the vertebra is similar. The capitulum of the rib also articulates to the parapophysis on the front edge of the centrum of the vertebra or to the facet between the vertebrae. The skull of the Apoda is also

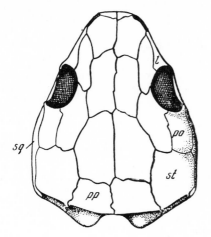

FIG. 70. Skull of the Permian micro-saur *Cardiocephalus*. *l*, Lachrymal; *pp*, postparietal. Other abbreviations as in Fig. 69. From J. P. Gregory *et al.*

stegalian. Although the number of bones in the skull roof is reduced, in onto-genesis many primordia of other bones are initiated which later merge with each other. Separate postparietals are developed which later fuse to the parietals; the prefrontals are merged with the frontals; the nasals with the premaxillae. Certain other bones of uncertain homology, not only dermal but also perichondral, are also developed. Almost all the bones of the lower jaw (total nine) characteristic of the Stegocephalia are also initiated. They are later merged into two large complexes with the dentary (five bones) and the angular (four bones). The palate of the Apoda is very primitive and contains all the typical components, including the transversa (ectopterygoid). As in microsaurs also, the posterior part of the parasphenoid is very broad and reaches the fenestra ovalis. The stapes consists of a broad base with a small columella (which in the Apoda sometimes shows a fenestra for the passage of the stapedial artery. The quadrate bones are directed forward. On the lower jaw there is a large processus retroarticularis. In some Apoda (*Ichthyophis* and *Rhinatrema*) there are small bony scales of the cycloid type in the skin. In the microsaurs the whole body was covered by scales of the cycloid type (but with radial striation which disappeared in the Apoda).

Some authors (e.g., Romer, 1950a) ally the Apoda with the Lower Permian *Lysorophus* and the Carboniferous *Cocytinus*, which Romer also assigns to the Microsauria. Notwithstanding a certain similarity, especially in the re-duction of some bones of the skull roof and in the expansion of the parasphe-noid, it must be noted that the Lysorophidae are highly specialized Micro-

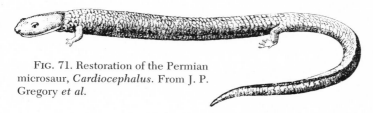

FIG. 71. Restoration of the Permian microsaur, *Cardiocephalus*. From J. P. Gregory *et al.*

sauria, in which characters of a transition to a burrowing way of life were present (e.g., *Cardiocephalus*).

We may also recall attemps to derive the organization of the Apoda from the structure of some Nectridia, particularly the Aistopoda (Marcus *et al.*, 1936). These were highly specialized limbless, wormlike forms with a narrow and rather weak skull. They were typically aquatic animals. The possibility of a derivation from such profound ultraspecialization seems to me of little likelihood now.

Although there is one aquatic form among the Apoda—*Typhlonectes*, it is a highly specialized carnivorous form which evidently transferred secondarily to aquatic life. This is evident in the absence of seismosensory organs. The larvae of some Apoda develop in water. However, the most primitive members of the Apoda, for example *Icthyophis*, deposit the eggs on land and guard them even until the hatching of the young. Evidently the Apoda arose from terrestrial Stegocephalia. It must be recognized that the Apoda are specialized descendants of the Microsauria which, in correlation with the burrowing way of life, lost the limbs, the limb girdles, and also the tail (a small swimming tail is present only in *Typhlonectes*). The skull roof was strengthened by fusion of a certain number of bones. The organs of vision were reduced. At the base of the lachrymal duct a unique suctorial palpus was developed.

16

The History of the Development and Origin of the Urodele Amphibia

In the most primitive representatives of the urodele Amphibia (Hynobidae and Cryptobranchidae) fertilization is external; in the higher members it is internal. The eggs are deposited in the water as a rule. From them are developed larvae with three pairs of external gills, very similar to the larvae of dipnoan fishes. In the latter there are four pairs of external gills, however in urodele Amphibia, as in *Ranodon* (Schmalhausen, 1955b), rudiments of a fourth pair of external gills are found. There were similar larvae in the Stegocephalia: in *Tungussogyrinus* carbonized remnants of three pairs of outer gills have been described. Larval development is definitely known in *Archegosaurus*. The Stegocephalia described as species of *Branchiosaurus* are mostly larval forms close to *Eryops* (Romer, 1945); they also had external gills. In addition, some Stegocephalia were "permanently branchiate," i.e., neotenic forms. Such, for example, were *"Gerrothorax"* and probably *Stegops* also. The most studied form of the neotenic Stegocephalia is *Dvinosaurus*, described by Amalitskii (1921), Sushkin (1900), Efremov (1933), and in especial detail by Bystrov (1938). This study has shown that the structure of the visceral apparatus, including the blood vascular system, is essentially the same as in the larvae of modern urodele Amphibia, taking the axolotl for comparison (Bystrov, 1939). In the general form of the head and the body as a whole, larval forms of Stegocephalia (especially *Branchiosaurus*) were reminiscent of the larvae of urodele Amphibia.

In this respect urodele Amphibia show a clear relationship to the Stegocephalia. However, the latter had a completely "stegal" skull roof. The reduction of this roof has been noted even in the Paleozoic among adelospondylous Stegocephalia—*Cocytinus* and especially *Lysorophus*. These were also neotenic forms, undoubtedly close to the primordial urodele Amphibia. In the larval development of the Caudata many features can be found indicating their origin from Stegocephalia and even some characteristics inherited from fish ancestors.

127

I. THE DEVELOPMENT OF EXTERNAL GILLS

The primordial branchial apparatus is initiated in Amphibia essentially as in fishes. In the embryonic stages of development there are observed, on the sides of the head under the otic capsule and posteriorly, prominent external transverse ridges with more or less deep furrows between them. The former correspond to the primordial visceral bars, the latter indicate the position of the future visceral clefts. In each of the ridges there are developed: (1) a central blood vascular vessel—the primordial arterial arch carrying blood from the arterial trunk to the dorsal aorta, (2) the arch of the visceral skeleton in the form of a condensation of mesenchyme lying medial to the arterial arch, and (3) primordia of the visceral musculature lying in a dense mass of myoblasts lateral to the arterial arch. Between the primordia of the visceral arches of the cephalic gut are wedged endodermal folds, expanding to meet the ectodermal furrows above to which they are joined. These are the primordia of the visceral pouches. The most highly developed visceral pouches, the branchial ones, break outward in the Amphibia, forming up to four pairs of gill slits. The first of the visceral pouches, the spiracular, is developed between the maxillary and hyoid arches, but in the Amphibia it never opens exteriorly. In addition, all the visceral arches with the exception of the first two (the maxillary and hyoid) develop gill partitions and gills proper in their outer part. In all of this we see processes common to both Amphibia and fishes (the spiracular cleft appears at an early stage in all higher fishes and does not break through at all in the Dipnoi). However, from the moment of the development of the gills proper, the paths of development of the respiratory apparatus of Amphibia and fishes noticeably diverge.

The formation of the rudiments of the external gills begins with the thickening of the ectoderm in the lateral portions of the primitive gill bars, protruding in the form of small ridges. Regions of thickened ectoderm quickly form protuberances, the primordia of the external gills. These primordia are located on the sides of the head, at about the middle of the region of the primitive gill bars (Fig. 72).

Later, when the formation of the prochondral and then the cartilaginous arches of the branchial skeleton begins, the primordia of the external gills are found lying at the level of the upper ends of the gill arches. However, the upper ends of the gill arches of Amphibia are in reality only the upper ends of

FIG. 72. Head of an embryo of *Hynobius* 8 mm long. On the rudiments of the primary gill septa the anlagen of external gills 1–3 are visible as protuberances. *hy*, Site of hyoid arch anlage; *md*, anlage of mandibular arch with a protuberance, the rudiment of the balancer; *n*, olfactory pit; *oc*, eye.

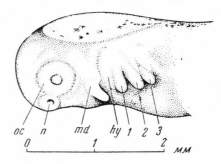

the ceratobranchialia, i.e., they correspond to the midpoints of the gill arches in fishes (at the point of the flexure). The dorsal sections of the gill arches were previously reduced in crossopterygian fishes, and this was obviously correlated to the transition to pharyngeal respiration (Schmalhausen, 1951) by loss of the mobility of the hyomandibula. Thus although the external gills of Amphibia were connected to the upper ends of the gill arches, their morphological position corresponds to the middle of the gill arches of more primitive fishes. This is shown quite clearly in the localization of their primordia in the early stages of their individual development.

The gill clefts are developed after the appearance of the primordia of the external gills, and cut through only in the ventral region. The opercular fold develops simultaneously and likewise only in the ventral region. On its upper margin the opercular fold only partly covers the lower part of the base of the first external gill. The second external gill lies not only behind but above the first, and the third is still farther dorsal. This favors a freer flow of water to the gills since they are only partly covered by each other (the same is observed in larval gills of sturgeons).

In accordance with the position of the external gills the posterior gill clefts are elevated above the anterior ones. While the first gill cleft is covered by the opercular fold, the second is covered on its upper part by the first external gill, and the fourth by the third gill.

The external gills are thus located, successively, between the upper ends of the gill clefts so that each gill covers the upper end of the gill cleft succeeding it. Therefore the outer and dorsal wall of each gill is connected to the body wall and covered by the same skin with the characteristic pigmentation and glands. The medial and ventral walls of the external gill pass proximally into the gill bar region and, covering the succeeding gill clefts posteriorly, still function in part as gill bars. The trunk of each external gill is connected proximoventrally to a gill bar, and is its direct continuation (Fig. 72).

Morphologically the trunk of the external gill is an external outgrowth of the dorsal part of the gill bar. This view is supported by numerous notes from further studies (involving the structure of the transitional area and the location of the gill filaments on it) and the arrangement of the blood vessels and musculature.

Each external gill is marked, as was noted, as an ectodermal thickening and a noticeable outer protuberance in the central area of the anlage of the primitive gill bar (Fig. 72). This protuberance emerges first in a lateral direction and then backward, forming a prominent projection rapidly elongating. On this process, the primordium of the gill trunk, secondary protuberances appear in definite sequence, extending into more or less elongate primordia of the gill filaments (Fig. 73).

The first outwardly visible rudiments of the gill filaments are the rudiments of the filaments of the anterior rank. They are initiated on the outer (morphologically anterior) edge of the lower surface of the trunk of the external gill. On the inner (morphologically the posterior) edge of the same surface the filaments of the second rank later develop. The filaments of the first

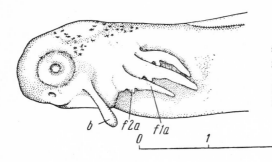

FIG. 73. Head of an embryo of *Hy-nobius* 9 mm long, showing external gills with large primary lamellae and rudiments of the succeeding lamella. *b*, Balancer; *f1a*, *f2a*, rudiments of front rank lamella.

rank are thus formed earlier than the filaments of the posterior rank, beginning at the distal (morphologically dorsal) end of the gills and progressing in a proximal direction (Fig. 74). In the young of sturgeons, in which the internal gill lamellae assume the role of "external" gills, the front rank lamellae are also initiated first and emerge from under the rudiment of the gill operculum. The posterior lamellae are initiated a little later and at first differ markedly from the anterior ones.

The gill lamellae are developed, as we have noted, in a distal-to-proximal direction and the first to develop is the most distal (dorsal) lamella in front. It elongates very quickly and flattens out, taking the shape of a narrow lamella, and undoubtedly assumes the first respiratory function of the whole gill. In the motile stages of the larva within the egg envelope this first lamella evidently already functions as a gill, and its accelerated development is apparently determined by this early function.

The earlier development of the lamellae of the anterior rank, especially of the first lobe, acquired through this terminal position, results in some assymmetry in the gill structure (Fig. 74). The primordia of the lamellae actually form a paired series on the edge of the ventral surface of the gills, but since the lamellae of the front rank, expecially the first of them, are developed earlier, and the lamellae of the rear rank are delayed, the primordia of the

FIG. 74. First (A) and second (B) gills of an embryo of *Hynobius* 9 mm long. *1a–4a*, Rudiments of front rank lamellae; *1p–4p*, rudiments of posterior rank lamellae.

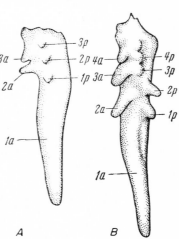

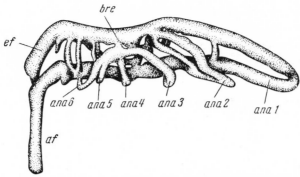

FIG. 75. Reconstruction of the vessles of the third gill of an embryo of *Hynobius* 8 mm long. *af*, *ef*. Afferent and efferent branches of the arterial arch; *ana 1-ana 6*, rudiments of vascular loops of front row lamellae; *bre*, efferent artery of external gill.

rear rank are caused to be turned in the proximal direction. This gives an appearance of lobes alternating in the anterior and posterior ranks. However, with later development of the lamellae of the rear rank the difference between them is equated and as a result there is established a quite definitely paired arrangement of lamellae. Departures from this arrangement occur not only in Amphibia but also in fishes (Moroff, 1902).

In *Ranodon* only one paired series of a small number of relatively wide and short primordial gill lamellae is developed in the gills (Fig. 76). In *Hynobius* a considerably higher number of primordial gill lamellae are developed and, supplementary to them, a second group regularly alternating with the first. In the axolotl an auxiliary, more medial, rank of lamellae is formed above these (Fig. 77).

We would consider the gill lamella arrangement in the form of a simple paired series primary and original for Amphibia, as it always appears in the early stages of ontogeny and as it is retained until late in larval life in such primitive forms as *Ranodon*.

The development of gill lamellae begins, properly, in the early appearance of their primordia in the form of protuberances on the trunk of the external gills. The appearance of the outer rudiments precedes the formation of the anastomoses between the efferent and afferent arteries of the outer gills. The first anastomoses are developed from the dorsal efferent vessels and turn downward to a union with the ventral vessel. They are usually archlike, curved under the ectoderm of the anterior (outer) surface of the gill. First to develop are the anastomoses on the anterior (lateral) side of the gill; later the posterior (medial) ones develop. The early primordia of anastomoses are formed as outgrowths from the efferent arteries (Fig. 75). Later the formation of matching (opposite) outgrowths from the afferent arteries is seen.

The very first anastomosis occupies a terminal position at the distal end of the gill and is completely transformed into the first vascular loop, connecting the distal end of the efferent artery to the afferent artery forming.

Subsequently, in the same way, all the new anastomoses are developed in back-to-front order and from them the vascular loops emerge ventrally. The latter are bent toward the ectoderm of the anterior edge of the lower surface of the gill and enter into the simultaneously emerging rudiments of lamellae of the front rank. With a short delay the same process of formation of vascular loops of the inner anastomoses goes on at the posterior edge of the lower surface of the gill (Fig. 75).

The earliest rudiments of the gill lamellae take the form of protuberances on the thickened ectoderm. These rudiments extend into rounded projections having a paired arrangement greatly resembling the rudiments of the internal gill lamellae of fishes—the "branchions" of Severtsov. With further growth these rudiments become more flattened dorsoventrally (proximodistally) and acquire the form of real lamellae.

Each pair of rudiments is supplied by blood vessels at first having the form of simple elongate loops penetrating each lamella. The outer branch of each loop is an efferent vessel running to the efferent artery of the external gill. The inner branch of any loop either of the front or rear rank is an afferent vessel directly leading from the afferent artery of the external gill to the efferent artery of the external gill. The efferent artery of the external gill passes along its upper wall (morphologically proximal) and the afferent artery along the lower wall, right between the bases of the gill lamellae of the front and back ranks. In this there is manifest an exceptional similarity of structure to the "branchions" of the gill arches of young sterlets (Fig. 76). In the external gills of Amphibia only the gill arch of the skeleton itself is absent, since the trunk of the gill is an external outgrowth of the gill septum. In all the rest we see such great similarity that we can frankly speak of the typical "branchions" of Severtsov in respect to the Amphibia.

Later, with flattening of the rudiments and their conversion into gill lamellae, a transverse anastomosis is developed between the vessels of each loop. One of them passes across the gill lamella under the dorsal (distal) surface, the other beneath the ventral surface (Fig. 77). The same is seen in the transformation of the gill filaments on the gill lamellae in sturgeons.

In the gill lamellae of Amphibia there gradually develops a very complex net of superficial anastomoses which functions as the main element of the organs of respiration in the larvae.

In fishes, further complexity in structure of the gill lamellae arises, leading to increase of their respiratory surface. On both sides of the gill lamellae many transverse folds, the secondary lamellae, are developed. Anastomoses running along the surface of the gill lobes penetrate into these lamellae and form a net of fine capillaries.

In Amphibia the gills do not reach this level of complexity. They are arrested at the developmental stage of simple gill lamellae. However, along with further, and undoubtedly secondary, adaptation of the larva to more prolonged life in water the structure of the external gills is also complicated. In such primitive urodele Amphibia as *Ranodon* and *Onychodactylus* (apparently also in *Cryptobranchus*) the gill lamellae, not especially numerous, are comparatively short and arranged in one double series, quite regularly

FIG. 76. Reconstruction of one pair of lamellae (branchions) with vascular loops of the third gill of an embryo of *Hynobius* about 11 mm long (A); reconstruction of a pair of lamellae (branchions) with vessels of a young sturgeon sterlet (B). From Severstov. *a* and *e*, Afferent and efferent branches of vascular loops; *aaf* and *eef*, afferent and efferent arteries of external gills; *Abr*, cross section of gill arch; *fa*, *fp*, rudiments of anterior and posterior lamellae; *n*, nerve.

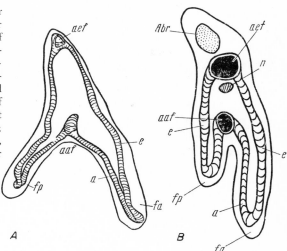

paired (Fig. 76). In a great proportion of urodele Amphibia the larval stage is prolonged and the outer gills have acquired a more complex structure. Thus, in *Hynobius* secondary gill lamellae are developed between the primordial lamellae in a similar paired arrangement. Later the increase in the respiratory surface goes as far as the development of a supplementary series of gill lamellae between the early series (in the axolotl). The lamellae are much elongated; however, in the supplementary series they always remain shorter than in the main series (Fig. 77). The primordial gill lamellae in the two main ranks remain the largest. In the permanently branchiate *Proteus* and *Siren* the outer gill structure is further complicated owing to the branching of the trunk of the gill itself, each branch of which bears some tufts of gill lamellae.

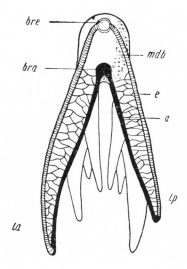

FIG. 77. Diagram showing arrangement of gill lamellae in the axolotl. In the front plane a pair of primary gill lamellae with vessels is seen; beyond there are a tertiary pair, a larger secondary pair, and finally another tertiary pair of lamellae. *a*, *e*, Afferent and efferent vessels of the gill lamellae; *bra*, *bre*, afferent and efferent vessels of the external gills (in cross section); *la*, *lp*, anterior and posterior lamellae; *mb*, muscle bundles of m. depressor branchiae.

Thus the external gills of Amphibia, starting their development very similarly to the internal gills of primitive fishes, do not fully reach the development of the latter. In the more advanced Amphibia the larval life is evidently prolonged, increasing the size of the larvae, and the respiratory surface of the outer gills is additionally increased. However, this is now attained by a different mode than in fishes. Evolution does not go backward, but attains the same biological effect by other means. Of later secondary adaptations for life in the water, not even the structure of the organs of aquatic respiration was changed in the Amphibia to resemble fishes. On the contrary, the divergences were increased and, living always in the water, the permanent branchiates, Sirenidae and Proteidae, departed even more from their fishlike ancestors than other urodele Amphibia in their larval state. This will be seen even more clearly when we examine the development and structure of the branchial septa.

A. Development of Branchial Septa and Musculature

The primordial gill septum of the larva (Fig. 72) projects its medial part outward in the form of knobs, which are the rudiments of the external gills. The gill clefts develop a little later, directly beneath these rudiments. Between the gill clefts, secondary gill septa are quickly differentiated from the proximal parts of the anlagen of the gill arches of the skeleton. Distal of the anlage of the gill arch lies the arterial arch, and then between the latter and the ectoderm, the primordia of the musculature. The developing efferent artery ("anastomosis") lies right along the outer wall of the gill arch; the afferent artery is curved a little outward, passing dorsally in the external gill. The outer part of the gill septum becomes thinner. Proximal to its posterior wall the muscle fibers depressing the external gills are differentiated and only mesenchyme with some small blood vessels is found farther distally in the septum. On the whole the gill septum takes the aspect of a falcate or semilunar curved plate. The gill septa turn caudolaterally in the upper part and ventrolaterally in the lower part. Succeeding septa partly cover each other, and all of those developing in front of the opercular fold are overlapped (Fig. 78).

In *Ranodon* the extension of the gill septum into the outwardly protruding dorsal part (the trunk) of the external gill, bearing two series of gill lamellae, is very clearly visible. Still more clearly marked is the unity of both formations, the gill septa and trunk of the outer gills, the similarity in the arrangement of the blood vessels (Fig. 79), and also the similarity in the arrangement of the musculature. In both this animal and in others there is also found a general similarity to the arrangement of these organs in primitive fishes.

Along the gill arches of the skeleton the efferent branchial arteries are arranged most proximally both in fishes and in Amphibia. In the external gill of Amphibia the efferent artery is also located proximally—along the upper wall of the trunk of the gill. The afferent branchial artery is situated a little farther along, also along the gill arch of the skeleton in fishes and Amphibia. In fishes it passes between the bases of the inner gill lamellae. In the external

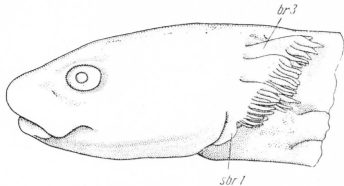

FIG. 78. Head of a larva of *Ranodon* 35 mm long, showing arrangement of the external gills. *br 3*, Third gill; *Sbr 1*, septum of first gill passing dorsally into the trunk of the external gill and partly covered ventrally by the opercular fold.

gills of Amphibia it is disposed along the lower surface, also passing between the bases of the gill lamellae.

The branchial septa of Amphibia are very distinctive and markedly differ outwardly from the branchial septa of fishes. In the latter they are not visible; they are covered on both sides by gill lamellae, and only in the Selachii does the outer edge of the septum project outward and continue as a more or less prominent dermal fold. In bony fishes the branchial septa are reduced, and in teleost fishes the gill lamellae hang free on the gill arches. Only in some primitive bony fishes—in modern sturgeons and in Dipnoi— are there well-developed branchial septa (in *Polypterus* and *Lepidosteus* they

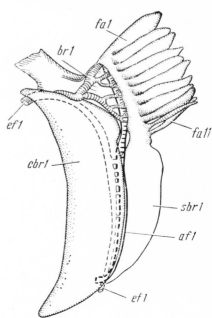

FIG. 79. Larva of *Ranodon* 56 mm long; first gill arch with septum and external gill. *af 1, ef 1*, Afferent and efferent gill arteries; *br 1*, efferent artery of external gill; *cbr 1*, ceratobranchial; *fa 1–fa 11*, gill lamellae; *sbr 1*, gill septum.

are somewhat reduced). However, they are entirely covered under both ranks of gill lamellae and are visible only in transverse sections through the gill arches.

In urodele Amphibia the gill septa are well developed and fully visible. They are completely exposed owing to the previous reduction of the gill lamellae (in the ancestral forms). Because the upper divisions of the gill arches of urodele Amphibia are reduced, the gill septa on them are set on the ventral divisions of the arches, namely on the ceratobranchials. They have a broad semilunar shape (Figs. 79 and 80) in which the most anterior of them partially covers the one behind (Fig. 78). Dorsally the first three gill arches pass directly into the external gills (Fig. 79). In forms with short external gills (*Ranodon*) it is clearly evident that the gill trunk is only the dorsal somewhat thickened part of the gill septum that retained its gill lamellae (Fig. 79). It lies outside, not within, the gill cavity, since the dorsal part of the opercular fold is totally reduced. Due to the elimination of the operculum the gills lying

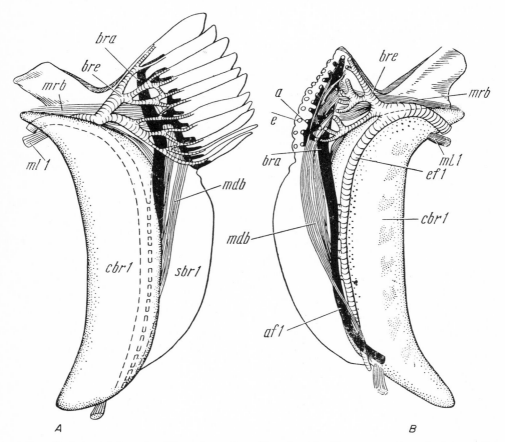

FIG. 80. Larva of *Ranodon* 57 mm long; first gill arch with gill septum and trunk of external gill, anterior (A) and posterior (lamellae removed) (B). *mdb*, m. Depressor branchiae; *ml 1*, m. levator arcus branchialis 1; *mrb*, m. retractor branchiae; other abbreviations as in Figs. 77 and 79.

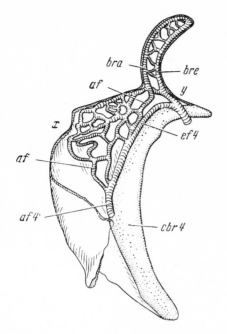

FIG. 81. Larva of *Ranodon* 56 mm long; fourth gill arch and gill septum with vascular net and external gill with one lamella. *af, ef,* Afferent and efferent gill arteries; *bra, bre,* afferent and efferent arteries of the gill lamella; *cbr 4,* ceratobranchial 4; *x–y,* thickened part of gill septum representing the rudiment of the trunk of the external gill.

beneath it are exposed. The gill septa and the trunks of the external gills represent one unit, and together they are homologous to the gill septa of fishes.

The gill septa are supplied with venous blood from the afferent gill artery. A small branch of this artery diffuses through them in a thin net of vessels (Figs. 79 and 80). The more important of these nets is in the fourth gill septum which, as a rule, lacks external gills (Fig. 81). In the upper (posterior) half of the fourth septum, at the base of this net, lies a system of fairly large vessels. It seems very likely to me that this vascular net plays some role in the respiration of urodele Amphibia. This assumption is supported by the presence of individual variations in structure of the fourth gill septum in *Ranodon*.

The gill septa themselves attain full development only in the larvae of urodele Amphibia, and even then not in all of them. In the permanently branchiate Proteidae they are reduced, particularly in *Necturus*. The fact of the reduction of gill septa, with maximum adaptation to permanent life in water, indicates that the gill septa of the larvae of Amphibia are not to be regarded as the result of secondary adaptation to the conditions of their existence. The gill septa were inherited from fishlike ancestors.

The opercular fold was reduced in all urodele Amphibia. However, it was more fully developed in the larvae of the most primitive forms, and most reduced in forms adapted to permanent life in the water. It is strongly reduced in *Necturus* and quite rudimentary in *Proteus*.

This circumstance also means that the opercular fold of amphibian larvae is a remnant of the gill operculum of fishes with their gill septa. It is not to be regarded as the result of secondary adaptation of amphibian larvae to life in the water (in larvae of anuran Amphibia, however, it undoubtedly secondarily reached considerable and unique development, completely covering the whole gill region of the head).

The development of the musculature in the gill septa of fishes has been especially well studied in the Selachii. Here it develops in association with canals of the coelomic cavity passing medially along the primary gill septa.

The development of the medial part of the visceral musculature, lying in the gill septa themselves, is of interest since it sheds light on the point of origin of the external gills of Amphibia. In the Selachii this musculature is arranged in a complete layer, median of the septa, between both ranks of gill lamellae. In bony fishes this musculature falls into separate muscle clusters lying between the gill lamellae and corresponding to them numerically.

In sturgeons the musculature of the gill septum is formed from the mesenchyme of the medial section of the general anlage. In the septa thin muscular tissues are differentiated leading off one by one to the posterior surface of the gill arches and extending to the epidermis at the boundary between the two ranks of gill lamellae. These muscle bundles pass to the gill septum behind the afferent and efferent arteries and behind the main branchial nerve (n. post-trematicus). The distal muscle bundles are attached between the gill lamellae of both ranks. Therefore, as they pass backward they cross the base of each gill lamella of the rear rank. Passing between the successive branchions they subsequently also cross the efferent and afferent vessels of each gill lamella of the rear rank (Severtsov, 1922).

In urodele Amphibia the musculature of the gill septum also develops from the mesenchyme of the medial part of the general anlage of gill musculature. Directly under the epidermis of the posterior (medial) wall of the gill septum there arises first an almost continuous layer of myoblasts, and then sections of muscular tissue which are converted into a group of bundles, together comprising the mm. depressores branchiarum. In the early stages, separate muscle bundles lead off from the posterior edge of the gill arch and these also originate directly in the mesenchyme of this region.

They pass along the medial wall of the gill septum backward and upward, and then by the medial (posterior) wall to the outer gill. Wedged in separate bundles between the blood vessels of the lamellae of the rear rank, this musculature enters the interstices between the lamellae of both ranks. Here it lies in a lengthwise strip along the lower edge of the external gill where it is attached to the skin, between the bases of the gill lamellae of both ranks (Fig. 80). Passing among the vessels the muscle bundles cross, to a small extent, the afferent vessels and also, in part, the efferent vessels of the lamellae of the rear rank (Fig. 80).

We see an amazing similarity in the development of the central musculature in fishes and in Amphibia. The difference is only that the muscular ligament arises from the gill arch in that part of the gill septum in which the lamellae are absent in urodele Amphibia, and therefore the muscle bundles pass dorsally to the external gill where all the gill lamellae are concentrated. The muscle tissue meanwhile loses the regularity of segmental arrangement (one bundle for each gill lamella). Notwithstanding these differences, correlated with the formation of external gills, the central musculature retained all its typical morphological relationships, and in general its functions also. On the one hand, muscle bundles serve for moving the gill lamellae (they are similar in fishes), and on the other hand they are organs facilitating the blood supply of the lamellae (through action on the afferent gill artery).

This is sufficient proof that the trunk of the external gill is only an outer extension of the gill septum with its lamellae, and that the lower edge of the external gill between the two ranks of lamellae is the outer edge of this part of the gill septum (Fig. 79).

In Amphibia there are, however, other specialized muscles also originating from the central musculature of fishes. They are developed from the same middle part of the general muscle primordia, dorsal of the anlage of the external gills. These are the mm. retractores branchiarum (mm. levatores branchiarum of Drüner). In the second and third gill arches these muscles also arise from the posterior edge of the ceratobranchial, but only from its upper tip. They lie beneath the epidermis of the rear (medial) wall of the external gill and pass backward to the bases of the gill lamellae, where they are attached to the skin. Parts of the fibers penetrate (in *Ranodon*) between the vessels of the lamellae of the rear rank and lie here with the fibers of m. depressor branchiale (Fig. 80). This shows clearly that mm. retractores branchiarum are the product of differentiation of the same central musculature. This musculature is distributed evenly in fishes; it arises in bundles from the posterior surface of the epi- and ceratobranchials and passes directly to the bases of the gill lamellae. In Amphibia it arises in bundles from the ventral and dorsal parts of the ceratobranchials and turns along the rear wall of the gill septum and the trunk of the external gill to the base of the gill lamellae. Correspondingly there is a concentration of the latter in the outer gill, i.e., at the upper end of the ceratobranchial. The central musculature in Amphibia is divided into two portions— a dorsal (m. retractor) and a ventral (m. depressor) which contribute to the movement of the whole gill.

B. THE NUMBER OF EXTERNAL GILLS

In *Ranodon* there is an especially thick net of blood vessels, connecting five to six channels to the fourth arterial arch (Fig. 81) in the fourth gill. Of these the first, according to the course of the vessels, apparently takes the role of the afferent artery, but the last two vessels are efferent arteries. They gather blood from several thickened isolated upper (or posterior) parts of the gill septum. This part of the septum (x–y) is separated by a pit or small cleft from the other parts, and is quite similar to the gill septa of the first three arches (Fig. 81). In some cases on the posterior end of this thickened section of the gill septum there is one well-developed and fully typical gill lamella with well-developed vascular loops and a net of capillaries between its branches (Fig. 81). In these cases it is clear that the thickened element of the gill septum is a rudimentary trunk (stem) of the external gill. The gill lamella is the first (i.e., most dorsal) lamella of the front rank, which in the typical gill is developed earlier than the other lamellae and occupies the terminal position on it.

The presence of the fourth external gill in the larvae of the urodele Amphibia clearly indicates that in more primitive Amphibia there were four pairs of external gills on four gill arches (as in the Dipnoi).

In this connection one cannot but recall the paper of Sushkin on *Dvinosaurus* (1936). Sushkin suggested that in this stegocephalian there was a fourth gill. Bystrov (1939) opposed the suggestion of Sushkin since neither in modern Amphibia nor in fossil Amphibia (larvae of *Tungussogyrinus* showing remnants of external gills) have remnants of a fourth external gill been found. However, the suggestion of Sushkin is based on faultless logic. The deep furrow on the fourth gill arch of the skeleton indicates strong development of the fourth arterial arch. Furthermore, in *Dvinosaurus* as in the neotenic (i.e., permanently branchiate) forms, pulmonary respiration could not have played a major role. In modern Proteidae the fourth arterial arch is completely reduced. Consequently the fourth arterial arch in *Dvinosaurus* could have supplied only a fourth gill. The finding of a rudimentary fourth gill in modern urodele Amphibia corroborates the belief of Sushkin.

C. The Origin of External Gills

At present, when the ectodermal origin of internal gills in fishes may be regarded as proved (Severtsov, 1922), we then cannot oppose this by saying that the external gills of Amphibia are new formations of a different origin. On the contrary, we are obliged to note the far-reaching similarity between the gills of Amphibia and fishes. Gills proper, in both fishes and Amphibia, consist of paired ranks of flat gill lamellae. As in higher fishes these lamellae are attached only at their bases. Elsewhere they are freely bathed in water on all sides. As a rule the lamellae of the front (outer) and rear (inner) ranks are arranged oppositely. They occasionally alternate, however, not only in Amphibia but in fishes also. The blood supply of the gills is very similar, and it differs only in that the gill blood circulation is developed from the primitive arterial arches, the continuity of which was destroyed in the formation of the early gill vessel loops. The similarity goes much farther (Schmalhausen, 1954). The efferent gill artery is fully developed at the expense of the arterial arch (as in higher fishes). The proximal part of the afferent gill artery is developed at the expense of the arterial arch and its distal part apparently grows at the expense of the ends of the branchial vascular loops (as in primitive bony fishes). The efferent artery passes right along the skeletal gill arch at the base of the gill septum and the afferent artery and in the same gill septum runs between the bases of the gill lamellae. In the lamellae themselves the afferent vessels are arranged medially, and the efferents laterally (as in fishes). In the lamellae, afferent and efferent vessels form a loop closed at the end, both branches of which are located at the edges of the lamellae, interconnected by a dual net of capillaries, one beneath the upper (posterior) and the other beneath the lower (anterior) surface of the lamella. In contrast to fishes, however, these capillaries lie right under the surface of the lamella itself and do not repeatedly penetrate its folded outgrowths—the lamellules. The latter are not present in Amphibia (apparently they were eliminated).

The similarity between the gill septa and gill lamellae of fishes and Amphibia is confirmed by the still greater similarity of their musculature. The muscles of the external gills of Amphibia (mm. depressores and mm. retractores branchiarum) are developed in a similar manner to the septal musculature of fishes—from the myogenic mesenchyme under the posterior (medial) surface of the gill septum (and the trunk of the exterior gill in Amphibia). These muscles arise in separate bundles from the rear surface of the skeleton of the gill arches (ceratobranchials) and, as in fishes, are turned toward the bases of the gill lamellae. All these similarities compel us to regard the external gills of Amphibia as formations homologous to the internal gills of fishes.

In the larvae of crossopterygian fishes there were also probably external gills in the hyoid and fourth gill arches. Originally they were only the organs of respiration in the youngest larvae (as in sturgeons). They were bundles of branchions located on the median sections of the visceral arches which protruded outward from under the still undeveloped gill operculum. With the expansion of the gill operculum the outer gills were covered and became internal gill lamellae (Fig. 10).

The reduction of the gill operculum had already set in with the transition to pharyngeal respiration, in particular with the restoration of the force mechanism of respiration. The delay in the ontogenetic development of the gill operculum maintained and stimulated the growing significance of direct water flow on the gill lamellae while in their external position.

The first step toward transformation of the internal gills into external larval gills was probably accomplished by an alteration in the conditions of embryonic development, during which the early activity of the larvae required early development of the respiratory organs. With a decrease in the amount of yolk in the egg, the role of the yolk vessels in the respiration of the embryo declined. In some cases a net of dermal vessels was developed. In other cases, as in the sturgeons, during the delay in the development of the gill operculum a progressively earlier development of the gill lamellae occurred. As a result the gill lamellae were found in an exterior position and were freely bathed in water. The flow of water over the gills was facilitated by ciliated epithelia of the oral cavity and the gill arches, and also by the motion of the larva itself. To this were later added the movements of the branchial folds and, finally, movement of the branchial lamellae themselves.

During feeding on larger objects (as in predatory larvae) the predominance of the external gills over the inner was more and more emphasized. The external gills, operating without pause, expanded and passed on to the later stages of development through delay in growth of the gill operculum. They became specialized and differentiated as larval organs located on the "upper" ends of the gill arches. At the same time, in the ventral section of the gill arches typical internal gill lamellae like the organs of adult fishes were developed.

The external gills of Amphibia were developed, consequently, as in fishes before, as special larval organs of respiration. They were characterized mainly by early development and continuous function and therefore acquired significance in larval predatory life as the main organs of respiration. In origin, however, they represent only a development of the first branchions (anlage) of the internal gills. They originally emerged from under the undeveloped gill operculum only by their distal ends. With the gradual development of the external gills these early branchions were moved farther outward due to the expansion of the dorsal part of the gill septa bearing them. This part of the septum was thickened and gave rise to a special outgrowth, the trunk (stem) of the external gill, on which typical gill lamellae were distally (ventrally) arranged in two ranks.

The branchions, developing ventrally from the external gills, gave rise in fishes to the definitive gill lamellae, i.e., the internal gills of the adult animal. In Amphibia, with the emergence of the adult animal onto land, the definitive gills lost their function and were reduced. Therefore, in Amphibia only the larval external gills are developed. Only the supporting structures, the gill arches and gill septa with their vessels and muscles, were retained from the original gills.

In the transition from predatory life to feeding on plankton or vegetation and animal detritus, the predominance of the external gills was lost. In fact, in this case their vulnerability was especially emphasized. Therefore, in anuran Amphibia the gill lamellae of the transitional region (between the trunk of the external gills and the gill septa) were secondarily transformed into internal gills of a distinct type with a dendritic form of branching, and the outer gills were reduced.

II. Development of the Arterial System

In terrestrial vertebrates, in comparison with fishes, there arose a fairly significant change in the blood circulatory organs. The main change was correlated with the addition of the respiratory function of the lungs. These changes had already begun in fishes, the brachiopterygids (*Polypterus*), and had advanced quite far (and in parallel to the Amphibia) among dipnoan fishes. The question of the origin of lungs, and their blood circulation have already been examined. We shall now dwell in more detail on the processes of individual development of the arterial system of the head of urodele Amphibia in connection with the significance of branchial, dermal, oropharyngeal, and pulmonary respiration.

In all fishes two more complete arterial arches, the maxillary and the hyoid, are developed anterior to the branchial arterial arches. They are usually initiated in terrestrial vertebrates, but are arrested early and sometimes suppressed. Frequently in Amphibia the hyoid arch is not developed, but is arrested very early by the connection of the maxillary arch with the arterial trunk. In fishes, however, during individual development, pronounced modifications in the arrangement of the arteries developing from the basis of the first two arterial arches occur.

In fishes, as in Amphibia, the arterial gill arch of the embryo is formed at the time of the formation of the gills on the afferent gill arteries connected to the arterial trunk, and the descent of the efferent gill artery is either direct, or through the paired trunks of the dorsal aorta. In fishes, along with the development of the hyoid hemibranch and the mandibular (spiracular) "pseudobranch" such a division occurs in the first two arterial arches also. In Amphibia neither the hyoid hemibranch nor the spiracular "pseudobranch" are developed. Therefore, properly speaking, one cannot deal with afferent and efferent vessels of the maxillary and hyoid arches in them. In the connections of the remnants of these arches to the arterial trunk or to the system of efferent arteries, however, we may judge the origin of one artery or another developing from the first two arches.

Indeed in fishes, beginning with Selachii, the afferent element of the maxillary arterial arch loses the connection with the arterial trunk fairly soon and joins in a long anastomosis to the lower ends of the efferent hyoid and first efferent gill artery. In the Selachii and in many other fishes (e.g., *Amia*) such anastomoses form one continuous hypobranchial artery, interconnecting the ventral ends of all the efferent gill arteries. The branch supplying blood to the front area of the visceral apparatus ("tongue"), the lower jaw, and the thyroid gland leads anteriorly from the hypobranchial artery.

With reduction of the hemibranch in higher fishes the afferent hyoid artery is also lost. The efferent hyoid artery retains its connection with the aortic root, and sometimes to the hypobranchial artery, and serves for blood supply to the gill operculum, hyoid musculature, and the overlying part of the head.

The maxillary arterial arch, as we have said, is interrupted under the spiracular gill. It is retained dorsally in connection to the root of the dorsal aorta and ventrally usually in the form of a small remnant associated with the hypobranchial artery.

Thus both anterior arterial arches give rise in fishes to arteries connected dorsally to the root of the dorsal aorta or ventrally to the hypobranchial artery.

It is interesting that in Amphibia there is developed not only a complete maxillary arch, but that the same connections are established as in fishes. Although, in Amphibia, a complete hyoid arch is apparently not developed, the same arteries derived of this arch are nevertheless found in them, which are present in higher fishes.

One can only speak of the carotid arteries, as a separate system supplying blood to the head, with respect to terrestrial vertebrates. However, in fishes there are homologous arteries supplying the same region. They simply are not differentiated from the rest of the arterial system to the same extent as they are in terrestrial vertebrates.

As in higher fishes (Moroff, 1902), the arterial arches of Amphibia develop by means of a merging of the primarily isolated bars without established walls, and appear in the central region of primitive visceral arches. In urodele Amphibia they are first fused dorsally to each other and to the dorsal aorta

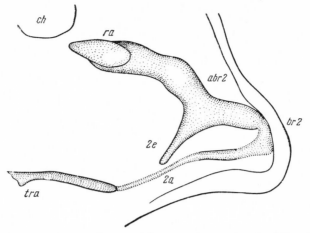

FIG. 82. Reconstruction of the rudiment of the second arterial arch of *Hynobius* 8 mm long; cross section. *abr 2*, Rudiment of arterial arch; *br 2*, rudiment of external gill; *ch*, notochord; *ra*, aortic root; *tra*, arterial trunk; *2a, 2e*, rudiments of afferent and efferent gill arteries.

(Fig. 82). Later the connection to the arterial trunk (Fig. 83) is established.

The maxillary arch is developed first. In the urodele Amphibia it is formed first as a very thick vessel. As in fishes it takes a major role at first, serving in the earliest stages of the development of the embryonic blood circulation as the single canal along which the blood is driven from the heart and arteries to the dorsal aorta system.

After the maxillary arterial arch there develop almost simultaneously the third and fourth arterial arches (Fig. 83). Later, in urodele Amphibia, the fifth arterial arch is developed, and finally, noticeably later, the sixth arch, lying in the last (i.e., fourth) gill septum. As we have said, they are formed initially in the dorsal sections (Fig. 83).

The internal carotid artery of Amphibia develops as a direct anterior prolongation of the main aorta (Fig. 84). In young larvae (particularly in embryos) it connects through the maxillary arterial arch to the arterial trunk. This connection is soon broken, however, due to the reduction of the anterior end of the arterial trunk. Following this the connection with the anlage of the outer carotid artery is broken as a result of the reduction of the ventral section of the maxillary arch.

The development and structure of the internal carotoid artery of larvae of urodele Amphibia is found to be quite similar to the development and structure of the internal carotoid artery of higher fishes, if one follows to the limit their points of homology and particularly if one considers them as originating from the main aorta at the place of origin of the efferent artery of the first gill arch.

The efferent artery of the first gill arch is developed in quite the same way as the succeeding arches. The dorsal part of the efferent gill artery develops directly from the corresponding part of the arterial arch. The ventral part of

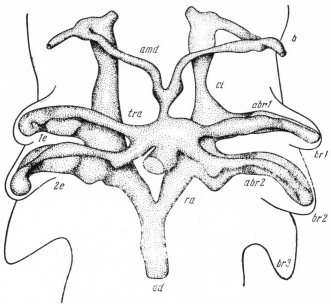

FIG. 83. Reconstruction of the arterial arches of *Hynobius* 8.5 mm long; frontal section, ventral aspect. *abr 1*, *abr 2*, Arterial gill arches; *ad*, dorsal aorta; *amb*, mandibular arterial arch; *b*, artery of balancer; *br 1–br 3*, rudiments of external gills; *ci*, internal carotid artery; *ra*, aortic root; *tra*, arterial trunk; *1e*, *2e*, rudiments of efferent arteries.

the efferent artery in all arches in urodele Amphibia arises as a rudiment lying at the base of the ventral outgrowth of the external gills from the dorsal half of the arterial arches (Fig. 82). It subsequently becomes an "anastomosis" between the dorsal efferent and ventral afferent part of the arterial arch. In its position on the skeletal gill arch, in its mode of development, and by the connections of the anastomoses, it is homologous to the efferent gill artery

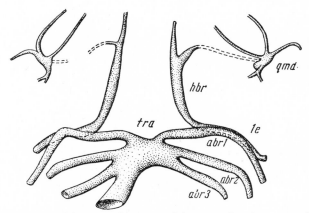

FIG. 84. Reconstruction of the ventral portion of the arterial arch system of *Hynobius* 10 mm long. *hbr*, Rudiments of hypobranchial (external carotid) artery; *l*, lingual artery; *qmd*, mandibular artery; *abr 1*, *abr 2*, arterial gill arches; *tra*, arterial trunk.

of the first arch. It develops much the same as the first arch and should be regarded as a remnant of the original efferent gill artery which never supplied the internal gill. The efferent artery of the external gill, from its origin, is the external outgrowth of the internal efferent artery. In anuran Amphibia the internal efferent artery was restored to its original function since these forms possess secondarily developed internal gills.

The first pair of gill arches develop vessels connected to the ventral ends of efferent arteries, being their anterior prolongations. These vessels are also differentiated in location, sometimes from separate initial rudiments. From such rudiments paired elongate vessels interconnecting the ventral ends of the first arterial arches are formed. By analogy with the vessels of fishes we should call this vessel the hypobranchial artery. In terrestrial vertebrates it becomes the basis for the formation of the external carotid artery.

In urodele Amphibia (*Hynobius*) there appear first small lateral protrusions at the base of the mandibular arterial arch. Then, between these protrusions and the lower ends of the efferent arteries, the first gill arches appear as indefinite cellular masses or separate cavities without definite walls. Thus there is noted an elongate connection between the ventral ends of the mandibular and first efferent gill arteries—the rudiment of the hypobranchial artery. Following this with exceptional rapidity, the anterior extension of the arterial trunk, bearing the mandibular arterial trunk, disappears and finally there is now established the single connection between the ventral termini of the mandibular arteries and the final efferent gill artery.

Directly following the establishment of these long new connectives, the hypobranchial arteries, the ventral part of the jaw is reduced, beginning from the area of the jaw articulation toward the elongated vessel (Fig. 84). Thus on account of the elongation of the anastomoses between the mandibular arterial arch and the first efferent gill artery (i.e., on account of the hypobranchial artery), the exterior carotid artery is developed. The ventral section of the mandibular arch is reduced.

At metamorphosis, when the gills disappear and the continuous arterial arch is restored, the first arterial gill arch is included in the structure of the internal carotid artery, forming its proximal elongation to the point of origin of the outer carotid artery. Thus the inclusion of both carotid arteries in one system occurs.

This system is divided from the dorsal aorta system by a gradual reduction of the passage of the aortic root over the space between the descent of the first and second efferent gill arteries. The carotid duct (ductus caroticus) thus formed loses its cavity and is completely obliterated. The carotid artery system is also separated from the arterial trunk to which it is only indirectly connected through the capillaries of the first gill and small anastomoses in the ventral region. At the time of metamorphosis, with reduction of the gills, the blood current passes through these anastomoses direct from the arterial trunk to the carotid artery system. At the same time, however, a septum develops in the arterial trunk separating the flow of blood from the heart to the carotid artery system from the remainder of the blood.

This separation is undoubtedly supported by the fact that in the presence of an undivided ventricle in Amphibia a mixing of arterial and venous blood occurs. The elongate valve in the conus arteriosus, the septum in the arterial trunk and, lastly, the separation of the carotid artery from the dorsal aorta were only a few elements in a complex system of adaptations leading toward the supplying of the head, especially the brain and its main sense organs, as well as the tongue (as an organ of food-taking), and the respiratory musculature of the hypoglossal region, with the most oxygenated blood, and the respiratory organs themselves, the lungs (in anurans, the skin also), with the most venous blood.

With the development of the septum in the ventricle of higher terrestrial vertebrates and the establishment of a complete separation of arterial and venous blood in the heart itself, the significance of a completely separate carotid artery system is lost. The carotid arteries have become branches of the ventral aorta, and to them there is sometimes joined the subclavian artery (in turtles, crocodiles, birds, and many mammals).

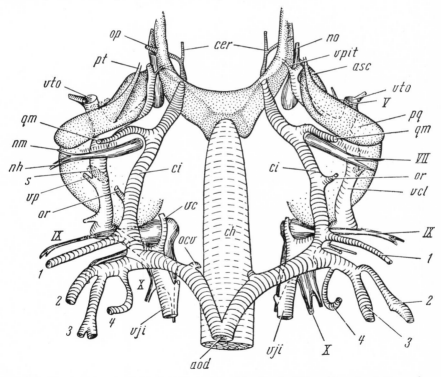

FIG. 85. Reconstruction of the dorsal vessels of the head of *Hynobius* about 15 mm long. *aod*, Dorsal aorta; *asc*, processus ascendens palatoquadrati; *cer*, cerebral artery; *ch*, choana; *ci*, internal carotid artery; *nh*, *nm*, hyoid and mandibular branches of facial nerve; *no*, oculoprofundus nerve (V); *ocv*, occipitovertebral artery; *op*, optic artery; *or*, orbital artery; *pq*, palatoquadrate cartilage; *pt*, pterygoid process; *qm*, arteria quadratomandibularis; *s*, anlage of stapes; *vc*, cerebral vein; *vcl*, lateral head vein; *vji*, internal jugular vein; *vp*, vena palatoquadrata; *vpit*, pituitary vein; *vto*, vena orbitotemporalis; *1–4*, branchial arterial arches; V, VII, IX, X, cranial nerves.

In the dorsal section of the arterial system of the head a large artery at the base of the mandibular aortic arch is first developed. While retaining its former position in the dorsal section, and also supplying much of the balancers, in the area of the jaw articulation it gives off new branches expanding anteriorly along the lower jaw. This is the art. quadratomandibularis, typical of Amphibia. It is situated directly behind the palatoquadrate and passes laterally between this cartilage and the hyomandibular nerve, parallel and directly anterior to the latter (Fig. 85). The jaw artery in the larvae of the dipnoans *Protopterus* and *Ceratodus* (Schmalhausen, 1951; Fig. 5) branches off in exactly the same position.

In front of the point of origin of the art. quadratomandibularis the internal carotid artery passes into the braincase through a foramen in the developing trabeculae. Beyond this it gives off two lateral ophthalmic arteries passing again through the wall of the trabeculae outward to the eye.

In the posterior part of the internal carotid artery, between the descent of the first efferent branchial artery and the exit of the mandibular artery, i.e., in the position of the dorsal element of the hyoid arterial arch, a small rudiment of a branch extending laterally under the otic region of the skull develops. At the same place, directly in front of this artery, the auditory ossicle, the stapes, is developed. In *Ceratodus* the art. hyoidea (art. opercularis; Greil, 1913), with its anterior branch transecting the anlage of the pharyngohyal (art. temporalis; Greil, 1913), is developed in a similar position. As shown in the later development, in position, branching, and region of supply this artery in the Amphibia is undoubtedly a homolog of the orbital artery of fishes.

In addition, well behind the principal aorta, lateral of the notochord in the occipital area of the head, there is developed a pair of dorsally turned branches, the occipitovertebral arteries, which ascend to the occiput and run backward along the spine to become the vertebral artery. Still later, in larger larvae, the art. palatonasalis develops in this region, running along the base of the skull anteriorly. This concludes the development of the main arteries of the head.

In other Urodela the arterial system is found to be more or less conspicuously divergent from what we have described for the Hynobiidae.

A. The Hyoid Artery

The hyoid aortic arch as a whole, as indicated above, apparently never develops in Amphibia (there is a trace of a rudiment of it in frogs). However, its dorsal part, which we designate as the art. hyoidea, not only develops early in some cases but attains considerable proportions.

The hyoid artery is developed in the region of the hypoglossal arch of the visceral skeleton directly behind the anlage of the auditory ossicle, the stapes, which is recognized after the formation of this arch. The hyoid artery mainly supplies the depressor mandibulae muscle, which in derivation is a hyoid muscle (m. adductor hyomandibularis of fishes, and m. levator hyoidei of the Dipnoi) and is innervated by the facialis nerve. Sometimes this artery is initiated early, even before the development of art. orbitalis (Fig. 87). In one case in *Ranodon* (Fig. 87) it is found branching off independently behind the origin of the orbital artery, but farther along both arteries fuse into one orbital artery. Sometimes in comparatively late stages (in larva 26 mm long), there is a thick art. hyoidea in the typical position.

Just as the original relationship between the hyoid and orbital arteries was maintained in *Pleurodeles* (Fig. 86), so it is present in the larvae of some fishes (particularly in sturgeons and Dipnoi), in which the orbital artery is the anterior branch of the hyoid artery.

In the Urodela, however, the orbital artery usually acquires an independent origin from the internal carotid artery or (as in fishes) anterior to the point of origin of the hyoid artery, or more often takes its place completely. In Amphibia, the hyoid artery as such is not developed in its original position in most cases, thus its remnant is actually its derivative, the orbital artery. In addition to the hyoid artery there also remains its peripheral element, however, with its typical region of supply, entering into the structure of a new jugular artery leading off from the aortic arch system (Fig. 87, right).

As was shown above, the orbital artery arises as the anterior branch of the hyoid artery. In a vast majority of vertebrates, however, it forms an independent artery with an origin from the internal carotid artery. In terrestrial vertebrates its place of origin usually lies in the region of the former hyoid arch

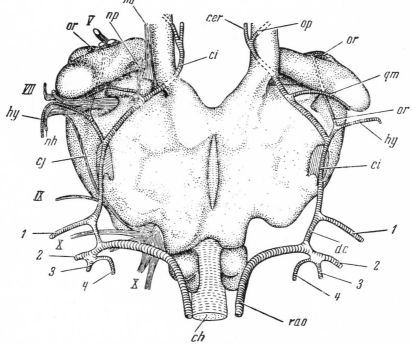

FIG. 86. Reconstruction of the dorsal arteries of a larva of *Pleurodeles waltlii* about 20 mm long. Ventral view. *cj*, Commissure between arteries VII and IX; *dc*, ductus caroticus; *hy*, hyoid artery; *np*, palatine nerve VII; *rao*, aortic roots; other abbreviations as in Fig. 85.

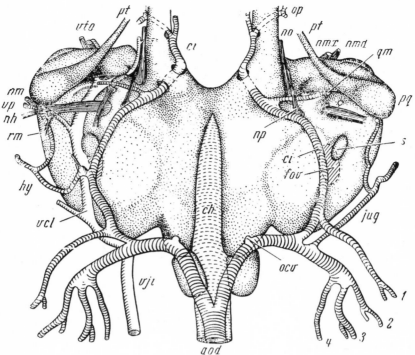

FIG. 87. Reconstruction of the dorsal vessels of the head of *Ranodon* 26 mm long. Ventral view. *fov*, Fenestra ovalis of otic capsule; *hy*, hyoid artery; *jug*, jugular artery; *nmd*, *nmx*, lower and upper jaw branches of trigeminal nerve; *np*, palatine nerve VII; *rm*, muscle branch of hyoid nerve VII; other abbreviations as in Fig. 85.

aorta. It is developed relatively late in urodele Amphibia. From its origin directly behind the rudiment of the auditory ossicle it leads anteriorly in a dorsal direction, going around the stapes backward and upward, or downward and forward. In some cases in the larvae of *Ranodon*, the orbital artery passes straight through the anlage of the stapes. In the cartilagenous precursor of the auditory ossicle, and sometimes after ossification, there is a very distinct canal through which this artery passes (Fig. 135).

The further path of the orbital artery is always highly characteristic. It lies along the head vein (v. capitis lateralis), at first beneath it, then lateral of it; it passes with it through the cleft between the palatoquadrate and the otic capsule of the skull (antrum petrosa lateralis, or cranioquadrate passage of English authors) forward to the region of the orbits, where it turns directly behind the processus ascendens palatoquadratum to the artery accompanying the main branch of the trigeminal nerve emerging there. These arteries supply the sides of the head in the region of the orbits, and especially the jaw musculature. The most important branch is that accompanying the n. mandibularis trigemini and passing beyond it to the outer wall of the lower jaw. Such an arrangement of the branching indicates not only the homology of this artery with the orbital artery of fishes which we discussed before, but also its homology with the stapedial artery of terrestrial vertebrates. In lizards particularly we find the same orbital artery typical of fishes in the division of the art. stapedia into art. supraorbitalis, art. infraorbitalis, and art. mandibularis. For us it is important to note, however, that in primitive Amphibia there is sometimes a fully typical stapedial artery, even passing through the canal in the auditory ossicle. The same is observed sometimes in the Gymnophiona (*Ichthyopsis*) and it is also known in many Stegocephalia. The above relation to the stapes and the further branching of the stapedial artery should be recognized as basic for all terrestrial vertebrates.

B. THE MANDIBULAR ARTERY

The mandibular artery, pronounced in the embryonic stages, is ventrally reduced simultaneously with the development of external gills in the young larvae. At the same time the dorsal part of the mandibular arch artery soon expands and in young larvae becomes the most important artery of the head (Fig. 85). From its position it acquires the name art. quadratomandibularis. The art. quadratomandibularis branches off from the internal carotid artery immediately below the above-noted basitrabecular articulation, in front of the exit of the facialis nerve (Figs. 86 and 87). It lies below the articulation (anteromedially) along with the exit of n. palatinus facialis, abruptly crossing it to the dorsal side and extending under the medial posterior edge of the quadrate cartilage below to the jaw articulation. Thus, the palatine branch of the facialis nerve passes downward and forward, crossing over ventrally through a loop formed by the spreading of the internal carotid artery and the quadratomandibular artery at an acute angle (Figs. 86 and 87). Such a relationship of the palatine nerve to the mandibular artery is to a great extent characteristic of fishes, *Polypterus, Acipenser, Lepidosteus, Amia,* and *Ceratodus* (Schmalhausen, 1951; Fig. 5), and it is retained even in those cases in which the exit of the palatine nerve is borne far forward.

This typical correlation is retained in Amphibia and shows with complete certainty the homology of art. quadratomandibularis of Amphibia with the art. mandibularis efferens of fishes.

The main trunk of the mandibular artery passes between the rear wall of the palatoquadrate cartilage and the muscles descending to the lower jaw (m. depressor mandibulae) to the jaw articulation, where it gives off posteriorly several small branches to the above-mentioned muscles, and small branches to the end of the hyoid, to the skin of the hyomandibular fold, and also to the ventral musculature. An important branch runs farther along the inner edge of the lower jaw (art. mandibularis medialis), a small branch leads off laterally to the skin, and one more branch curves around the jaw joint and lies along the outer edge of the lower jaw (art. mandibularis lateralis).

This artery, so thick in young larvae, is reduced, however, with the development of a new artery, art. jugularis, which not only has the area of distribution of the former hyoid artery, spreading from m. depressor mandibularis forward to the jaw region, but also joins the jaw artery system and completely replaces it. It takes the name of art. mandibulojugularis (Fig. 87).

The jugulomandibular artery originally developed from the peripheral element of the hyoid artery, which makes a new connection to the aortic arch system by means of an elongate anastomosis, and loses its original connection to the internal carotid artery (Fig. 87). Having developed in this way the jugular artery is connected at the front edge of m. depressor mandibulae to the mandibular artery and, replacing it, takes over its whole peripheral element.

This region of blood supply in young Amphibia receives purely arterial blood from the internal carotid artery, and later, with the development of the jugulomandibular artery, similar blood from the second efferent branchial artery. However, after metamorphosis of the systemic aortic arch, and consequently of the jugulomandibular artery, they only receive a mixture of arterial venous blood. Since this artery is fully developed late in larval life (in the Plethodontidae especially during metamorphosis) this is apparently correlated to the conditions of terrestrial life in Amphibia. This is likewise affirmed by the absence of this artery in forms living constantly in the water.

C. The Blood Circulation of the Head of Adult Amphibia in Relation to the Mode of Respiration

In Amphibia leading a typically amphibiotic way of life and spending a considerable proportion of their time on land there is, as is well known, not branchial, but pulmonary respiration. That in itself, however, turns out obviously to be insufficient in modern Amphibia possessing a bare skin, and it is always supplemented by dermal respiration. In addition, in urodele Amphibia, the strongly vascularized mucous membrane of the oral cavity, pharynx, and even the esophagus (Salamandridae and Plethodontidae) plays a large role in respiratory gas exchange. Since in small bodies the external surface is relatively greater the role of dermal respiration is enhanced in small Amphibia. Here lungs are sometimes reduced altogether (*Salamandrina perspicillata* and Plethodontidae).

The dermal arteries of the head, carrying purely arterial blood from the carotid artery, certainly cannot take part in dermal respiration. In this case the whole surface of the head remains unused for these purposes. However, some arteries carrying a mixture of blood from the systemic arch forward in the head may take part in respiration. Such, for example, is the occipital artery, remaining relatively small in urodele Amphibia. However, in its place (or right along with it) in more recent larvae the palatine artery is developed, which at metamorphosis reaches high capacity (Fig. 88, art. palatonasalis). This artery abundantly supplies the mucous membrane of the oral cavity, which in urodele Amphibia has a prominent role in respiration after metamorphosis.

Dermal branches of the hyoid artery and especially the quadratomandibular artery (Fig. 88) are present. However, while these branches receive arterial blood from the carotid artery they evidently cannot take part in respiration. In Urodela a prolonged anastomosis linking the hyoid artery and the mandibular artery with the systemic arch of the aorta is developed. From the latter a mixture of blood is now carried to the lateral head areas which can be

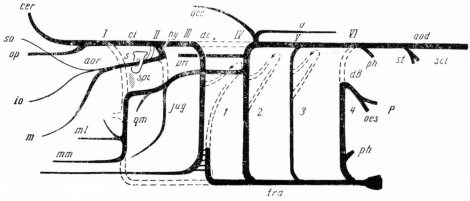

FIG. 88. Scheme of the arteries of the head of Urodela, left side. Broken lines indicate provisionary larval vessels. *aod*, Dorsal aorta; *aor*, orbital (stapedial) artery; *ce, ci*, external and internal carotid arteries; *cer*, cerebral artery; *dB*, ductus Botalli; *dc*, carotid duct; *hy*, hyoid artery; *jug*, jugular artery; *io, m, so*, suborbital, mandibular and supraorbital branches of the orbital artery; *mm, ml*, art. mandibularis medialis; *occ*, occipital artery; *oes*, aerteria oesophagea; *op*, principal optic artery; *p*, pulmonary artery; *ph*, pharyngeal artery; *qm*, quadratomandibular artery; *s*, stapes; *scl*, subclavian artery; *spi*, remnant of spiracle; *st*, pectoral artery; *tra*, trunk of ventral aorta; *v*, vertebral artery; *1–4*, branchial arterial arches; *I–VI*, aortic arches.

completely oxygenated in the skin. Thus the blood supply of the most important artery of the head takes part in the dermal respiration process.

That the art. mandibulojugularis was developed from the long anastomosis linking the mandibular and hyoid arteries with the systemic arch aorta is evident from the fact that in *Amphiuma* it is essentially an anastomosis between the retained art. quadratomandibularis and another aorta (Druner, 1902, 1904). The art. mandibulojugularis is thus a special collector, bringing together the dermal vessels of the sides of the head and linking them to the systemic arch aorta. Thus the dermal vessels of the head are included within the respiratory system. In the Plethodontidae, in which the lungs are reduced, dermal-oral respiration fully satisfies the oxygen requirement of the organism. The dermal branch of the jugulomandibular artery was expanded. Along with this artery, in adult animals, arteries branch out to the esophagus, and a large branch passes to the skin. In the jaw region it also gives off more substantial dermal branches. In salamanders branches from the pulmonary artery also lead off to the esophagus. These branches receive almost pure venous blood which is oxygenated in the mucous membrane of the pharynx and esophagus. In *Salamandrina perspicillata*, with reduction of the lungs, the pulmonary artery carries all its blood to the mucous membrane of the pharynx and esophagus alone.

Of the larval vessels inherited from the fishlike ancestors of the Amphibia, transformations of the hyoid and mandibular arteries are successively connected with the adaptation of modern Amphibia, possessing smooth, constantly moistened skin, to life on land in relatively humid air, while dermal respiration takes on ever-increasing importance. The main artery serving this

respiration, in the head region, in urodele Amphibia is the large jugulomandibular artery supplying the skin of the sides of the head and the mandibular
region and being precisely the result of this transformation. To this there is
joined only the still small occipital artery. Besides dermal respiration there
is still oropharyngeal respiration, served by the large art. palatonasalis supplying the mucous membrane of the oral cavity, the small art. pharyngeae,
going to the pharynx wall (Fig. 88), and art. esophagea distributing to the
esophagus walls. In some cases pulmonary respiration completely replaces
oropharyngeal and dermal respiration (in Plethodontidae, *Ranodon,* and
Onychodactylus).

The most pronounced transformation of the arterial system is correlated
particularly with the development of dermal respiration. In anuran Amphibia
this transformation goes even farther than in urodeles. The occipital artery
is very widely expanded, enclosing the whole upper part of the head including the temporal region, the region of the orbits (replacing the orbital artery),
and the nasal area. It is connected by an anastomosis to the system of pulmonary dermal arteries in the region of the mandibular branch. On the other
hand the jugulomandibular artery moves its exit still farther back to the pulmonary (fourth gill) arch and is found as a considerable part of a new large
dermal artery (art. cutanea magna) receiving almost pure venous blood. The
importance of the jugulomandibular artery in the respiratory process is sub-
stantially increased as a result of this. Thus a mode of unique specialization
originates among urodele Amphibia leading a more or less terrestrial way
of life.

In adaptation to constant life in water there is no metamorphosis and the
animal retains external larval gills, and consequently branchial circulation,
throughout life (Sirenidae and Proteidae). In these cases predominant significance is acquired anew by the art. quadratomandibularis and its original
larval form. Another branch of the carotid artery which usually appears later,
art. hyoidea and its derivative art. orbitalis, is not developed at all. Art. palatonasalis, serving the oral respiration of terrestrial forms, is also reduced. A
similar larval blood circulation in the head is also present in the axolotl. In
adult *Ambystoma* it is retained, however, after metamorphosis. Both the
axolotl and *Ambystoma* possess a typical art. quadratomandibularis. In them
neither the hyoid artery nor its derivatives, art. orbitalis and art. jugularis, are
developed. On the other hand there is a well-developed art. palatonasalis.
Thus in *Ambystoma* the phenomenon of neoteny is seen well developed;
even after metamorphosis they retain some larval characters.

The phenomenon of neoteny, to greater or lesser degree, involves all
urodele Amphibia. It is little developed in the arterial system of the Hynobiidae, Salamandridae, and Plethodontidae; it is noticeable in the Cryptobranchidae and especially in the Amphiumidae. It is clearly manifested in
the Ambystomidae and reaches its maximal extent in the Proteidae and
Sirenidae.

As a result the arterial system of the head in aquatic Amphibia is found to
be considerably simplified.

III. THE SEISMOSENSORY SYSTEM

Of the sense organs we call especial attention to the seismosensory organs since they are limited exclusively to life in the water, are inherited from fishes, and disappear in terrestrial life. In fossil forms they are indicative of aquatic life. Moreover, they are distinguished by an exceptional constancy in their occurrence which is determined by the complexity of correlations to certain other organs, primarily in the connections to the nerves supplying them. This connection is established at the simultaneous development of both the seismosensory organs and their nerves from a system of lateral placodes which occupy a key position in the body of the embryo (preotic, otic, and postotic placodes). Second, to the lines of the seismosensory organs there are connected the primordia of the dermal bones which, as canal bones, enter into the structure of the skull roof and also the lower jaw as particularly stable components. This correlation is so close that it is now used as the method for determining the homologies of the bones in bony fishes and Stegocephalia.

In the distribution of the canals of the seismosensory organs two different types are clearly manifested: the actinopterygian fish type and the type represented by the crossopterygians and Dipnoi. In the first case the cheek region of the skull is bisected by the preopercular canal starting from the main temporal canal in the otic region (Figs. 11 and 99). In the second case the preopercular canal starts behind the eye from the infraorbital canal (Figs. 48 and 101), first goes backward, then curves downward along the preoperculum and descends to the lower jaw, as in the first case. The difference between the two types is so great that it was formerly presumed that in crossopterygian and dipnoan fishes there is a special jugal canal. Stensiö (1947) showed, however, that it is one and the same as the preopercular canal, which may occupy several different positions in lower fishes. In *Acanthodes,* of the Acanthodii, it leads off from the orbital canal as in actinopterygian fishes, and in the more primitive *Euthacanthus* (Fig. 6) it is disposed in almost the same way as in crossopterygian fishes. It lies in an almost similar position in various sharks. In some paleoniscids it takes an intermediate position. Furthermore, in the ontogenesis of the Dipnoi (*Ceratodus* and *Protopterus*) there was established a shift of the preopercular series of organs from the upper (branch from the main line) to a lower position (lead-off from the infraorbital line). Nonetheless in bony fishes the difference in the position of the preopercular canal in the actinopterygians on the one hand, and in the crossopterygians on the other, is shown quite clearly. According to the above characteristics the Brachiopterygii (*Polypterus*) belong indisputably to the actinopterygian fishes; in them the preopercular canal leads off from the main temporal canal (Fig. 99).

According to this same characteristic the Stegocephalia are indisputably classed as the same type as the crossopterygian fishes and the Dipnoi (Fig. 52). The history of the development of the seismosensory system in urodele Amphibia not only maintains this position but allows one to make some further conclusions. Comparison with the Stegocephalia clarifies the picture of a gradual sinking of the dermal bones beneath the skin and a segregation of the seismosensory organs, attaining an ever more superficial position. The connection with definitely grooved bones is lost in modern Amphibia; however, the developmental dependence on the arrangement and mode of expansion of the lateral placodes and on the arrangement of the corresponding nerves is also retained. As a result, in the early stages of development of young larvae or urodele Amphibia the typical arrangement of the seismosensory organs is retained in the form of lines fully corresponding to the canals and rows of pits in crossopterygian fishes.

The development of the seismosensory system of urodele Amphibia was studied by Platt (1896b) in *Necturus,* Stone (1922) in the axolotl, more recently by the author (Schmalhausen, 1955b) in *Hynobius* and *Ranodon,* and by Medvedeva (1961b) in *Ranodon* (Fig. 89). According to these accounts the principal parts of the seismosensory system of the head are developed from the large preotic placodes in correlation with the development of the facial nerve (VII lateralis), from small supratemporal placodes in connection with the glossopharyngeal nerve (IX lateralis), and the occipital placodes growing backward along with the lateral branch of the vagus nerve (X lateralis). The preotic placode, differentiated early, gives rise to the supraorbital and suborbital canals, a small otic branch and a large hyomandibular thickening. The first two branches spread around the eye and give rise to the supraorbital and infraorbital rows of seismosensory organs which are correspondingly innervated by n. ophthalmicus superficialis VII and n. buccalis VII. The otic branch gives off a small row of organs behind the orbit. It is innervated by a special branch of the facial nerve, n. oticus. The supratemporal placode gives off a small transverse row of organs innervated by a branch of the glossopharyngeal nerve (n. supratemporalis IX). The occipital placode extends backward and gives rise to a row of organs innervated by a branch of the vagus nerve (n. auricularis X). The hyomandibular part of the preotic placode divides into two parts. The posterior part grows downward and then forward along the lower jaw. It gives rise to the preopercular row or organs, leading anteriorly to the mandibular row. Behind, it branches off the transverse row of organs of the gular line. The anterior part of the anlage likewise produces an anterior offshoot to the lower jaw and thence it dissociates into an oral row of organs. The remaining part of the anlage differentiates into a system of organs, dispersed between the preopercular and suborbital rows, which from their position in the facial region we call the jugal row.

The gradual differentiation of the placodes, their expansion and breakup into rows of isolated organs is shown in Fig. 89 for *Ranodon sibiricus.* In *Hynobius keyserlingii* the same thing is generally found (Schmalhausen, 1955b). This whole picture is remarkably similar to what is known for fishes. The general distribution of the seismosensory organs, not only in the main line areas, which are represented by canals in fishes and by grooves in Stegocephalia, but also in the secondary lines in the facial region on the dorsal side of the head and on the throat (gular line), which in fishes are manifested in the form of rows of small pits (pit lines) is also very similar. We shall not repeat the descriptions of the distribution of the seismosensory organs in

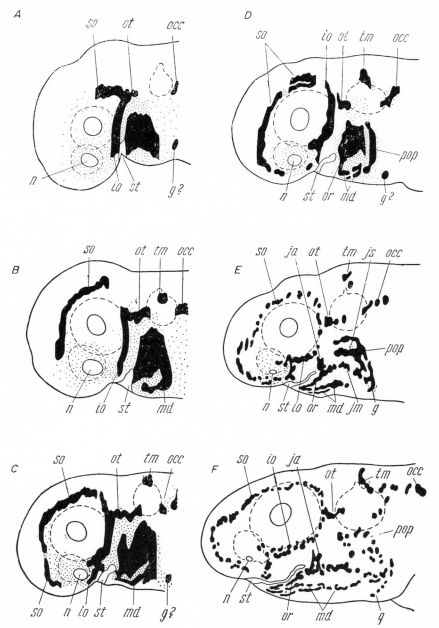

FIG. 89. Graphic reconstruction of the seismosensory placodes of the head of *Ranodon*. Placodes in black; thickened ectoderm between placodes indicated by dots. Embryo of 10 mm length
(*A*); 12.5 mm (*B*); 14.5 mm (*C*); 15 mm (*D*); 16 mm (*E*); 19 mm (*F*). *g*, Gular line; *io*, infraorbital
line; *ja, jm, js*, anterior, median, and dorsal part of jugal line; *md*, mandibular line; *n*, nostril;
occ, occipital part of temporal line; *or*, oral line; *ot*, otic line; *pop*, preopercular line; *so*, supraorbital line; *st*, outer boundary of oral invagination; *tm*, transverse supraorbital line. From
Medvedeva.

urodele Amphibia (cf. Schmalhausen, 1955b, 1957a). We will only indicate the similarity to the Stegocephalia and the mode of the evolution of the seismosensory system in the Amphibia (Figs. 90, 91, and 92).

In fossil Amphibia there has long been a regular distribution of the grooves which form a characteristic figure on the dermal bones of the skull roof that paleontologists call the "lyre." In arrangement they fully correspond to the canals of the seismosensory organs of fishes, in particular, crossopterygian fishes. There can be no doubt that these grooves mark lines of the seismosensory organs arranged in dermal canals on the surface of the bones or, rather, in open dermal channels.

The arrangement of the lateral line organs in Stegocephalia and in urodele Amphibia is very similar, as is evident in comparison of Figs. 48 and 101, showing the position of the grooves on the skull of Stegocephalia, and Figs. 93 and 94 in which the pattern of distribution of lines of sensory pits in urodele Amphibia (on the basis of their distribution pattern in *Ranodon*) is given.

The comparison shows very small differences:

1. The preopercular line at its upper anterior end closely approaches the postorbital branch of the infraorbital line, but in modern Amphibia, as a rule, it is not connected to it. In the Stegocephalia the preopercular ("jugal") groove, on the contrary, is usually connected to the posterior branch of the suborbital groove. However, in *Paleogyrinus, Lyrocephalus kochi,* and *Wetlugasaurus* this connection is similarly absent.

2. The temporal line in urodele Amphibia is moved to the supratemporal region, so that a gap in the horizontal line between the otic and occipital regions is formed. In Stegocephalia the temporal groove usually extends without interruption from the upper end of the postorbital branch of the infraorbital canal along the dorsal surface of the skull back to the occipital region (to the tabular). However, the temporal groove is occasionally broken in *Lyrocephalus, Peltostega, Capitosaurus,* and *Wetlugasaurus,* and does not extend to the posterior border of the skull in *Dvinosaurus, Cyclotosaurus, Metoposaurus, Benthosuchus,* and others. The temporal groove is almost fully re-

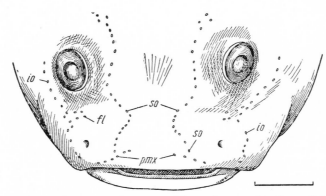

FIG. 90. Larva of *Ranodon* 30 mm long. Head from above and in front. *fl,* Lachrymal bulge of infraorbital line (*io*); *pmx,* premaxillary row of organs; *so,* supraorbital lines.

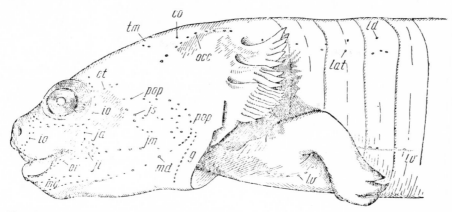

FIG. 91. Larva of *Ranodon* 55 mm long. Lateral view. *co*, Organs of transverse occipital line; *g*, gular line; *io*, infraorbital row; *ja, ji, jm, js*, anterior ventral, median, and dorsal parts of jugal line; *lat*, lateral line of trunk; *id*, accessory dorsal line; *lv*, ventral line; *md*, mandibular line; *occ*, occipital part of temporal line; *or*, oral line; *ot*, otic portion of temporal line; *pop*, preopercular row of organs; *tm*, transverse supratemporal row.

duced or unknown in *Paleogyrinus, Colosteus, Archegosaurus*, and *Eryops*. Thus the reduction of the temporal line in any case is also noted in many Stegocephalia.

3. The transverse occipital commissure is already reduced in most of the Stegocephalia. It is developed in rare cases and then it is weakly manifested (*Dolichopareias, Keraterpeton, Trematosaurus*, and *Benthosuchus*). In some cases it is incomplete and is represented only by its lateral elements. In urodele Amphibia there are remnants of the occipital commissure in the form of

FIG. 92. Larva of *Ranodon* 22 mm long. Head from below. *g*, Gular row of organs; *jm*, median section of jugal line; *md*, mandibular line with two branches; *or*, oral row of organs; *pop*, preopercular row of organs.

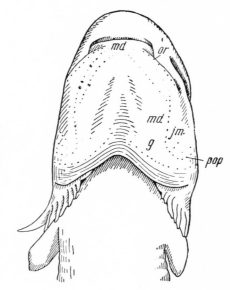

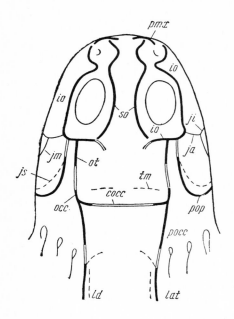

FIG. 93. Arrangement of the lateral lines on the head of Caudata (Hynobiidae); view from above. Broad lines indicate rows of organs represented by grooves in Stegocephalia and by canals in crossopterygian fishes; double lines indicate grooves as in Stegocephalia; broken lines as in Urodela; thin lines indicate rows of organs only occasionally present as grooves in Stegocephalia; looped lines indicate rows of organs which are usually pit lines in fishes. *cocc*, Occipital commissure; *io*, infraorbital line; *ja, ji, jm, js*, anterior, ventral, median, and dorsal jugal lines; *lat*, lateral line of trunk; *ld*, accessory dorsal line; *occ*, occipital part of temporal line; *ot*, otic part of temporal line; *pmx*, premaxillary line (anterior commissure); *pocc*, postoccipital part of temporal line; *pop*, preopercular line; *so*, supraorbital line; *tm*, transverse supratemporal line.

a group of scattered seismosensory organs. In *Ranodon* it is represented only in its lateral elements, by one or two organs.

4. Finally it should be noted that in *Trimerorhachis, Benthosuchus, Dvinosaurus*, and probably most of the Stegocephalia there was, as in urodele Amphibia, in addition to the mandibular groove (c. marginalis), a still very well-manifested oral groove (c. dentalis of Williston) which, passing along the outer edge of the jaw to the anterior end of the dentary bone, is obviously homologous to the oral line of sensory pits of urodele Amphibia. In contrast to the latter, however, both of these lines begin in the region of the supra-angular as one general groove and only later is it divided into two. Meanwhile in the Urodela the oral line begins at the angle of the mouth independently of the mandibular line.

It is evident that there is an exceptional similarity in the disposition of the lines of seismosensory organs in urodele Amphibia and the corresponding

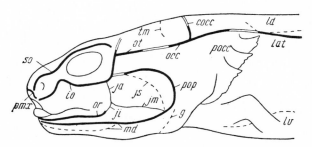

FIG. 94. Arrangement of the lateral lines of the head of Caudata (Hynobiidae). Lateral view. *g*, Gular line; *lv*, ventral line; *md*, mandibular line; *or*, oral line; other abbreviations as in Fig. 93.

grooves in the Stegocephalia. In addition to those lines homologous to the grooves of Stegocephalia, however, there are still other rows of organs in urodele Amphibia. These lines cannot be regarded as newly acquired by Amphibia since they are clearly homologous to definite lines of sensory pits (pit lines) of crossopterygians and many other fishes (Stensiö, 1947). Evidently they were also present in the Stegocephalia but on account of a superficial position in the skin no trace of them remained on the bones. As was shown before, however, in some cases such rows of organs are buried deeper under the skin and appear in the form of homologous grooves or canals. This is seen both in fishes (especially in crossopterygians) and in Stegocephalia. For example, in the stegocephalians *Lyrocephalus*, *Colosteus*, and *Aphaneramma*, there were grooves corresponding to the central transverse lines of the head (the dorsal, elongate postorbital branch of the suborbital line is present in *Menopoma* and embryonically in the Hynobiidae). In *Trematosaurus* there was a small posterior offshoot, leading backward and downward from the infraorbital groove and homologous to the anterior part of the jugal line. In *Paleogyrinus decorus* there was a groove leading from the preopercular groove to the corner of the mouth and homologous to the median and lower parts of the jugal line (Fig. 31). In *Ichthyostega* in the quadratojugal bones there was also an elongate canal corresponding to the lower postmaxillary part of the jugal canal (Fig. 31).

In the Stegocephalia the lines of seismosensory organs are noticeable on the dermal bones of the skull as superficial grooves and only in the Ichthyostegidae were the canals of the lateral line enclosed in the bones as in fishes. It is usually thought that these grooves are impressions of dermal canals in which the above-noted organs are distributed. There is very little probability of this. With the close connection of the skin to the dermal bones of the skull indicated by the superficial sculpturing of the bones, the space between the epidermis and the bony skull roof would have been negligible. Moreover, the grooves of the lateral line are very wide and if canals lay in them they could not have shifted in such a narrow space. The lateral line grooves are especially wide in *Palaeogyrinus*, *Lyrocephalus*, and *Benthosuchus*, and reach a width up to 10 mm in *Metoposaurus*, *Cyclotosaurus*, and *Batrachosuchus*. In *Batrachosuchus* they are extremely broad, not only absolutely but relatively, reaching almost one-third the diameter of the orbit of the eye. Such canals could not be located in the very thick skin and would have had to be on the surface in the form of open channels.

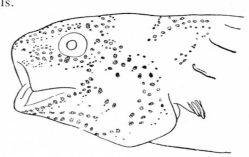

FIG. 95. Head of axolotl (*Ambystoma tigrinum*) 25 mm long. Secondary proliferation of sense organs by division (groups of organs) and new formations (small organs).

The exceptional width of the grooves of the lateral line is probably correlated with a secondary proliferation of the sense organs (as in many modern aquatic Amphibia after metamorphosis, Fig. 95), but perhaps they were also differentiated for the development of the dermal glands which, with their secretions, maintain these organs in a humid state during the life of the animal on land. The great width of the grooves facilitated easy washing away of mucous during the shift of the animal to water (the mucous would have prevented reception of vibrations and water movements by the hairs of the sensory cells).

THE MODIFICATIONS OF THE SYSTEM OF SEISMOSENSORY ORGANS IN AMPHIBIA

In the system of seismosensory organs of Stegocephalia certain ontogenetic and (particularly) age modifications may be defined and certain phylogenetic transformations may be shown. Incidentally, in the Stegocephalia, the paths leading to modern Amphibia may also be noted.

In the Ichthyostegidae (Fig. 31) the system of seismosensory canals is constructed on the crossopterygian fish pattern, with certain simplifications. The simplifications consist of the presence of simple excretory pores together with ramifications such as are present in crossopterygian fishes. In the ontogeny of *Amia calva* (according to Allis, 1889) the formation of simple pores precedes the development of the complex pattern. Therefore, as Säve-Söderbergh (1932) notes, the canal structure of ichthyostegids may be understood if it is regarded as the result of arrested development. In favor of such an interpretation is the form of the canals themselves. The canals in *Amia calva* are developed from individual points corresponding to the position of each sense organ which develops in those positions. At the end of each canal there are exit apertures and it takes an overall archlike form. By the growth of each of these plates the ends of the adjacent canals are united and their excretory openings are fused into one common external pore lying between the neighboring seismosensory organs. Thus continuous canals are formed, consisting of individual links containing one organ each. Each link has an archlike shape since both of its ends are raised to the surface of the epidermis where the common outer pores for the two adjacent links open. With further development, an elongate excretory canalicule (usually branching later) is developed, and the entire canal as a whole is straightened. This later phase of the straightening of the canal (and also the branching of the excretory canal and the proliferation of external pores) has declined in the ichthyostegids. According to Säve-Söderbergh each section of canal between two neighboring excretory pores has an archlike form in *Ichthyostega*, and their middle sections are deeply sunken into bones (where the sense organs are located).

The seismosensory canals were located within bones in ichthyostegids. In all later Stegocephalia they lay in grooves on the surface of the bones. This modification can be regarded as the result of two processes: (1) delay in the formation of the canals of the lateral system, and (2) modification of the dermal canals into superficial open grooves. In Stegocephalia, both of these processes evidently took place.

In bony fishes the dermal bones of the skull (and also the scales in the skin of the trunk) are initiated after the formation of the lateral line canals. Bones bearing such canals are initiated at the very start in the form of a tube around the pre-existing canal, and therefore the latter is included in the bone from the first moments of ossification. In most of the Stegocephalia the canals of the lateral line were formed later when the dermal bones of the skull were already developed, and therefore the seismosensory canals were not included in the early stages of the bones at all. The branchiosaurs (Branchiosauria) are undoubtedly larval forms and indisputably there were lateral line organs in them; they even retained indications of this in two rows of pigmented scales on the tail of *Micrerpeton* (Moodie, 1908); however, no traces of these lines were left on the bones of the skull. One imagines that in the branchiosaurs the seismosensory organs lay on the surface, in the actual epidermis, as in larvae of modern Amphibia. It should not be forgotten that such a superficial position in the epidermis is characteristic not only of amphibian larvae, but also of young fish larvae. In the Stegocephalia the superficial position of the seismosensory organs was maintained longer than in fishes in correlation with extension of the larval phase in their development.

In the larvae of fishes the superfical position of the sense organs is maintained briefly. These organs are sunken in pits, and ridges are developed which are elevated above them so that the lines are found sunken in grooves. Then the ridges come into contact and the grooves are converted into canals buried under the epidermis. This latter phase evidently declined in most Stegocephalia. If, in Stegocephalia, enclosed canals lying under the epidermis were developed, then they inevitably would have been involved in the process of ossification and would have been included in the superficial expansion of the dermal bones (as even the net of dermal blood vessels was included). It must be presumed that in the labyrinthodonts the seismosensory organs lay in open dermal grooves which were formed only in late larval life. After metamorphosis they were depressed and enclosed below and laterally by ossification. Further modifications with age must be noted. In larger individuals the grooves are more fully developed. They cut deeper into the bones; they grow farther and are connected to each other, while in young individuals elongation of the grooves is scarcely noticeable or connections are not present (Moodie, 1908; Bystrov, 1935).

In the labyrinthodonts the lateral line grooves attained great width and in life were undoubtedly complex, unique, and highly specialized organs (probably with increased numbers of sensory hillocks and rich in the development of glands).

The reduction of the seismosensory canals in Stegocephalia occurred through omission of the later stages of their differentiation. This is clearly evident in a comparison of the lateral line systems of teleost fishes, ichthyostegids, and more recent Stegocephalia. Following this reduction, which led to the formation of systems of superficial grooves in the place of the previous canals, a new phase of gradual development and unique specialization began, evidently correlated with the secondary return of labyrinthodonts to life in water.

Certain features of the structure and age modification of the grooves in labyrinthodonts lead to some further conclusions. The groove became less noticeable and simultaneously declined to small patches and rows of alveoli. The development of such grooves was delayed and sometimes they became noticeable as chains of alveoli only in aged individuals, as for example the occipital commissure in large *Benthosuchus* (Bystrov, 1935). The breakup of the grooves into sections and rows of alveoli is seen in many cases. In *Capitosaurus nasutus* the supraorbital groove throughout its length was broken up into a chain of alveoli. The same is seen in *Pteroplax cornuta* (Attey, 1878, cf. Säve-Söderbergh, 1935). In *Lyrocephalus kochi* the anterior ethoid commissure was broken apart into rows of short grooves or long alveoli. This same commissure is broken into alveoli in *Trematosaurus* and *Metoposaurus* and is totally reduced in *Capitosaurus*, *Wetlugasaurus*, and many other labyrinthodonts. In *Branchiosauravus*, *Trematosaurus*, *Lonchorhynchus*, and *Benthosuchus* the occipital commissure takes the form of a transverse row of alveoli lying along the posterior edge of the postparietal and tabular bones (Bystrov, 1935). In other labyrinthodonts it is usually absent altogether. In *Metoposaurus* and *Benthosuchus* the posterior ends of the temporal canal are broken into rows of alveoli. In *Wetlugasaurus*, *Cyclotosaurus*, *Dvinosaurus*, and many other labyrinthodonts the ends are reduced altogether, and the temporal groove ends blindly in the region of the supratemporal bone. In *Benthosuchus*, *Mastodonsaurus*, *Cyclotosaurus*, *Lonchorhynchus*, and *Trimerorhachis* the posterior ends of the supraorbital groove are broken into rows of alveoli (in *Metoposaurus* this breakup extends to the upper ends of the suborbital canal). In *Colosteus*, *Trematosaurus*, *Capitosaurus*, *Wetlugasaurus*, and other labyrinthodonts a total fragmentation is attained.

If it is considered that the archlike form of the section of each canal between two excretory pores in ichthyostegids indicates development from separate anlagen corresponding to each sensory hillock in the development of *Amia calva*, according to the description of Allis (1889), then we may interpret the fragmentation of the grooves of Stegocephalia as restricted development. Probably in Stegocephalia also the grooves were initiated in ontogeny in separate units, i.e., in depressions corresponding to each sensory hillock. After this, late in larval life, the rows of elongate depressions were fused into continuous grooves. In phylogeny the grooves were broken up into rows of alveoli by modification of the later stages of the formation of the continuous grooves.

In the labyrinthodonts such a reduction occurs only in certain sections of the lateral line grooves. The entire system as a whole was developed in correlation with a secondary transition to life in water in a rather progressive although unique form.

In the lepospondylous Stegocephalia which are basically more terrestrial forms than the labyrinthodonts (although a secondary return to water occurred to a minor extent in one branch of them), the system of lateral line organs underwent further reduction and in a majority of cases grooves were not left on the skull bones. Nevertheless, Moodie (1908) found scarely noticeable grooves on the lower jaw of *Diplocaulus*. In *Keraterpeton galvani* the lateral line organs just take the form of rows of elongated pits (Fig. 66). Among the Microsauria the same rows of pits are present in *Microbrachis* (Fig. 69). All this indicates that with reduction of the canals and grooves, according to the trend of reduction of the terminal stages of development, they are first broken up into sections and elongated pits evidently corresponding to separate seismosensory organs; after this, with further reduction the sensory buds remain in the larval position in the epidermis, only sinking into scarcely noticeable pits.

Upon a secondary return of lepospondylous Stegocephalia and modern Amphibia to life in the water the phase of continuous groove formation was completely lost and in the further evolution of the seismosensory system it was not restored. The lateral line organs were left on the surface or buried only in certain small pits.

In the ontogenesis of modern Amphibia, sensory hillocks are initiated in all lines. They develop a typical distribution even in land-dwelling viviparous forms which never occur in the water, such as *Salamandra atra*. In this case the primordial one-rank arrangement of the sensory organs is especially well defined, however, the whole system is simplified as in a large proportion of other Urodela. During prolonged or permanent life in the water in urodele Amphibia (and also in the anuran Aglossa) there is seen a secondary increase in the number of seismosensory organs (Fig. 95). In some cases the main lines are converted into broad strips with a multiranked arrangement of the sensory organs or with scattered groups and rows of numerous neuromasts (Proteidae).

In those cases in which this secondary proliferation is absent, particularly in the larvae of more primitive members of the urodele Amphibia such as the Hynobiidae, the main seismosensory lines consist of one simple row of organs (in *Ranodon* only the upper part of the jugal line has lost the regularity of distribution of the organs). The number of organs in these rows is relatively small. It is interesting that the number of sensory buds in modern Amphibia is very similar to the number in Stegocephalia and even in fishes.

In *Ichthyostegopsis* the infraorbital canal, including the lachrymal region (but without the subnasal section), had 27 external pores. Since the sensory organs were located between neighboring pores, there were about 26 of them. In *Ranodon* in this particular region, i.e., including the lachrymal fold, there are 22 to 26 organs. In *Triton cristatus* 26 sensory buds have been found also.

In *Ichthyostegopsis* the horizontal part of the preopercular canal in its posterior downward curve had 11 pores. In *Ranodon* in the preopercular line up the point of branching off of the jugal line there are 12 to 18 organs, in *Triton cristatus* 9 organs.

Apparently the number of primordial seismosensory organs in Amphibia is fairly constant and differs but little from the number of organs in the corresponding canals of crossopterygian fishes.

In *Osteolepis macrolepidotus*, according to the reconstruction by Säve-Söderbergh (1933) the number of primary external canals and consequently the number of sensory organs in the very short supraorbital canal is about 10, in the suborbital canal about 28 to 30, in the length of the temporal canal 32 to 33, in the occipital commissure about 10 on each side, in the preopercular canal about 28, and in the mandibular canal about 40. These numbers are somewhat higher on the average than in Amphibia, but are nevertheless very close.

The number of organs in the suborbital canal of *Osteolepis* is the same as in *Ranodon* and in the supraorbital canal of *Osteolepis* it is less than half. This is plainly correlated with the elongation of the preorbital (olfactory) region in terrestrial vertebrates.

In conclusion we note the following:

1. In the larvae of Hynobiidae and particularly in *Ranodon* the well marked and typically distributed main lines of the seismosensory organs are all homologous with the canals of fishes and the grooves of Stegocephalia.

2. In addition to the lines homologous to canals of fishes, in the larvae of Hynobiidae there are also all the principal rows of characteristic lines (or grooves) of the superficial organs (pit lines) occurring in fishes. Particularly, the jugal and gular lines are well developed.

3. In the larvae of Hynobiidae the lines of seismosensory organs consist of sensory hillocks distributed almost regularly in one row throughout. The numbers of primary sensory hillocks in the lateral line system of urodele Amphibia is approximately the same as in the canals of crossopterygian fishes. In adult aquatic Amphibia there sometimes occurs a considerable increase in the numbers of sensory organs. In some cases, in the place of former uniseriate lines, broad strips consisting of numerous rows of organs are developed.

In crossopterygian fishes the seismosensory system reached a very high level of development which was obviously determined by its great importance in the ambushing habits of benthic predators. The Stegocephalia inherited this system, but on transition to life in the aerial medium it was finally eliminated.

IV. The Olfactory Organs, Nostrils, and the Nasolachrymal Duct

Among the higher sense organs in crossopterygian fishes the organs of olfaction and hearing were dominant. The olfactory organs displayed a noticeably more complex differentiation than in other bony fishes. This progress was definitely dictated by the predatory way of life in which the presence of long-range receptors had exceptional significance, and vision could not have been sufficiently utilized in the turbid stream water. The capability for increasing utilization of olfaction was improved by structural modifications providing for rapid exchange of water, in particular by a shift of the nostrils to the edge of the mouth and the formation of a choana.

According to Jarvik (1942) even in the Porolepiformes there was, in addition to the main olfactory cavity, a lateral diverticulum as in modern Caudata. In the Osteolepiformes the olfactory cavity was even more complex and, according to Jarvik, was similar in structure to that of anurans. Jarvik also indicates another difference: in the Porolepiformes the olfactory capsules were widely separated and a precerebral cavity was located between them, while in the Osteolepiformes (*Eusthenopteron*) the nasal capsules were turned inward and there was only an internasal septum between them. These differences, however, do not have great significance. As Kulczycki (1960) pointed out, the lower members of the Porolepiformes differ but little from the Osteolepiformes. According to Vorobjerva-Blokhina (1959, 1962) the structure of the olfactory region indicates the biological type. In Osteolepiformes with a broad flat head (*Panderichthys* and *Platycephalichthys*) indicating benthic life, there were widely separated olfactory capsules between which there was an anteriorly prolonged cranial cavity. Nevertheless, judging by the cast of the cranial cavity, there was a very simple olfactory sac in *Megalichthys* (Fig. 24). Obviously there was no uniformity in the structure of the olfactory organ of crossopterygian fishes. Moreover, it should be affirmed that in the brain there were long and quite distinct, but not massive, paired forebrain "hemispheres." These divisions passed directly into long olfactory lobes. Obviously the forebrain, like that of Dipnoi and also of Amphibia, was an olfactory brain, and this indicates the great importance of olfaction in their lives. However, the structure of the olfactory sac itself was relatively simple. In *Porolepis*, according to Kulczycki (1960) there was not even the lateral outgrowth which Jarvik described as being the likely site of Jacobson's organ.

In the Stegocephalia there was apparently a relatively simple olfactory sac which only acquired a more complex structure in the terrestrial forms. Thus in *Eryops* there was undoubtedly a well-developed Jacobson's organ, judging from the presence of a large nerve which lay ventromedial of the main olfactory nerve (in a cast of the brain cavity; Dempster, 1935).

The development of the olfactory organ in urodele Amphibia proceeds at first in approximately the same way as in higher fishes. In connection with the front edge of the neural plate paired olfactory placodes are developed in the form of thickened basal layers of the ectoderm. The placodes sink down and give rise to olfactory pits and then to deeper sacs, the external openings of which form the external nostrils (Fig. 96). The later development varies in fishes, Amphibia, and higher vertebrates. In teleost fishes the nostrils become somewhat elongated along the axis of the animal and then two folds divide them into nostrils, anterior and posterior. In higher vertebrates an oronasal groove, which develops from the nostril to the corner of the mouth, is enclosed as a canal leading to the oral cavity where it opens as a internal nostril or choana. In Amphibia a diverticulum develops from the olfactory sac, extending deep toward the oral cavity from which a small matching diverticulum develops. The union of two diverticula forms the choanal canal (Fig. 96).

The olfactory sac itself is also variously differentiated. In bony fishes the dorsal wall of the olfactory sac remains relatively thin in the region of the two nostrils, and the opposite lower wall is thickened and forms olfactory epithelia. The surface of this epithelium is then increased by the formation of folds which are often arranged radially or form two transverse rows arranged laterally from a median suture.

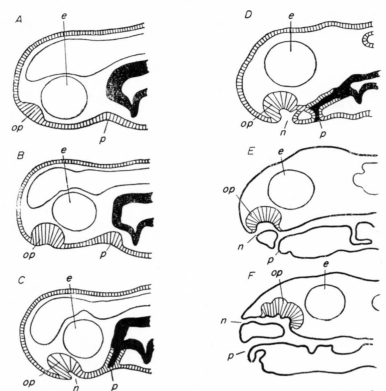

FIG. 96. Plan of the anlagen and movements of the nostrils and mouth. Ectoderm, hatched; endoderm, black. *e*, Eye; *n*, nostril; *op*, olfactory placode, orbital pouch; *p*, oral invagination, mouth. From Medvedeva.

The olfactory organ is quite highly developed in *Polypterus*. In addition to the main sac there is an auxiliary sac located anterodorsally. The olfactory sac is divided by longitudinal septa into five compartments with rows of transverse folds in each. The auxiliary cavity is of similar structure (O. I. Schmalhausen, 1962). A vestibular cavity is placed ventrolaterally with a covering of ciliated epithelia. This cavity leads to the protruding anterior nostril and to the posterior nostril, opening not far from the eye. Apparently the olfactory organ in *Latimeria* is constructed similarly.

In dipnoan fishes the olfactory sac is located on the ventral side of the head and both nostrils are moved downward to the edge of the mouth (Fig. 97). Correspondingly the dorsal wall of the olfactory sac is thickened, and the ventral one, between the two nostrils, remains thin. The olfactory epithelium forms rows of transverse folds.

In urodele Amphibia the olfactory sac is moved laterally to the side of the head. Its lateral wall remains thin, and the medial wall is thickened and forms olfactory epithelia. The surface of the latter is increased by the formation of a series of transverse folds. As we have noted, the similarity to the higher fishes is very great (Fig. 99). The distinctions are mainly in the different position of the nostrils and correspondingly in a different orientation of the olfactory sac with its folds (Schmalhausen, 1958d, fig. 2).

The position of the nostrils varies in fishes; however, the most significant variations in crossopterygian fishes are correlated with the formation of the choana. These modifications also continued into the terrestrial vertebrates and led to the formation of a respiratory air passage through the olfactory organ. Apparently the new differentiation of the olfactory sac is associated with the transition to life in the aerial medium. Even in the urodele Amphibia, having a relatively very primitive olfactory organ, there is a special diverticulum of the olfactory sac which is apparently homologous with Jacobson's organ in higher vertebrates.

In urodele Amphibia this organ develops in a somewhat different position than in Anura. In the latter, as in higher vertebrates, it develops in the form of a ventromedial diverticulum of the olfactory sac. In urodele Amphibia Jacobson's organ is initiated ventrally, but it then turns in a lateral direction. This, undoubtedly a secondary shift, is no obstacle to its homology as in either case a typical complex of Jacobson's glands is developed.

Jacobson's organ undoubtedly has an olfactory function; it is lined with olfactory epithelium and is supplied by a branch of the olfactory nerve. The isolation of part of the olfactory organ in a ventral saclike diverticulum is probably explained by its inheritance from the olfactory sac of fishes. Its function consisted of chemical testing of the water. Upon emergence of the animal into the air most of the olfactory organ became filled with air (especially during respiratory movements), and water was retained longer only in the ventral part. This led to a differentiation of the dorsal area which, through development of glands, was gradually converted to an organ of aerial olfaction, and of the blind sac to a temporary organ of aquatic olfaction. Later on, larger lateral and medial glands were developed, maintaining all the epithelia in a moist state. Especially prominent glands were developed in connection with Jacobson's organ; their function consisted in maintenance of the moisture reserve necessary for effecting aquatic olfaction.

In riparian Stegocephalia, Jacobson's organ was probably a very important ventral part of the olfactory organ (in *Eryops*) and an adequate reserve of water was constantly retained in it. With extended development of the glands and adaptation of the olfactory sac to aerial respiration the volume and im-

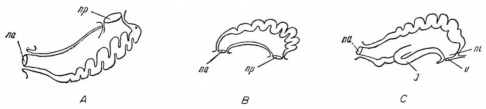

FIG. 97. Arrangement of the olfactory pouch of larvae of *Amia calva* (A), *Ceratodus forsteri* (B), and *Ranodon sibiricus* (C), lateral view. *J*, Jacobson's organ; *na*, *np*, anterior and posterior nostrils; *ni*, internal nostril (choana); *v*, valve of choana.

portance of Jacobson's organ decreased. Its close connection to the choana obviously determined the new function of olfactory testing of food material in the oral cavity, which continued in the reptiles. On the other side, the connection with the nasolachrymal duct determined the development of a unique olfactory palpus in the Gymnophiona.

The flow of respiratory air was only carried over the main organ in which there was a special passage leading from the outer nostril along the lateral wall of the olfactory sac to the choana. In this part of the organ the usual dermal epithelium is retained.

The choanae of urodele Amphibia are developed from two sources, from the olfactory sac and from the oral cavity. This separation of the primordia into two parts explains the peculiar development in the Amphibia (Medvedeva, 1961a). In Amphibia the development of the nostrils is determined in part by a complicated relationship with the arrangement of the placodes of the seismosensory system in this segion. This dependency sheds light on the history of the shift of the posterior nostrils and the formation of the choanae.

In crossopterygian fishes the nostrils were shifted downward to the edge of the mouth. Obviously this gave a better exchange of water in the olfactory organ, especially with the location of the posterior exhalant nostrils on the margin of the oral cavity. With opening of the mouth and the drawing of water into the oral cavity a region of lowered pressure was created which induced a flow of water in the olfactory organ, from the anterior to the posterior nostrils. The posterior nostril was divided into two, an outer and an inner nostril (the choana). Thus in some crossopterygian fishes there were three pairs of nostrils lying very close to each other. In *Porolepis* and in *Panderichthys* (Fig. 42), both posterior nostrils emerge from the olfactory sac through one common opening. In other crossopterygians this was divided by a septum into two openings, and the nostrils were spread wide apart. The anterior nostrils were next shifted forward and upward, the outer posterior nostril moved backward, and the inner posterior nostrils moved deeper into the oral cavity along the sides from the vomers. The outer posterior nostril apparently gave rise to the nasolachrymal duct of terrestrial vertebrates. In primitive Stegocephalia the anterior nostrils and choanae are still located side by side at the edge of the mouth (*Ichthyostega* and *Megalocephalus*). In the developmental history of the urodele Amphibia traces of the movement of these nostrils are plainly seen.

The olfactory placode is initiated at the anterior end of the head; from here the olfactory sac shifts to the ventral side. The nostrils are directed downward and approach an oral invagination. The choanal canal is then developed and the outer nostril is again shifted forward on the dorsal side of the head. This stage is shown in Fig. 96. As shown, it duplicates in general the situation seen in crossopterygian fishes. There is also proof that the choana arose by a shifting of the posterior nostril from outside to inside the oral cavity. This proof is linked to a peculiarity in the development of the suborbital row of seismosensory organs.

The nerves of the seismosensory system are developed, as is well known, in close connection with the ectodermal placodes—the anlagen of the sense organs of this system. The corresponding nerves grow in proportion to the expansion and differentiation of the placodes into a strip of thickened ectoderm, and become differentiated beneath them. After the dispersal of the placodes into separate primordia of the seismosensory organs, the nerves are separated from the ectoderm but retain their superficial position under the skin and their original branching connections with the sensory organs. The suborbital placode accompanying n. buccalis usually grows forward under the eye under the olfactory organ in front of which it is connected to the placodes of the opposite side, forming an anterior, i.e., ethmoid, commissure of the seismosensory system.

In lower urodele Amphibia—the Hynobiidae—the suborbital placode on its path forward meets the olfactory sac and does not extend beyond. The corresponding nerve, n. buccalis, going to the olfactory sac, turns steeply downward, passes medial of the choana and the olfactory sac, and emerges again in the ectoderm in front of the olfactory organ (Fig. 98). Here, in connection with the extension of n. buccalis, an anterior differentiated parting of the suborbital placode is developed, which gives rise to the premaxillary row of seismosensory organs (Schmalhausen, 1955b, 1957a). Thus the suborbital placode is found to have been divided into two parts, suborbital and

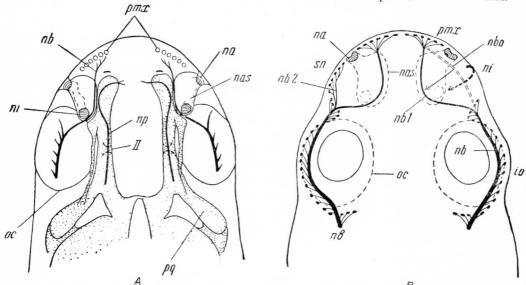

FIG. 98. Reconstruction of the anterior part of the head of a larva of *Ranodon* 22 mm long, ventral view (*A*); diagram of the infraorbital line of Hynobiidae (*B*) and its innervation (double broken line shows original path of facial nerve in crossopterygian fishes, arrows show the movement of the posterior nostril and migration of facial nerve). Dorsal view. *io*, Infraorbital row of organs; *na*, external nostril; *nas*, olfactory sac; *nb*, facial nerve VII; *nbo*, original position of facial nerve; *nb 1*, position of anterior part of facial nerve in the Hynobiidae; *nb 2*, secondary branch of facial nerve; *ni*, movement of posterior nostril; *np*, palatine nerve VII; *oc*, shape of eye; *pmx*, premaxillary row of organs; *pq*, palatoquadrate cartilage; *sn*, subnasal row; *II*, position of otic nerve.

premaxillary, by the olfactory sac. Under the olfactory organ a gap is formed in the seismosensory system, which, however, is then filled at the expense of a secondary expansion of the suborbital placode with separate branches of n. buccalis. The unique pathway of the main trunk of the facial nerve is perhaps easily explained in terms of the historical shift of the posterior nostril downward to the edge of the mouth and then inward to the oral cavity. The movement unavoidably crossed and broke up the suborbital canal of the seismosensory organs, and the nerves turned inward with the choana. The position of n. buccalis of the Hynobiidae and certain Salamandriidae clearly documents the movement of the choanae. A secondary extension of the suborbital row into the subnasal area sometimes leads to a restoration of the whole maxillary row of seismosensory organs with their appropriate innervation from subnasal branches of the facial nerve (*Ambystoma*).

The break in the suborbital row of organs is thus caused by the shifting of the posterior nostrils and the formation of the choana. Correspondingly it may be found either in crossopterygian fishes or in lower Stegocephalia. While in all Holostei (Fig. 99) the suborbital canal passes without a break to the anterior end of the head, in some Crossopterygii this canal is interrupted in the region of the posterior nostril. In *Osteolepis* the suborbital canal terminates at the anterior end of the lachrymal bone at the edge of the jaw under the olfactory organ. The position is the same in *Dipterus*. In modern Dipnoi (*Ceratodus* and *Protopterus*) the suborbital canal terminates below the olfactory organ.

In the more ancient rhachitomous and embolomerous labyrinthodonts the position of the suborbital groove is amazingly similar to the position of this canal in *Osteolepis*. In *Megalocephalus* (Fig. 100) the suborbital canal terminates at the rear edge of the nostril. The same is true in *Palaeogyrinus*, *Eogyrinus*, and *Colosteus* (Fig. 101) in which the canal does not go beyond the border of the lachrymal bone. The same is occasionally seen in more recent Stegocephalia as, for example, in *Lyrocephalus*. In most of these Stegocephalia, after the movement of the external nostrils, the suborbital canal secondarily expands anteriorly beneath the olfactory organ again and thus restores its continuity. We have also seen this repeated expansion and restoration of continuity of the suborbital row of seismosensory organs in the modern urodele Amphibia in which it is retraced with full clarity. In crossopterygian fishes this evidently

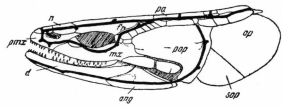

FIG. 99. Skull of *Polypterus*, lateral view; seismosensory system in black. *ang*, Angular bone; *d*, dentary; *fr*, frontal; *mx*, maxilla; *n*, nasal; *op*, operculum; *pa*, parietal; *pmx*, premaxilla; *pop*, preoperculum; *sop*, suboperculum. From Jarvik.

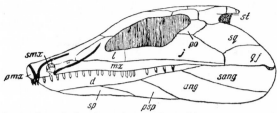

FIG. 100. Skull of *Megalocephalus*, lateral view; lateral line grooves in black. *ang*, Angular; *d*, dentary; *j*, jugal; *l*, lachrymal; *mx*, maxilla; *pmx*, premaxilla; *po*, postorbital; *psp*, postsplenial; *qj*, quadratojugal; *sang*, surangular; *smx*, septomaxilla (nariale); *sp*, splenial; *sq*, squamosal; *st*, supratemporal. From Watson.

originated in *Eusthenopteron* in which the suborbital canal passes without interruption beneath the outer nostril. In *Ichthyostega* it apparently crosses the outer nostril on the bony bridge of the septomaxilla (Fig. 34). In any case the shift of the posterior nostril into the oral cavity and the formation of the choana must have been accompanied, if only temporarily, by a break in the suborbital canal of the seismosensory system. We can prove this both on fossil material and by the developmental history of the seismosensory system in urodele Amphibia (Hynobiidae) and, lastly, by the aberrant passage of the facial nerve (n. buccalis) detouring around the choana from the medial side (Schmalhausen, 1955a, 1957a).

The secondary expansion of the suborbital placode in Amphibia led to further modifications in ontogenesis. This placode transected the oronasal groove, i.e., the rudiment of the choanal canal, and as a result this rudiment is found to be divided into two parts, nasal and oral, which were initiated independently but are later united (Fig. 96). Naturally this occurred only in forms with larval development and a secondary expansion of the seismosensory system, i.e., in urodele and anuran Amphibia, but not in the apodous forms (Medvedeva, 1961a, 1963).

The question of the shift of the posterior nostrils is also correlated with the question of the origin of the nasolachrymal duct of terrestrial vertebrates. At present there is still no agreement on this subject. Most authors state that the nasolachrymal duct is a new formation having originated only in terrestrial vertebrates. Again Allis (1932) took an opposite stand on this issue, advancing the suggestion of an homology of nasolachrymal duct with the canal of the posterior nostril of bony fishes (*Amia* and *Polypterus*). This belief was sup-

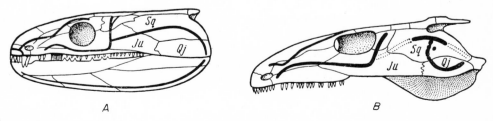

FIG. 101. Skull of *Colosteus* (A) and *Palaeogyrinus* (B), lateral view. Canals in black. *Ju*, jugal; *Qj*, quadratojugal; *Sq*, squamosal. From Romer and Watson.

ported by some paleontologists on the basis of a study of the position of the nostril in crossopterygian fishes (Jarvik, 1942). On the other hand, this theory encounters some difficulties and this compels us to turn to a critical examination of older views (Born, 1883), supported by such paleontologists as Watson (1913) who saw in the nasolachrymal duct a modification of a canal of the seismosensory organs.

A study of the history of the development of the nasolachrymal duct in urodele Amphibia (Hynobiidae and others) has shown that it is initiated in the ectoderm quite independently of both the olfactory organ and the eye, behind the outer nostril and in front of the anlage of the orbital ring. In all cases the middle section of the nasolachrymal duct is originally initiated by differentiation in the dorsal bulge in the orbitonasal part of the suborbital placode. The anlage is marked by a condensation of mesenchyme at its base. It is sunken somewhat below the level of the exterior ectoderm and expands both forward to the rear edge of the nostril and back to the anterior edge of the eye. The front end reaches to the nostril in Hynobiidae (Fig. 102) and along its back wall it ranges deep to the lateral wall of the olfactory sac. The anlage is cut off from the ectoderm in its anterior part earliest, behind the nostril. It is bounded by a well-marked basal membrane and is covered by a layer of mesenchyme. As the anlage separates it sinks deeper beneath the skin and its middle section lies on the surface of the cartilage capsule. The front end enters the nasal opening of the capsule (fenestra narina) at its posteroventral margin and is joined to the base of the narial canal on the lateral wall of the olfactory sac, descending to its lateral diverticulum. The distal end passes to the ectodermal thinkening surrounding the eye (anlage of the orbital ring) and opens on the surface of the ectoderm, as first one opening (mediodorsal), and then a second at the end of a shorter lateral branch.

In the Salamandridae the development of the nasolachrymal duct is a little simpler and the connection to the nostril is apparently lost altogether. There

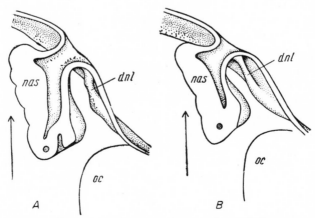

FIG. 102. Larvae of *Hynobius*, 23 mm long (A) and 24 mm long (B). Reconstruction of two stages of the differentiation of the nasolachrymal duct and the migration of its anterior end to the wall of the nostril. Ventral view. *dnl*, Rudiment of nasolachrymal duct; *nas*, olfactory sac; *oc*, eye.

remains no doubt that in this we have a secondary simplification of the onto-genetic processes.

Relationships in the Hynobiidae are undoubtedly more primitive; how-ever, while in the Hynobiidae there is a clearly developed connection of the anlage of the duct to the outer nostril, it is nevertheless initiated indepen-dently of the nostril behind it in the dorsal part of the orbitonasal bulge of the lateral placode.

In all cases in the Amphibia, and especially in the Hynobiidae, an early concentration of mesenchyme at the anlage of the nasolachrymal duct is seen. With the differentiation of the latter there is formed around it the connective tissue membrane noted by many authors. In this membrane the anlagen of two dermal bones, the septomaxilla and lachrymal, later originate.

A. DERMAL BONES OF THE NASOLACHRYMAL DUCT

Two bones are developed in close connection with the nasolachrymal duct, surrounding it more or less completely. The connection of the naso-lachrymal duct to the lachrymal bone is well known, and no one disputes the dermal origin of this bone. It is a highly characteristic bone of the skull roof of terrestrial vertebrates and is obviously homologous with the anterior infraorbital bone of fishes. In the latter it includes the preorbital part of the infraorbital lateral line canal, in Stegocephalia the corresponding groove passes along it. A second bone related to the nasolachrymal duct is the septo-maxilla or, better, the nariale (Wegner, 1922) which is present in most Am-phibia and in many reptiles (also in monotremes). Its homolog in fishes is not as clear. In *Amia calva* there is a dermal bone lying in a similar posi-tion between the premaxilla and the lachrymal. It extends from the anterior to the posterior nostril and includes the subnasal part of the infraorbital lateral line canal and also the dorsal branch of this canal, descending to the posterior nostril. It is very likely that this bone is homologous to the nariale of terres-trial vertebrates (Wegner, 1922). An homologous bone—rostrale laterale (Jarvik, 1942)—was clearly present in crossopterygian fishes in which it was bounded by the lower margin of the exterior nostril and sometimes gave off an extension entering into the olfactory capsule (as the nariale in Anura and Amniota). Nonetheless it included part of the infraorbital lateral line canal. The dermal nature of this bone in higher terrestrial vertebrates (Amniota) is not to be doubted. In Amphibia, however (especially in urodele Amphibia), a close association of the nariale with the cartilage of the olfactory capsule has sometimes been described. The association of this bone with the cartilage is sometimes so close that it has prompted several authors to regard the nariale as a bone of mixed origin.

The anlage of the nariale appears in the larva of *Hynobius* of about 26 mm length at the same time as initiation of the lachrymal. It is located in the pos-teroventral part of fenestra narina in the ventrolateral wall of the nasolachry-mal duct. The ossification center is quite independent of the cartilage and is situated fairly distant from both the lower and posterior edges of the fenestra narina. It arises as a typical membranous ossification in a mesenchyme aggregation which surrounds the nasolachrymal duct even in the early stages of its formation. The anlage of the nariale quickly encloses as a half-ring around the anterior and dorsomedial walls of the nasolachrymal duct (Fig. 103), and is closed posteriorly as a complete ring, surrounding its proximal end at the place of descent to the lateral diverticulum of the olfactory sac. The anlage of the nariale retains its independence of the cartilage of the olfactory capsule throughout the larval period. Not until the time of metamorphosis does the ventral edge of the nariale fuse to the cartilage of the olfactory capsule at the posteroventral edge of the fenestra narina. Since this originates at the same time as the development of m. dilator naris, which is attached to the nariale, this is easily explained as a secondary fusion of this bone to the cartilage as a functional requirement. The m. constrictor naris envelops the nostrial posteriorly and becomes attached to the edge of the fenestra narina, and in part to the narial bone also. All this requires an attachment to the internal cartilaginous skeleton.

In *Ranodon* the nariale is initiated relatively later than in *Hynobius*. The position and shape of the anlage are the same, however, the bone is more weakly developed, and it does not always form a complete ring around the base of the nasolachrymal duct. In *Onychodactylus fischeri*, on the other hand, the nariale is considerably more developed. The nariale completely envelops the base of the nasolachrymal duct. However, in addition, a medial process leads off from its ventral wall enclosing the lateral diverticulum of the olfactory sac below at the point of origin of the canal of the outer nostril. In this sequence it is easy to recognize the medial process (processus intrafenestralis; Wegner, 1922), the nariale (septomaxilla) present in anurans and reptiles, and also the internal process (processus dermintermedius; Jarvik, 1942) homologous to the lateral rostral bone of crossopterygian fishes (*Eusthenopteron*).

The nariale of *Onychodactylus* shows the most complete development of

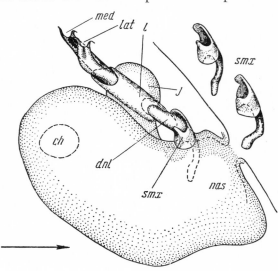

FIG. 103. Larvae of *Onychodactylus fischeri* 85 mm long, at the end of metamorphosis. Reconstruction of the left olfactory sac; the septomaxillae are shown separately, and the right one in outline in the drawing. *ch*, Choana, *dnl*, nasolachrymal duct; *J*, Jacobson's organ; *l*, lachrymal; *lat*, *med*, lateral and medial rami of nasolachrymal duct; *nas*, olfactory sac; *smx*, septomaxilla (nariale).

this bone in urodele Amphibia. There can be no doubt of its homology with the septomaxilla of anurans and reptiles, just as there can be no doubt of its primary membranous character.

The lachrymal is initiated as a membranous ossification in the middle part of the nasolachrymal duct at the same stage of larval development as the nariale, that is, in larvae of *Hynobius keyserlingii* of about 26 mm length. The anlage of the lachrymal is located ventromedially directly below the duct. Later is grows around the nasolachrymal duct, enclosing it anterolaterally and posteromedially (Fig. 103). At the time of metamorphosis, in larvae of about 30 mm length, the anterior part of the lachrymal encloses the duct as a complete ring. The nasolachrymal duct consequently passes through this ring on its way backward from the olfactory sac and then lies on the dorsolateral surface of the bone. The posterior part of the lachrymal bone adjoins the anterior under-edge of the prefrontal bone. In *Hynobius* the branched nasolachrymal duct is located on the surface of the posterior part of the lachrymal bone surface.

The same is seen in *Onychodactylus*, in which the annular element of the lachrymal is such that the entire bone takes the form of a tube, enclosing the nasolachrymal duct. In *Ranodon* the nasolachrymal duct is developed in the central region of the lachrymal bone and this is markedly reflected in its shape. The lachrymal bone is clearly developed under the influence of the nasolachrymal duct and its.development is similar to the manner in which a dermal bone develops, enclosing a canal of the seismosensory organs.

Thus both bones associated with the nasolachrymal duct, the nariale (septomaxillare) and the lachrymal are developed as membrane bones closely connected with this canal in its connective tissue envelope (nariale) or, in any case, directly below it (lachrymal). In the early stages they both underlie the nasolachrymal duct (nariale ventrolaterally, lachrymal ventromedially) and, quickly growing around it, enclose the duct in a complete ring or fairly long tube at the time of metamorphosis (in *Ranodon* and *Onychodactylus*). In their development and relationship to the nasolachrymal duct both bones are very similar to the seismosensory canals of the dermal bones of this system in bony fishes.

The experimental investigations of Medvedeva (1959, 1960) in removal of the ectoderm in the region of the oronasal bulge of the suborbital placode showed that the presumptive material of the nasolachrymal duct is contained in this region. In addition, the complete dependency of the anlage of the lachrymal and the formation of the septomaxilla on the presence of the nasolachrymal duct was established.

B. THE ORIGIN OF THE NASOLACHRYMAL DUCT

In determining the origin of the nasolachrymal duct it is necessary to consider on the one hand, the fate of the posterior nostril in crossopterygian fishes, and on the other hand, its similarity to the infraorbital canal in relation to its dermal bones, in the connections of the anlage of the duct with the placode of the seismosensory system, and in its independence of the orbito-

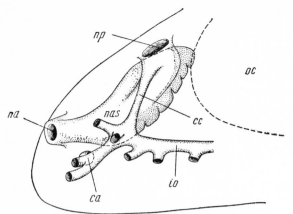

FIG. 104. Larva of *Amia calva* 26 mm long, showing the infraorbital canal and its connection to the nostrils. *ca*, Anterior commissure; *cc*, connecting branch of the canal leading to the nostril; *io*, subnasal part of suborbital canal; *na*, *np*, anterior and posterior nostrils; *nas*, olfactory sac; *oc*, eye.

nasal sac. The only possible answer may be the accepted hypothesis of a dual origin of the duct, into the composition of which the posterior nostril and part of the infraorbital canal entered (Schmalhausen, 1958c,d).

A connection of the seismosensory canals with the nostrils occasionally occurs in fishes (Fig. 104). Such connections to the posterior nostril should have occurred in crossopterygian fishes also. It is very likely that the suborbital canal was connected to the posterior nostril in primitive Coelacanthidae. This is evident from the position of the lateral rostral (a homolog of the septomaxilla), including the infraorbital canal in the nostrils in the Devonian *Diplocercides*. Anterior and median notches on these bones make it very probable that connections of this canal to both nostrils existed. In any case, in the Porolepiformes and Osteolepiformes such a connection of the suborbital canal of the seismosensory system to a lesser degree with the posterior nostril would have been unavoidable. In the shifting of the posterior nostril downward to the edge of the oral opening it would have unavoidably cut across the suborbital canal. The connections between the anterior and pos-

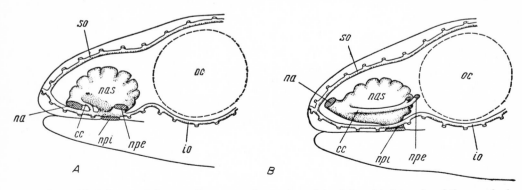

FIG. 105. Scheme of the transformation of a section of the infraorbital canal and the canal of the posterior nostril into the nasolachrymal duct (*A* and *B*). *cc*, Connecting branch of the infraorbital canal; *io*, infraorbital canal; *na*, anterior nostril; *nas*, olfactory sac; *npe*, *npi*, external and internal (choanal) sections of posterior nostril; *oc*, eye; *so*, suborbital canal.

terior parts of the canal could then have been maintained only through the cavity of the posterior nostril. In Osteolepiformes, however, the anterior nostril had shifted to the edge of the mouth. In this case a similar connection should have been established with this nostril also. Since the position of both nostrils at the edge of the mouth is seen not only in some Osteolepida (*Osteolepis*) but also in primitive Stegocephalia (*Ichthyostega, Megalocephalus,* and others), we can assert with some certainty that this position is original for terrestrial vertebrates (in some Stegocephalia, *Colosteus, Palaeogyrinus,* and later forms, the nostrils are again elevated to the lateral surface of the head and occupy a more dorsal position). In such cases it must be considered highly likely that a subcutaneous superficial connection was established between the anterior and posterior nostrils by means of the seismosensory canal (Fig. 105) lying within the anterior nostril in the nariale, and at the posterior nostril in the lachrymal. On the other hand, with the division of the posterior nostril into two, an outer (nasolachrymal duct) and an inner (choana), and with the shift of the choana into the oral cavity, the connection between them should have been broken (with the formation of the primitive palate). Then the posterior outer nostril would have remained connected with the olfactory sac by means of the canal of the seismosensory system (Fig. 105). This connection was quite necessary for fishes living in water since only in this way could a constant flow of water have been maintained from the anterior nostril through the olfactory organ into the posterior external nostril. The water current from the anterior nostril into the choana could be only of a periodic nature—it began on opening of the mouth—and therefore was linked to respiratory action and especially to seizing prey while feeding. The connection of the posterior nostril to the seismosensory canal is consequently secondary, and therefore is manifested as such in the history of individual development of the nasolachrymal duct.

Thus we come to the conclusion that the nasolachrymal duct has a dual origin, being derived as a connection of the canal of the posterior nostril to a section of the suborbital canal of the seismosensory system. This hypothesis takes cognizance not only of the similarity of the nasolachrymal duct to the canal of the posterior nostril of crossopterygian fishes, but it also explains the peculiarity of the relation of its anlage to the placode of the seismosensory system and its independence of the olfactory sac, and also the establishment of the secondary connection with the anterior nostril and olfactory sac. Recognition is taken also of the organic connection of the nasolachrymal duct with the dermal bones of the seismosensory system, the nariale (septomaxilla and lateral rostral) and the lachrymal (anterior infraorbital).

We will not discuss anuran Amphibia here, but one cannot but observe that in *Xenopus calcaratus* the nasolachrymal duct is developed, albeit very tardily, before metamorphosis; it is, however, of the same type as in urodele Amphibia. Canalization of the primordium sets in only during metamorphosis. However, after metamorphosis the nasolachrymal duct acquires a very definite aperture. The place of union of the duct with the nostril is converted into a fairly large chamber. The distal end of the duct is forked and is terminated at the apex by a marked protuberance below the eye. This protuberance is described as a unique "palpus." The "palpus" is borne at the tip of the naso-lachrymal duct, i.e., the posterior outer nostril. Undoubtedly this duct cannot take the normal function of the nasolachrymal duct in *Xenopus,* especially since *Xenopus* is a purely aquatic animal. The broad aperture of the duct stands as evidence of a secondary restoration of its initial function as the posterior nostril of fishes—maintaining a steady flow of water from the anterior nostril through the olfactory organ into the posterior outer nostril. The elongation of the nostril into a tubular palpiform process occasionally occurs in fishes (*Polypterus, Amia,* and many bony fishes). The nasolachrymal duct in the gymnophiones (Apoda) is even more strongly developed. It lies in a long drawn-out "palpus" which is moistened by a secretion of the prominently developed Harderian glands. The duct is associated with a highly developed Jacobson's organ and clearly takes the role of an extended nostril. At the end of the palpus there is also a tactile organ.

Naturally in the transition to terrestrial life in the aerial medium the function of the nostril is altered. The anterior external nostrils and the choanae have become canals for respired air. The posterior external nostril, which facilitated a steady flow of water through the olfactory organ, lost this function and was then utilized for secreting the product by the nasal glands. Our conclusions on the origin of the nostrils of terrestrial vertebrates may be formulated as follows:

1. The external nostrils of terrestrial vertebrates are homologous to the anterior nostrils of fishes.

2. The posterior nostrils of crossopterygian fishes (and sometimes the anterior nostrils also) were shifted downward to the edge of the oral opening. This provided better passage of water through the olfactory organ in less active animals. Water flow was initiated with each opening of the mouth, i.e., during respiratory movements and seizing of food. The rate of the water intake through the olfactory sac was increased with the approach of the posterior nostril to the very edge of the mouth below the edge of the lip.

3. The posterior nostril in Rhipidistia was divided into two parts, the outer and inner. The outer part retained the original function of maintaining a steady flow of water through the olfactory organ when the animal was at rest (by the action of ciliated epithelia). This water current was amplified by the movements of the animal (due to the setting up of a difference in pressure). The internal medial part of the posterior nostril served for periodic intaking of water through the olfactory organ at the opening of the mouth. This part of the nostril acquired more significance in less active predators, awaiting their prey and sucking it in through the open jaws. The two different functions of the posterior nostrils—maintaining a steady flow of water and periodic active drawing-in of water through the olfactory organ—led to its division into two independent organs, the posterior outer nostril and the posterior inner nostril (i.e., the choanae).

4. The position of the nostrils at the edge of the mouth and the shifting of the medial part of the posterior nostrils into the oral cavity led to union of the

infraorbital seismosensory canal with the nostrils. The continuity of this canal was maintained only through the medium of the posterior nostril (Fig. 105). By separation of the choana the canal was left in communication with the external nostrils and provided a direct subcutaneous connection between the anterior and posterior nostrils.

5. The posterior external nostril retained its function only during life in the water. Upon emergence of the animal into the aerial medium this function was eliminated and in its place was substituted a new function, that of carrying excess liquid from the eye. Thus there arose a nasolachrymal duct consisting of two parts, the canal of the posterior nostril and a part of the infraorbital canal of the seismosensory organs. This explains the independence of the anlage of the nasolachrymal duct from the olfactory organ, its connection to the infraorbital placode, the secondary connection of this anlage to the anterior nostril, and the close connection of the nasolachrymal duct to the two dermal bones of the infraorbital canal, the nariale (septomaxilla) and lachrymal.

V. ORGANS OF HEARING AND THE SOUND TRANSMISSION APPARATUS

In fishes the ear is very weakly developed since in water sound vibrations are not of much consequence biologically. A major role in the life of fishes is played by vibrations of lower frequency, infrasonic, for which there are special receptors, the seismosensory organs. In the air, on the contrary, the latter lose their value, and acoustic organs take on great significance. Immediately upon the emergence of fishes onto land exceptionally favorable conditions were created for the latter. In crossopterygian fishes the gill operculum was connected to the suspensorium (hyomandibula) through a special articulation. On emergence of the animal onto land the branchial chamber beneath the operculum was filled with air. This in itself created a suitable medium which allowed free vibrations of the gill operculum from the most negligible disturbance. These vibrations were transmitted to the hyomandibula, and from the latter to the otic capsule. In crossopterygian fishes the movable attachment of the hyomandibula to the otic capsule was effected at two points, laterally on the crista parotica, and medially at the base of the capsule. The lateral connection on the otic region gave the firmer support. The medial connection lay on the thinner wall of the otic capsule, opposite the sacculus of the inner ear. If we regard the lateral joint as a point of support, the hyomandibula took the role of a lever-type transmitter from the gill operculum to the base of the otic capsule. The outer "arm" of the lever, from the gill operculum to the support point on the crista parotica, was considerably longer than the medial "arm" from the supporting point to the base of the capsule (Fig. 41). Thus, the transmission of vibrations from the gill operculum occurred with some loss of amplitude and increase of force. Such transmission increased the capacity for the reception of vibration of the gill operculum by the receptors of the inner ear (macula sacculi and macula lagenae). Through evolution the

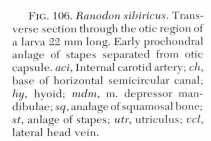

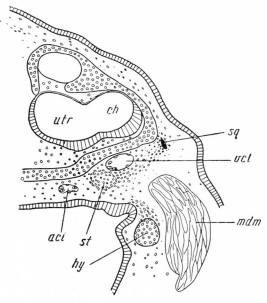

FIG. 106. *Ranodon sibiricus*. Transverse section through the otic region of a larva 22 mm long. Early prochondral anlage of stapes separated from otic capsule. *aci*, Internal carotid artery; *ch*, base of horizontal semicircular canal; *hy*, hyoid; *mdm*, m. depressor mandibulae; *sq*, analage of squamosal bone; *st*, anlage of stapes; *utr*, utriculus; *vcl*, lateral head vein.

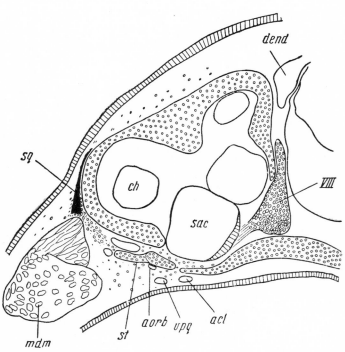

FIG. 107. *Ranodon sibiricus*. Cross section similar to that in Fig. 106. Larva 29 mm long. *aorb*, Orbital artery; *dend*, endolymphatic duct; *sac*, sacculus; *st*, cartilaginous anlage of stapes with rudiment of columella; *vpq*, vena palatoquadrati; *VIII*, otic ganglia. Other abbreviations as in Fig. 106.

massiveness of the hyomandibula was reduced, and it took the form of a thin bony columella retaining, however, the dorsal point of support and all the important leverage transmission by decreasing the amplitude of vibration and increasing the force. The auditory ossicle is constructed in this way in modern Anura. It transmits sound disturbances of the air from a membrane with a relatively large surface, the tympanic membrane, to the small membrane of the fenestra ovalis of the otic capsule. In urodele Amphibia this system of sound transmission from the air became reduced and was replaced by another system of sound reception. The developmental history of the middle ear in urodele Amphibia, especially in the Hynobiidae, gives a clear indication of the historical transformations in the sound transmission mechanism.

In *Hynobius* and *Ranodon* the stapes is initiated in a condensation of mesenchyme extending from the anterior part of the basal fenestra of the auditory capsule to the posterior edge of the squamosal in the region of the otic process of the palatoquadrate cartilage (Fig. 106). A cartilaginous anlage is formed in the aggregation as an independent center of chondrification, lying between the internal carotid artery and the lateral head vein, below the wall of the otic capsule (Fig. 107). In *Ranodon* the anlage of the stapes at first lies in front of the basal fenestra; in *Hynobius* it lies at its anterior edge. In its formative stages the stapes lies with its base in the anterior part of the fenestra and it very soon becomes united to its anterior inner edge. The orbital artery in *Hynobius* apparently consistently passes below the shaft of the stapes and misses it anteriorly. Occasionally in *Ranodon* (in 40% of the cases) it passes through a fenestra in the shaft of the stapes, forming the typical art. stapedia (Fig. 108).

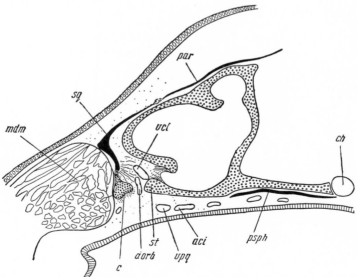

FIG. 108. *Ranodon sibiricus*. Cross section of larva 57 mm long. *aorb*, Orbital artery passing through canal in columella; *c*, capitulum of columella; *ch*, notochord; *par*, parietal bone; *psph*, parasphenoid; *vpq*, vena palatoquadrati. Other abbreviations as in Fig. 106.

The mesenchyme condensation connecting the anlage of the stapes with the edge of the squamosal in *Hynobius* is differentiated into two parts, a small dorsal part enclosing the lateral head vein and passing to the edge of the otic capsule, and a more conspicuous lateral one passing to the posterior edge of the squamosal bone. Accordingly, this mesenchyme rudiment expands and chondrifies in the form of a process of the auditory ossicle. A small dorsal process fully encloses the latter vein (Fig. 109) and in later stages of development closes over it, forming a complete cartilage ring in the dorsal part of the base of the auditory ossicle. The lateral process, the shaft of the columella (stilus columellae), is considerably larger (Fig. 109) and it expands anteriorly toward the rear edge of the squamosal. The mesenchyme coagulation in which it is developed links the end of the columella to the rear edge of the squamosal and extends farther along this margin, and consequently along the posterior wall of the palatoquadrate cartilage, in a ventrolateral direction. It is clearly seen in the form of a flat strand of rodlike cells in larvae of *Hynobius* of 20 mm length or larvae of *Ranodon* 35 mm long (Fig. 110). Later on this mesenchyme strand gradually chondrifies laterally and distally, forming a cartilaginous shaft running from the columella of the stapes along the rear edge of the palatoquadrate to its hyoid process with which it merges. Between the hyoid process and the hyoid proper a thick hyoquadrate ligament develops. Although the cartilage of the hyoid process also develops a continuous connection with the palatoquadrate cartilage, it is of peculiar significance since it appears much later and from another source—from a mesenchyme condensation lying between the palatoquadrate cartilage and the hyoid, i.e., between elements of two distinct visceral arches. At the expense of this condensation the hyoquadrate ligament is first formed, and then, much later, from the so far unused basal part of the same coagulation, a hyoid processus is formed on which is placed the proximal part of the hyoid ligament. The unique significance of the hyoid process is also shown by the relation of this chondrification to the anterior mandibular artery.

The remnant of the mandibular arterial arch, the art. quadratomandibu-

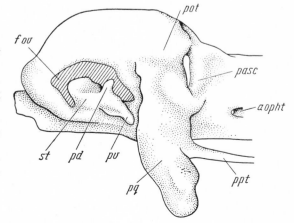

FIG. 109. *Hynobius keyserlingii* larva 25 mm long. Reconstruction of otic region of head, lateral view. *aopht*, Passage for orbital artery; *fov*, fenestra ovalis (hatched); *pasc*, ascending process of palatoquadrate cartilage; *pd*, dorsal process of columella, enveloping lateral head vein; *pot*, otic process of palatoquadrate cartilage; *ppt*, pterygoid process of palatoquadrate cartilage; *pq*, palatoquadrate cartilage; *pv*, ventral process of columella; *st*, stapes.

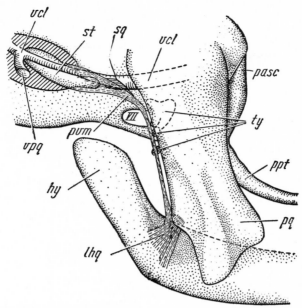

FIG. 110. *Ranodon sibiricus* larva 35 mm long. Reconstruction of palatoquadrate cartilage and parts of the otic capsule and hyoid, lateral view. Membrane of fenestra ovalis hatched; outline of lateral head vein and tympanic cavity lying medial of palatoquadrate indicated by broken lines. *hy*, Hyoid; *lhq*, hyoquadrate ligament; *pasc*, ascending process of palatoquadrate cartilage; *pq*, palatoquadrate cartilage; *pvm*, mesenchyme anlage of ventral rod; *sq*, outline of posterior edge of squamosal bone; *st*, stapes; *ty*, rudiments of tympanic cavity; *vcl*, lateral head vein; *vpq*, palatoquadrate vein; *VII*, seventh cranial nerve.

laris, transects the posterior end of the palatoquadrate cartilage on its way to the lower jaw, directly above the place of attachment of the hyoquadrate ligament. In young larvae it passes through the anterior part of the hyoquadrate mesenchyme condensation, i.e., through the anlage of the hyoid process and here gives off a further branch. By the time of the chondrification of the hyoid process the primary mandibular artery is usually already completely reduced. If it is retained longer, it passes through the cartilage into the canal lying between the hyoid process and the ventral shaft on the one hand, and the palatoquadrate cartilage proper, on the other hand. Later on the art. quadratomandibularis in the Hynobiidae always degenerates and is replaced by art. mandibulojugularis (Schmalhausen, 1953b). Such a passage for an artery which is derived from the primary mandibular arterial arch may be explained if it is recognized that in a given case the fusion of parts of the mandibular and hyoid arches of the skeleton occurred. The mandibular artery, found to be compressed between these parts, passes through the canal of the inner cartilage (Fig. 111) as the result of this fusion.

In Fig. 112 is an illustration of a plastic reconstruction of the skull of a larva of *Hynobius* 27 mm long. The ventral cartilaginous shaft is fully developed and its end fuses to the hyoid process, and consequently to the palato-

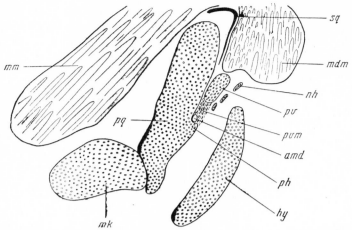

FIG. 111. *Hynobius keyserlingii* larva 33 mm long. Sagittal section through palatoquadrate cartilage and lower part of ventral shaft of columella. *amd*, Arteria quadratomandibularis; *hy*, hyoid; *mdm*, musculus depressor mandibulae; *mk*, lower jaw; *mm*, temporal muscle; *nh*, hyoid nerve; *ph*, rudiment of hyoid process; *pq*, palatoquadrate cartilage; *pv*, ventral shaft of columella; *pvm*, its prochondral end; *sq*, squamosal bone.

quadrate cartilage. Its position in life resembles the position of the hyomandibula of fishes. The similarity is further enhanced by the presence (as individual variation) of an opening through which the hyomandibular nerve emerges (Fig. 113). This nerve usually goes around the ventral side of the shaft of the columella.

In adult *Hynobius* the auditory ossicle takes the form of a very short massive formation. In a young specimen, of 65 mm length, at the base of the auditory ossicle lies a thin bony plate surrounded by a cartilage ring. It is set in the fenestra ovalis, with the anterior edge of which it is articulated by a cartilaginous commissure. From the center of the basal plate extends the mushroom-shaped columella, consisting of a narrow bony foot and a wide cartilaginous cap, passing anteriorly to a cartilaginous protuberance on the

FIG. 112. *Hynobius keyerslingii* larva 27 mm long. Plastic reconstruction of posterior half of skull. Lateral view, slightly from above. *ff*, Foramen in columella for hyomandibular nerve VII (variant); *pd*, process of columella enveloping vein; *ph*, hyoid process; *pv*, ventral shaft of columella (hyomandibula); *II*, *IV*, foramina for nerve exits; other abbreviations as in Fig. 109.

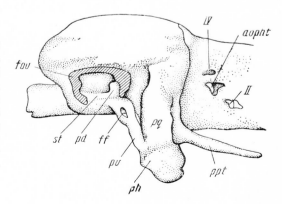

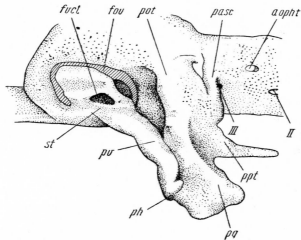

FIG. 113. *Hynobius keyserlingii* larva 34 mm long, nearing metamorphosis. *aopht*, Foramen for orbital artery; *fov*, fenestra ovalis; *fvcl*, foramen for lateral head vein; *pasc*, ascending process of palatoquadrate cartilage; *ph*, hyoid process; *pot*, otic process of palatoquadrate cartilage; *ppt*, pterygoid process of palatoquadrate cartilage; *pq*, palatoquadrate; *pv*, ventral shaft of columella (hyomandibula); *st*, stapes; *II*, *IV*, formaina for nerve exits.

quadrate. The latter is essentially completely ossified. Cartilage is retained only in the area of the processes (processus pterygoideus, ascendens, basalis, and oticus). The above cartilaginous protuberance, developed from the ventral shaft of the columella, is connected by a small strand to cartilage retained in the basal area of the processus oticus. The rest of the cartilaginous protuberance lies as a distant mass on the rear surface of the ossified quadrate. In the deep notch through which passes the hyomandibular nerve (Figs. 135 and 136), this cartilaginous protuberance is divided into a dorsal mass, "processus columellaris," and a ventral, rather long, posteriorly directed process, the "processus hyoideus." This cartilaginous mass, as a whole (Fig. 136), is part of the upper division of the hyoid arch, developed from the described mesenchyme strand behind the palatoquadrate cartilage. According to its position and connections it is homologous to the suspensorium (hyomandibular) of fishes.

We note, as a fact of great phylogenetic significance, that in fully developed larvae of *Hynobius* and *Ranodon* there are complete hyoid arches in addition, consisting almost entirely of cartilaginous elements. The cartilaginous auditory ossicle with a lateral thickening is prolonged without discontinuity into a fairly stout ventral cartilaginous shaft running along the rear edge of the palatoquadrate cartilage to the hyoid process. The latter is connected by a flat ligament to the ventral part of the hyoid arch, i.e., to the hyoid.[1]

The continuity of the hyoid arch was also established in some reptiles

[1] Reinbach (1950) suggested that the stapes is produced from a portion of the otic capsule, and that the remaining part of the columella of Amphibia is derived from the palatoquadrate, specifically from a hypothetical ray of the mandibular arch.

(in the tuatara *Sphenodon punctatus*) and embryonically in lizards, crocodiles, and birds. However, only in the Hynobiidae has the upper part of the hyoid arch retained the typical position and all the characteristic ligaments of the suspensorium (hyomandibula) of fishes, to say nothing of the fact that only in urodele Amphibia has the hyoid proper retained its original structure. In this respect, the urodele Amphibia of family Hynobiidae particularly show the most primitive relationships which are obviously fundamental to all terrestrial vertebrates.

A comparison with other urodele Amphibia shows the primitiveness and uniqueness of the position of the Hynobiidae. An examination of some series, or of the development of *Ambystoma*, *Pleurodeles*, and *Salamandrina*, shows a sharp reduction of the auditory ossicle and its columella. However, according to published reports (Thyng, 1906), in *Amphiuma* the stapes is prolonged into a cartilaginous shaft running along the posterior edge of the quadratum and merging into it. Perhaps this indicates a less remote position for the Amphiumidae than is assumed, and its affinity to the Hynobiidae.

Of the published reports there should still be noted certain discoveries apparently having some pertinence to the facts I have noted. Litzelman (1923) described as a rudiment of the hyomandibula in *Triton alpestris* an elongate cartilage adjoining the palatoquadrate posteriorly and later fused to it. Its position in the stages of metamorphosis is reminiscent of the hyoid process.

Since the ventral cartilaginous shaft is developed from the columella of the auditory ossicle as a ventral prolongation later connected to the ventral part of the hyoid arch, we can regard this shaft as derived from the latter, i.e., we see in it a homolog of the suspensorium (hyomandibula) of fishes. The relation of the hyomandibular nerve to this portion is quite similar to the relation of that nerve to the hyomandibula in sturgeons. However, the position of these parts differs from that in most bony fishes, in which the hyomandibular nerve emerges outward through an opening in the hyomandibula itself. This difference should not be overestimated since the reduction of part of the hyomandibula in front of the above opening may lead to freeing the nerve and its emergence anterior to the hyomandibula (as in the codfish, among teleosts), and the reduction of the posterior part may lead to the situation seen in sturgeons and in terrestrial vertebrates, particulary in urodele Amphibia.

The hyomandibular nerve curves posteriorly around the anlage of the ventral shaft of the columella as shown. Sometimes, however, in *Hynobius*, the condensation of mesenchyme here partly envelops the nerve. In one case in *Hynobius* (larva of 27 mm length) and in a later (prechondrification) stage of development, the ventral shaft of the hyomandibular nerve (without the inner mandibular branch) passes not through the notch but through an opening in this anlage (Fig. 112). In another case of a larva of *Hynobius* in a stage close to metamorphosis (34 mm), on the right the whole hyomandibular nerve (along with the inner mandibular branch) passes through the opening in the cartilaginous shaft; on the left side, only the outer branch (n. lateralis) passes through this opening. This reconstructs the original picture of the passage of the nerve through the opening in the hyomandibula.

The anlage of the auditory ossicle takes a typical position between the two large blood vessels, the inner carotid artery lying medially and the lateral head vein passing dorsally of the anlage (Fig. 106). The correlation of the auditory ossicle with these two vessels is retained in later stages and becomes still clearer owing to its branching, developing directly behind the auditory ossicle and closely enveloping it.

The orbital artery (art. orbitalis) is developed as a branch of the internal carotid artery in the chondrifying stages of the stapes in larvae of *Ranodon* of 23–25 mm length. In some cases in about the same place the orbital artery is developed as an anterior branch of the hyoid artery. Since the orbital artery is a branch of the hyoid artery in origin, the above mode of its development represents a recapitulatory variation.

In the formative stages of the orbital artery the development of the auditory ossicle is still not complete and it passes partly through the mesenchyme condensation which provides the material for the construction of the columella of the auditory ossicle (stilus columellae). In the chondrification of the latter (in larvae of *Ranodon* of 25–29 mm length) the orbital artery is sometimes enclosed by cartilage and it then passes into the canal through the columella (Fig. 108). The latter occurs occasionally in *Ranodon* (in 40% of a total number observed). In these cases the orbital artery occupies the typical position of the stapedial artery of reptiles and mammals (Fig. 135). More often, however, in other urodele amphibia, particularly in *Hynobius,* the orbital artery passes anteriorly below the columella, as is often the case in higher terrestrial vertebrates.

Very closely associated with the anlage of the stapes is the lateral vein of the head. Even in the early stages of the formation of the auditory ossicle this vein directly adjoins the stapes on the dorsal side and underlies the mesenchyme process protruding from this anlage. The cartilaginous columella developing in the latter partly covers this vein below. An especially close connection is established between the auditory ossicle and the lateral head vein in *Hynobius.* Directly below the vein on the stapes the dorsal cartilaginous protuberance is developed in the form of a loop, enveloping the lateral vein laterally (Fig. 109). The cartilaginous loop is prolonged into the mesenchyme shaft, extending to the wall of the otic capsule lateral of the vein, and is then converted into a ligament. Then the vein becomes entirely surrounded. At metamorphosis the cartilage expands around the vein and sometimes forms a complete ring on the base of the auditory ossicle, through which the lateral head vein passes. During metamorphosis, however, this ring disappears and the vein, in adult *Hynobius,* lies free on the ossified plate of the auditory ossicle. Directly behind the stapes the lateral head vein gives off a lateral branch, vena palatoquadrata, running anterolaterally along the mesenchyme shaft and (later) the cartilaginous columella, but turned toward the palatoquadrate cartilage. The lateral head vein with the palatoquadrate vein branching off from it thus forms a fork fully enclosing the auditory ossicle posteriorly.

The tympanic cavity of anurans is developed as an outgrowth of the dorsal wall of the first visceral fold in the form of an aggregated cellular mass, taking the form of a bubble set on a long pedicel. This cellular mass then loses its connection with the pharyngeal epithelium. The tympanic cavity proper is formed from these primordia only during metamorphosis. It is located anterior to the hyomandibular nerve. The Eustachian tube is formed anew. If one considers the features of the development of the tympanic cavity in anurans, then it is easy to recognize the same process seen in the development of urodele Amphibia.

In *Hynobius* the anlage of the dorsal diverticulum of the first visceral fold is of considerably larger mass than in the axolotl or *Triton*. Its general form is the same: it is a small pyriform formation set on a long pedicel. It is, however, retained much longer without reduction and its original connection to the pharyngeal epithelium sometimes persists until metamorphosis. In one case, in a larva of 33 mm length near metamorphosis, a well-preserved pear-shaped anteroposteriorly flattened mass of cells set on a long, flat, rather thick pedicel has been observed. In *Ranodon*, however, this formation is even more strongly developed although the connection of the primordium to the pharyngeal epithelium is broken earlier than in *Hynobius*.

In the youngest larvae of *Ranodon* (before hatching from the envelope) there are fairly large dorsal processes of the epithelium of the first visceral fold, in the form of dense masses of cells, packed with yolk grains. Even before hatching they are pear-shaped (i.e., they have the pyriform shape only in cross section) and make connections with the epithelium by thin pedicels. This connection is broken well before hatching, as in the axolotl, and consequently much earlier than in *Hynobius*. The anlage is converted into a mass of cells taking the form of a band with a slightly irregular outline (Fig. 114). This strip lies parallel to the posterior surface of the palatoquadrate cartilage in front of the hyomandibular nerve (Fig. 110); consequently it is placed almost transversely. As in the visceral clefts, however, the lateral edge of the

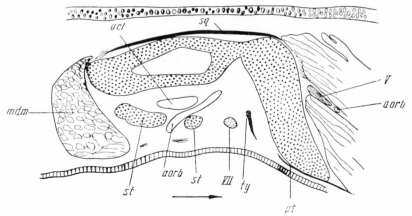

FIG. 114. *Ranodon sibiricus* larva 50 mm long. Sagittal section through auditory ossicle at the plane of the canal for the orbital artery. *aorb*, Orbital artery; *mdm*, m. depressor mandibulae; *pt*, pterygoid; *sq*, squamosal; *st*, stapes; *ty*, tympanic rudiment; *vcl*, lateral head vein; *V, VII*, nerves.

anlage turns a little posteriorly, and the medial edge turns anteriorly. Occasionally the anlage is broken up into separate sections of various sizes (Fig. 110) at the outset. Thereafter, further disintegration and resorption occurs sooner or later. Sometimes, however, such rudiments are retained up to metamorphosis in the form of dense cellular masses. Of especial interest is the fact that in some cases cavities are developed in the rudiments of dorsal diverticula. And after metamorphosis (in *Ranodon* of 80 mm length) bladders with thick epidermal walls are sometimes seen which plainly represent remnants of the formations described.

The rudiments described, and especially the epithelial formations developing from them in the larvae of *Ranodon,* are quite similar to the anlagen of the tympanic cavities of anuran Amphibia both in their mode of development and in their position between the palatoquadrate cartilage and the hyomandibular nerve. The independence of these anlagen from the potential material of the analagen of the frontal glands is definite, since cases of simultaneous development of both anlagen are found in *Ranodon.* Thus the developmental history of the dorsal diverticulum of the first visceral cleft in *Ranodon* and other urodele Amphibia in comparison to the developmental history of this same region in Anura shows fairly clearly that the homolog of the tympanic cavity is included in it. The considerable variability of these formations accords well with their rudimentary nature. In some cases, however, they have nevertheless also formed cavities which may be retained as remnants after metamorphosis.

All this taken together gives a quite clear indication that in the ancestors of urodele Amphibia there was actually an apparatus for sound transmission from the air, i.e., a tympanic cavity and tympanic membrane.

A. Muscles of the Dorsal Section of the Hyoid Arch and the Middle Ear

One of the muscles of the otic region associated with elements of the hyoid arch at its very origin is the m. depressor mandibulae which is originally the suspensor muscle (m. adductor hyomandibularis) and in urodele Amphibia is initiated as a muscle elevating the hyoid. In early stages of development (at hatching) the rudiment of this muscle branches off from the anlage of the otic capsule in the area of the horizontal semicircular canal and turns downward to the end of the hyoid where it is attached in these stages. Thus the phase of the development of m. levator hyoidei is repeated. Soon however, at the time of larval hatching, the original muscle shifts backward along the wall of the capsule, and then leads off ventrally from the posterior part of the otic capsule. On the other side, the distally attached muscle is borne along the hyomandibular ligament downward to the protruding corner of the lower jaw (Schmalhausen, 1955a). Originally it is located laterally and a little posteriorly of the anlage of the auditory ossicle. Later it is expanded, approaches the rear edge of the palatoquadrate cartilage and covers the otic region exteriorly. In larvae near metamorphosis, m. depressor mandibulae later rests with its anteromedial wall close to the head of the columella and on the ventral shaft (and also on the hyoid process).

In *Ranodon,* in some cases, bundles of small anterior fibers of this muscle are attached to the distal end of the columella. The same thing is found in one larva of *Hynobius* of about 34 mm length. In these cases we apparently have remnants of muscles in their original positions (m. adductor s. retractor hyomandibularis).

In the early stages of development (before hatching) when the rudiments of m. depressor mandibulae (s. levator hyoidei) still lie in the central part of the otic capsule in the area of the horizontal semicircular canal, in *Ranodon* there are regularly seen directly under it bundles of many cells taking a characteristic position between the otic capsule (in the horizontal semicircular canal area) and the lateral head vein. At the time of hatching of *Ranodon* larvae (of 21–23 mm length) there are quite often seen small but well-formed bundles of myoblasts arranged on the front edge of the anlage of the stapes, between the lateral head vein and the otic capsule (Fig. 115). Usually these anlagen quickly disappear. In one case however, in a larva of *Ranodon* 26 mm long, a definite muscular bundle has been found leading off anteriorly from the front edge of the stapes below the trunk of the hyomandibular nerve to the basipterygoid process at the base of the skull (Schmalhausen, 1953b). In another case, in a large larva of *Hynobius* 36 mm long, there is a large muscle bundle attached to the base of the stapes and running in a lateral direction along the trunk of the hyomandibular nerve and farther down to the connection with the tendon of m. depressor mandibulae (of which it is thus a part). In another case, in a larva of *Hynobius* 31 mm long, from the distal capitulum

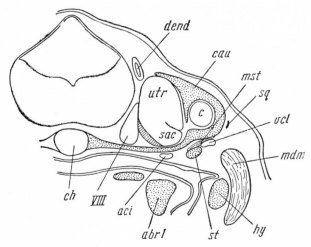

FIG. 115. *Ranodon sibiricus* larvae 21–22 mm long. Cross section through otic region. *abr 1,* Branchial arch; *aci,* internal carotid artery; *c,* external semicircular canal; *cau,* otic capsule; *ch,* notochord; *dend,* endolymphatic duct; *hy,* hyoid; *mdm,* m. depressor mandibulae; *mst,* m. stapedius; *sac,* sacculus; *sq,* anlage of squamosal; *st,* anlage of stapes; *utr,* utriculus; *vcl,* lateral head vein; *VIII,* auditory ganglia.

of the auditory ossicle a large muscle extends straight downward, attaching to the end of the hyoid. This muscle is separate but closely continuous (interlocked) with m. depressor mandibulae. In this case the muscle retained attachment to the stapedial muscle on the one hand, and secondarily acquired the lost function of m. levator hyoidei on the other hand.

Thus in *Ranodon* during ontogenesis segregation of a small muscle rudiment regularly occurs contiguous with the anteriomedial edge of the rudiment of m. depressor mandibulae (i.e., being in the typical position of the rudiment of the stapedial muscle, m. extracolumellaris stapedius). This rudiment sometimes even gives rise to a small bundle of myoblasts adjoining the rudiment of the stapes. Later on this embryonic material disappears, but sometimes it is converted into quite differentiated muscular bundles which, retaining their connection with the auditory ossicle, expand in various partly random directions. The existence of temporary anlagen and rudimentary muscle bundles in the larvae of Hynobiidae shows quite plainly that in the ancestors of urodele amphibians as in the reptiles there was a distinct musculum stapedius.

B. Comparisons with Fishes, Stegocephalia, and Reptiles

The position of the auditory ossicle (stapes) in the otic capsule and its relationship to the hyomandibular nerve and blood vessel differ from the position of the hyomandibula in bony fishes; however, it is analogous to its position in chondrostean fishes. A closer examination of this matter led to the conclusion (Schmalhausen, 1923b) that the hyomandibula was originally attached to the skull at two points between which the lateral head vein passed (Fig. 40). Since the main bulk of the hyomandibula by all accounts is epihyal, evidently the median attachment of the hyomandibula to the otic capsule of the skull is served by the pharyngohyal (Schmalhausen, 1923b). In that case the primary structure of the upper division of the hyoid arch is very similar to the structure of the upper divisions of the gill arches in sturgeons, which also have a dual connection to the braincase (Fig. 40). In sturgeons there is a ventromedial attachment of the gill arches through the common (infra-) pharyngobranchials and a lateral attachment by the special suprapharyngo-branchials, which by all accounts are the product of a secondary articulation of the dorsal processes of the epibranchials. As proof of the original existence of a dual attachment of the hyoid arch in bony fishes, I considered the correlation found in the dipnoan fish *Ceratodus* in which there is both a rudiment of the hyomandibula in the dorsolateral position and a rudiment of the pharyngo-hyal in the ventromedial position. Nevertheless the auditory ossicle of many reptiles is also characterized by a dual attachment to the braincase. The columella of lizards has a dorsolateral attachment to a parotic process (processus paroticus) of the skull and a ventromedial attachment in the fenestra ovalis of the otic capsule. Both the capital lateral vein and the hyomandibular nerve pass backward between the two attachments.

At the time that this hypothesis was proposed (Schmalhausen, 1923a,b) paleontological proof was found of the existence of a dual connection of the hyomandibula to the skull in crossopterygian fishes (*Rhizodopsis, Ectosteorhachis,* and *Eusthenopteron*), i.e., it is the same in those fishes which are apparently most closely related to terrestrial vertebrates. As may be judged by the evidence of a notch in the inner side of the hyomandibula of *Ectosteorhachis* (*Megalichthys*), the lateral head vein passes between the two attachments of the hyomandibula to the skull. Between the two articular heads the trunk of the hyomandibular nerve passed backward and later entered a canal on the inner side of the hyomandibula and emerged from it on the outer side (in *Ectosteorhachis* and *Eusthenopteron*). The dorsal head of the hyomandibula of *Ectosteorhachis* articulated with a parotic process of the skull (processus paroticus) and the ventral head articulated with the wall of the otic capsule in the region of the sacculus (Romer, 1941; Westoll, 1943a).

In urodele Amphibia of the family Hynobiidae, chondrification of the whole columella begins with the stapes and progresses laterally. However, in the lateral parts (extracolumella) the anlage is of a different nature and chondrification sets in much later. Between the two parts, and at late stages, a band of juvenile cartilage is sometimes retained, plainly indicating the boundary between the stapes and the extracolumella and externally resembling the articulation present in lizards. The extracolumella is developed in the Hynobiidae in a mesenchyme condensation extending from the anlage of the stapes to the edge of the squamosal bone and then along the rear wall of the palatoquadrate cartilage to the hyoquadrate ligament.

If the stapes is pharyngohyal in origin and since in any case the ventral head of the hyomandibula of crossopterygian fishes is, then the extracolumella is itself homologous to the hyomandibula (epihyale) with its dorsolateral head. This homology is indeed generally accepted for reptiles. However, in urodele Amphibia (Hynobiidae) an even clearer similarity of the position and relationships is maintained. The dorsal head of the columella of Hynobiidae is attached to the rear edge of the squamosal bone in the region of the origin of the horizontal semicircular canal of the otic capsule. In crossopterygian fishes (e.g., *Ectosteorhachis*) the dorsal head of the hyomandibula was articulated to the lateral otic process (processus paroticus) which lies at the base of the horizontal semicircular canal, an undoubtedly similar position. The only difference is that in Hynobiidae the parotic process of the skull is reduced.

Thus the two attachments of the columella of Hynobiidae to the skull, the medial (stapes) and the dorsal (capitulum of the columella), occupy a position in the skull similar to the two attachments of the hyomandibula of crossopterygian fishes. In both cases the lateral head vein passes between them. From the head of the columella the "ventral cartilage shaft" (Fig. 112) runs in a ventrolateral direction parallel to the posterior wall of the palatoquadrate cartilage and to its hyoid process. The position of this shaft is quite similar to the position of the hyomandibula of fishes. At its ventral end it is attached to cartilage developing at the base of the hyoquadrate ligament, and consequently to the palatoquadrate cartilage. The association of the hyomandibula with the palatoquadrate cartilage in fishes also becomes very close. Occasionally, in early stages of development it is found to be united by its lower end to the palatoquadrate cartilage (*Polypterus, Clupea, Amiurus, Ictalurus,* and others). This connection is a manifestation of a close interrelation between both primary visceral arches and is established not only in higher fihes, but also in the lower cartilaginous and chondrostean fishes, in their common forms of hyostyly or amphistyly (Crossopterygii).

The "ventral cartilaginous shaft" along with the dorsal capitulum of the columella is quite homologous in both its position and connections to the hyomandibula of fishes. Only in larvae of Hynobiidae is it retained in its original form and typical correlation to a much greater extent than in any other terrestrial vertebrate. The hyoid process of the palatoquadrate cartilage is also derived from the hyoid arch. In this manner it (1) develops the connection to the quadratum, and (2) makes a connection by the hyoquadrate ligament to the lower division of the hypoglossal arch, the hyoid. As to the first, it takes the position of the symplectic and fills its function. In the second, it is similar to the interhyal and supplements it.

A few words remain to be said concerning the relation of these parts of the skeleton to the hyomandibular branch of the facial nerve. In sturgeons this comes out to the surface detouring around the suspensor posteriorly. Meanwhile in almost all higher fishes, particularly in crossopterygians, the hyomandibular nerve passes through a canal or opening in the hyomandibula itself. In the Hynobiidae this nerve passes through a notch in the posterior edge of the ventral cartilaginous shaft (Fig. 135). This notch may be regarded as a remnant of the opening which has broken open through reduction of the posterior part of the hyomandibula. In support of this presumption would be the fact that the hyomandibular nerve passes through a mesenchyme analage and, in two cases in the Hynobiidae through a clearly outlined opening in the ventral shaft (Fig. 112), i.e., in the hyomandibula. Commonly even in the Hynobiidae, as in all terrestrial vertebrates, the hyomandibular nerve passes around the columella of the ear posteriorly. Such a passage of the nerve is explained with no special difficulty in terms of reduction of the posterior element of the hyomandibula.

In light of the facts of the larval development of Urodela (Hynobiidae), explanations of some relationships described earlier in some Stegocephalia and fossil reptiles are seen. In the very primitive Stegocephalia, *Megalocephalus (Orthosaurus)*, there was a pit in the posterior wall of the quadrate which evidently served for attachment of the large ventral process of the auditory ossicle (Watson, 1926b). The latter was often retained. It was ossified dorsally and one end rested in a pit (in the site of the fenestra ovalis) in the wall of the auditory capsule, and the other ended freely at the otic notch of the skull where the tympanic membrane was located. The supposed process articulating with the quadrate evidently remained cartilaginous. In position it corresponded precisely to the ventral cartilaginous shaft in the Hynobiidae. In other cases, at the lower end of the quadrate posteriorly there was a small protuberance with a roughened surface, the tuberculum supratrochleare (in *Benthosuchus*; Bystrov and Efremov, 1940), which probably bore a cartilaginous process comparable to the hyoid process of urodele Amphibia.

For comparison with urodele Amphibia on a higher level, however,

Dvinosaurus is of interest as a neotenic stegocephalian which lost the otic notch and consequently, the tympanic membrane. The auditory ossicle of *Dvinosaurus* (Fig. 136) (Sushkin, 1927, 1936; Bystrov, 1938) is very massive. Its bulky medial end apparently rested in the fenestra ovalis (lying in cartilage and therefore not preserved). The narrower distal end was divided into two forks. A small dorsal process pointed dorsolaterally to the edge of the tabular bone where it was probably suspended by a stout ligament, the cartilaginous parotic process (processus paroticus). A bulky ventral process was turned ventrolaterally toward the quadrate. Its roughened surface apparently merged into cartilage. Sushkin presumed that the cartilage was connected to the end of the hyoid by the addition of a long ligament. Bystrov believes that the cartilage merged into a broad ligament connecting it with the quadrate, as in the axolotl and other urodele Amphibia. In the light of the information uncovered by study of the Hynobiidae it would appear that the ventral process of the auditory ossicle in *Dvinosaurus* merged into a bulky cartilaginous shaft leading posteriorly to the quadrate and passing parallel to its posterior wall to the place of attachment of the hyoquadrate ligament. Probably this connection was achieved by means of the cartilaginous hyoid process.

In other Stegocephalia there was usually an otic notch in which the tympanic membrane was placed. In these cases the distal end of the columella terminated freely in the otic notch where it was evidently connected by cartilage to the tympanic membrane. Sometimes, however, the distal end was forked and a small dorsal process turned to the parotic process of the skull and the edge of the tabular bone (in *Trimerorhachis* and *Eryops*, Sushkin, 1927; *Edops*, Romer, 1941). Other processes were not found; even the dorsal processes in Stegocephalia evidently usually remained cartilaginous and were not preserved.

In the more ancient reptiles there occurred anew the above-mentioned primary connection of the columella of the ear to the quadrate. Thus in *Captorhinus* (Cotylosauria) there was a large auditory ossicle in the form of a long, slightly curved rod. It rested mainly in the fenestra ovalis; a little distant was an opening for the orbital artery (arteria stapedia). Farther laterally the columella was curved toward the quadrate bone. At the point of the bend a dorsal convexity was probably connected to the parotic process of the skull (processus paroticus) and is evidently a remnant of the dorsal head of the hyomandibula of crossopterygian fishes and the dorsal process of the columella of reptiles. The lateral end of the columella terminated in a rounded head articulated to a special pit on the posterior surface of the quadrate. The tympanic membrane evidently was not present and the columella was generally very similar to the larval columella of Urodela (Hynobiidae). The same type of auditory ossicle was present in *Labidosaurus* and some other cotylosaurs, in the pelycosaurs (*Casea, Varanosaurus,* and *Dimetrodon*), and in the theriodonts. In these cases no definite dorsal process was present. In some pelycosaurs, however, like *Ophiacodon* and *Sphenacodon,* there was a stout dorsal process extending to the parotic process of the skull. In this case the original dual attachment of the auditory ossicle to the skull, inherited from the crossopterygian fishes with a dual attachment of the hyomandibula, is clearly shown.

However, in modern reptiles also (*Sphenodon*, the lizards, and crocodiles) the primordial relationships were well preserved. In comparison with Urodela (Hynobiidae) the columella of these reptiles in general arrangement are superficially much less similar to the hyomandibula of fishes. In particular it is only a relatively slender and light auditory ossicle. In its thin processes and ligaments, however, the whole typical articulation of the original hyomandibula was retained. The stapes proper was homologous with the stapes of urodele Amphibia (and probably represents the pharyngohyale). Its position in the fenestra ovalis corresponds to the medial attachment of the ventral head of the hyomandibula of crossopterygian fishes. The extracolumella of reptiles is homologous with the cartilaginous ventral shaft of the larvae of Hynobiidae and the main part of the stapes (epihyale) with the dorsal head in crossopterygian fishes. The dorsal process and intercalare of reptiles mark the dorsal attachment of the hyomandibula.

The extension of the columella of reptiles (extrastapediale) attaching to the tympanic membranes, is evidently not homologous with the outer part of the columella of labyrinthodonts and Urodela. In urodele Amphibia, correlated with reduction (evidently secondary) of the tympanic cavity and membrane, this part is absent. The homology of the other parts of the auditory ossicle in urodele Amphibia and reptiles is generally clear. There are, however, differences in connection with the hyomandibular branch of the facial nerve. In urodele Amphibia this nerve as a rule emerges outward under the columella, i.e., from under the ligament of the columella to the dorsal head. In reptiles, as in urodele Amphibia, it emerges posterior of the dorsal process, i.e., above its connection to the stapes. This is explained by a secondary shift of the nerve after the reduction of the outer portion, the extrastapediale. In the Proteidae, only the inner mandibular branch (n. mandibularis internus) emerges under the ligament connecting the stapes with the edge of the squamosal. The hyoid nerve (n. hyoideus) emerges over this ligament, i.e., it takes the general position of the nerve in relation to the stapes seen in other terrestrial vertebrates.

The correlations we have established may be explained in the accompanying diagrams (Figs. 116 and 117) illustrating the mandibular and hyoid arches of crossopterygian fishes and lower terrestrial vertebrates. In order to represent these in one plane we are obliged for visual clarity to make certain modifications in the position of the upper half of the hyoid arch. The ventral head of the hyomandibula and its homolog in the auditory ossicle are shifted forward of the dorsal head, whereas in reality they are located below the dorsal capitulum medially. Correspondingly the extrastapedial is illustrated in the diagrams posterior of the other parts. In reality it lies lateral of them. Thus the dorsal part of the hyoid arch should be rotated about 90 degrees, i.e., in a position perpendicular to the plane of the figure.

In Fig. 116 the relationship in crossopterygian fishes is illustrated. In Fig. 117 the original situation in Amphibia is shown. The only difference from

FIG. 116. Diagram of the mandibular and hyoid arches of crossopterygian fishes. *asc*, Ascending process of
palatoquadrate cartilage; *d*, dorsal capitulum of hyomandibula; *hy*, hyoid; *hm*,
hyomandibula; *mk*, Meckel's cartilage;
nh, *nm*, hyoid and mandibular rami of
hyomandibular nerve VII; *pq*, palatoquadrate cartilage; *v*, central capitulum
of hyomandibula; *vcl*, lateral head
vein.

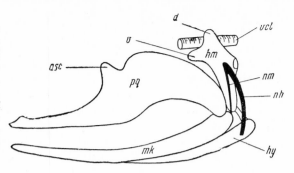

crossopterygian fishes is that the hyomandibular nerve emerges not through
an opening in the hyomandibula but behind it. The ventral head of the
hyomandibula is transformed into the basal part of the auditory ossicle
(stapes). Laterally, above the nerve exit, an external connection to the tympanic membrane (extrastapediale) is developed, possibly at the place of the
cristal process of the hyomandibula. In Fig. 117 a diagram is given of the
relationships in Stegocephalia. The position of the hyomandibular nerve is
shown in correlation with its position in urodele Amphibia. In urodele Amphibia it is secondarily modified as the path of the vessels and variations in
its orientation in larvae of *Hynobius* show. Of urodele Amphibia the most
completely developed auditory ossicle is in the Hynobiidae (Fig. 118). It
differs from the auditory ossicle of Stegocephalia in the absence of the extrastapedial (owing to a secondary reduction of the tympanic cavity and mem-

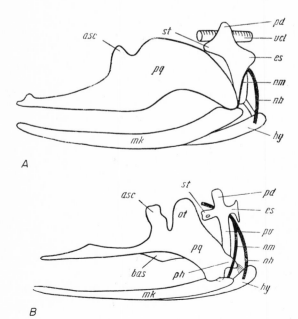

FIG. 117. Diagrams of mandibular
and hyoid arches: original position for
Amphibia (A); scheme in Stegocephalia
(B). *bas*, Basal process of palatoquadrate cartilage; *es*, extrastapedial; *ot*,
otic process of palatoquadrate cartilage; *pd*, dorsal process of stapes; *ph*,
hyoid process; *pv*, ventral extension of
columella; *st*, stapes; other abbreviations as in Fig. 116.

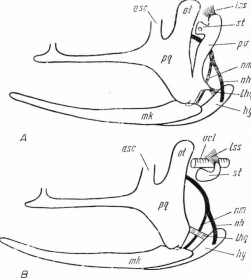

FIG. 118. Diagrams of mandibular and hyoid arches. Hynobiidae (A); other urodele Amphibia (B). *lhq*, Hyoquadrate ligament; *lss*, squamosostapedial ligament; other abbreviations as in Figs. 116 and 117.

brane) and the position of the nerve, emerging from beneath the stapes. In Fig. 118 the arrangement in most urodele Amphibia is shown. Of the whole dorsal section of the hyoid arch there remains only the base of the stapes and the ligament connecting it to the squamosal bone.

For completeness of comparison two more designs for reptiles are shown. Figure 119 shows the original arrangement. The difference from primordial Amphibia is only that the extrastapedial is developed not above the nerve exit but beneath it, between its two branches (this is an hypothesis, but it gives the simplest solution to the question of the different positions of the

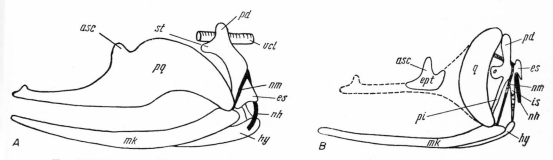

FIG. 119. Diagrams of the correlations of the mandibular and hyoid arches. Original position for reptiles (A); scheme for Lacertilia (B). *ept*, Epipterygoid; *is*, infrastapedial; *pi*, processus internus; *q*, quadrate; other abbreviations as in Fig. 116.

extrastapedial and the tympanic membrane in Amphibia and reptiles). The whole story may be summarized as follows:

1. The Hynobiidae have retained in their larval characteristics, especially in the later stages of development, many features of primitive organization. This applies in particular to the apparatus of sound transmission, built much more elaborately than in other urodele Amphibia.

2. The auditory ossicle (stapes) is initiated quite independently of the wall of the otic capsule and independent (anterior) of its basal fenestra. The anlage of the stapes is connected with the posterior edge of the squamosal bone (squamosum) and the otic process of the palatoquadrate cartilage by means of a mesenchyme condensation in which there is later differentiated, beginning from the stapes, its columella (stilus columellae). The basal part of the auditory ossicle extends posteriorly and then expands in the form of a broad base (plate) in the membrane of the fenestra ovalis. The anteromedial edge of the plate fuses to the edge of the otic capsule bordering the fenestra ovalis.

3. As a prolongation of the mesenchyme condensation running from the stapes with its columella to the rear margin of the squamosal bone, a ventral mesenchymal shaft develops running in a ventrolateral direction along the margin of the squamosal bone and the rear side of the palatoquadrate cartilage up to the place of attachment of the hyoquadrate ligament, where the hyoid process is developed. The latter is initiated in the mesenchyme condensation at the base of the above-mentioned ligament, but it is differentiated as a connection to the palatoquadrate cartilage. The hyoid origin of the process is documented by the passage of the primary mandibular artery (art. quadrato-mandibularis) through the canal between the palatoquadrate cartilage and its hyoid process. In the later stages of larval development, a cartilaginous shaft (processus ventralis columellae) develops in the ventral mesenchyme shaft starting with the end of the columella and extending to the hyoid process. In metamorphosis the end of the ventral cartilaginous shaft fuses to the palatoquadrate cartilage in the vicinity of its hyoid process.

4. In the middle stages of larval development there is sequentially established in the Hynobiidae the continuity of the elements of the hyoid arch, which at the time of metamorphosis consist of the cartilaginous elements of the dorsal division—stapes, processus ventralis (epihyale), processus hyoideus—and of the ventral division—hyoideum, interconnected by the hyoquadrate ligament.

5. Developing in the Hynobiidae in association with the distal end of the stapes, the "ventral cartilaginous shaft" occupies a position characteristic of the hyomandibula of fishes and shows all its typical relationships.

6. The hyomandibular nerve emerges on the surface behind the cartilaginous shaft, as in all terrestrial vertebrates. This is obviously explained by the reduction of the posterior part of the hyomandibula (as in sturgeons). However, in contrast to other terrestrial vertebrates, in urodele Amphibia it passes under the ligament between the stapes and the extracolumella, and not above it. The intermediate position in the Proteidae shows that in urodele

Amphibia the nerve was secondary shifted over the above ligament in a ventral direction.

7. The anlage of the stapes occupies a characteristic position on the otic capsule between the internal carotid artery and the lateral head vein. Branching off directly behind this anlage, the branch of the carotid artery (art. orbitalis) passes forward either below it, or (in *Ranodon*) sometimes through a foramen in the stapes. In the latter case it takes a position typical of the stapedial artery of reptiles and mammals.

8. The lateral head vein lies at the base of the auditory ossicle on its dorsal side. In *Hynobius* a cartilaginous dorsal process is developed here, which partly or fully envelops this vein.

9. In urodele Amphibia a small epithelial outgrowth is developed from the dorsal wall of the first visceral fold. In the Hynobiidae it has a more definite bulk, sometimes maintains a lengthy connection to the pharyngeal epithelium located directly behind the palatoquadrate cartilage, and occasionally gives rise to isolated epithelial vesicles. In position and mode of development these anlagen are similar to the anlagen of the tympanic cavities in anura. They are obviously its rudiments.

10. In the otic region of young larvae of *Ranodon*, there are very often groups of myoblasts in the immediate vicinity of the anlage of the auditory ossicle. In the more fully developed larvae of Hynobiidae fully formed muscle bundles attached to the stapes are sometimes seen as individual variations. They are variously placed but are always found genetically linked to m. depressor mandibulae. This anlage may be only a rudiment of m. stapedius.

11. No special difficulty is encountered in the comparison with Stegocephalia and reptiles. The homology of the stapes is definite and clear. The dorsal process is reduced in urodele Amphibia and replaced by a ligament, the ligamentum squamosostapediale. The extrastapedial is reduced in connection with the reduction of the tympanic membrane. The ventral shaft, processus ventralis columellae, was present in some Stegocephalia (*Megalocephalus, Dvinosaurus,* and probably, in *Dendrerpeton*), and in primitive reptiles (*Captorhinus* and others). In modern reptiles it obviously corresponds to processus internus columellae. The hyoid process was also present in the Stegocephalia; this is indicated by the presence of a roughened protuberance on the quadrate.

12. Urodele Amphibia arose from Stegocephalia which had a very primitive sound transmission apparatus consisting of a columella, which had a dual attachment (stapes and processus dorsalis) to the skull, and a large processus ventralis. The latter took the place of the hyomandibula of fishes and was articulated by its lower end to the quadrate at the place of attachment of the hyoquadrate ligament (or interhyale). In these ancestral forms the tympanic cavity and the stapedial muscle were present; consequently the columella of the ear served for transmission of sound vibrations of the air received by the tympanic membrane. It is sometimes suggested that sound transmission from the ground and not from the air was the original condition for terrestrial vertebrates (Tumarkin, 1949; Tatarinov, 1958). One of two possible

ways is suggested here: by the bony route, from the lower jaw through the quadrate bone and the auditory ossicle to the fenestra ovalis; or by a more complicated route, through the anterior limbs and muscles, ascending the scapula and the opercular cartilage to the same fenestra ovalis. The first route is presumed for animals in a position with the head resting on the surface of the soil; the second route of transmission is presumed for animals supported on appendages with the head elevated. This hypothesis (by Kingsbury and Reed, 1909) passed from scholar to scholar for over half a century without any criticism. Nevertheless its unsoundness is quite obvious. Sound transmission over a complicated system consisting of bones, cartilage, articulations, and muscles is practically impossible owing to almost complete dissipation of the sound waves at each border of two different media. In addition, the opercular cartilage itself could be regarded as an "auditory ossicle" only through ignorance. The relatively large mass (and consequently, inertia) and the position of the cartilage in its own frame (allowing only the passage of sound along the linear axis) in the otic capsule, does not favor the transmission of vibrations. By contraction of the corresponding portion of m. levator scapulae the opercular cartilage is drawn backward and lowers pressure in the perilymph of the ear. This would indicate an accommodation of hearing to piercing sounds but may also simply serve as protection from excessive concussions during irregular movements or saltation of the animal especially in the Salientia (Schmalhausen, 1957b). The first route of sound transmission through the lower jaw is quite another matter. The bony route of sound transmission from the ground is not only possible but also was realized in apodous Amphibia, snakes, many fossil reptiles, and microsaurs. Traces of this mechanism are also present in urodele Amphibia. The only question is the primacy of the mechanism of sound transmission from the ground for terrestrial vertebrates. It is indisputable that a fish having crawled out on the shore can perceive sounds from the ground; it does not require any new adaptation for that since the bony route of sound transmission was perfected in fishes in the aquatic medium. We will not dwell here upon the other question—whether or not these sounds were of much biological significance. It is necessary to note, however, that the connection of the auditory ossicle (hyomandibula) to the fenestra ovalis arose extremely early in the more ancient Stegocephalia (unfortunately nothing is known of ichthyostegids in this respect). Also early established was the position of the distal end of the auditory ossicle in the otic notch of the skull where the tympanic membrane was located. In some lower Carboniferous Stegocephalia there was as yet no fenestra ovalis, but in any case the pit in which the auditory ossicle rested was there. Meanwhile, for bony sound transmission from the ground neither the fenestra ovalis, nor the pit, nor even the auditory ossicle itself was needed—for this the connection of the quadrate bone to the braincase was sufficient. The advantage acquired by the primordial terrestrial vertebrates consisted not in that they could utilize the auditory apparatus of fishes, but that there was opened to them a whole new world of sound in *the air*, which immediately assumed for them vast biological significance.

The developmental history of the middle ear of urodele Amphibia, particularly in the Hynobiidae, clearly shows that they had a system of sound transmission from the air, but that it has been reduced. The existence of rudiments of a tympanic membrane[2] and the stapedial muscle (in *Ranodon*) serves as an adequate indication for this history of the middle ear.

C. MECHANISMS OF SOUND TRANSMISSION IN URODELE AMPHIBIA

One might attempt to explain the reduction of the apparatus of sound transmission from the air in urodele Amphibia in terms of their secondary return to life in the water. On one hand, however, many labyrinthodonts which returned to life in the water retained the typical structure of the middle ear, and the most aquatic of modern Amphibia, the Aglossa, have an excellently developed tympanic cavity and membrane. On the other hand, many urodele Amphibia and also lepospondylous Stegocephalia led a wholly terrestrial way of life, and there are no grounds whatever to presume that they all arose at a stage of secondary aquatic existence in their history. A more probable supposition is that the ancestors of the urodele Amphibia, i.e., terrestrial lepospondylous Stegocephalia (the Microsauria) led a cryptic life and were concealed from danger, hiding under stones, semiburrowed in moss, plant detritus, turf or loose ground. Such a way of life, as in snakelike forms crawling over the ground, always leads to a reduction of the tympanic membrane and cavity (e.g., the early stages of reduction in *Sphenodon* and in various stages of the Agamia). The merging of the extracolumella with the quadrate in the ontogenesis of the Hynobiidae apparently demonstrates the biological significance of sound transmission from the ground in the ancestors of urodele Amphibia. This, in turn, gives indication of a burrowing or creeping life habit in the ancestral forms.

In consideration of the problem of transmission of sound vibrations in the discontinuous media, from the external medium to the body of the animal and through the tissues to the auditory receptors, it is necessary to consider the very great refraction of the sound waves at the border of the two phases. Sound waves are even reflected at the boundaries of air layers of different densities. In the passage from air to water (and also from water into air) only 0.07% of the sound wave energy passes into the other medium. All the remaining energy is reflected (coefficient of reflection, $r = 0.9993$). In transition from the air to a solid body the energy loss is even higher (for the boundary between air and steel, $r = 0.99998$, i.e., only 0.0027% passes into the other medium). In this case there may be transferred further only a few hundred thousandths of the volume of total energy falling on a solid body. Consequently, from the impact of sound waves on the covering bones of the skull practically the whole energy of the sound vibrations of the air is reflected. For the boundary

---

[2] Tatarinov states that the spiracle cavity is not only present in urodele Amphibia, but even breaks out (to the surface) in the cryptobranchs (1958). This is an error, brought about by the adoption of the ambiguous term "spiraculum" for the external gill opening of Amphibia, which has nothing in common with the first visceral cleft.

between a solid body and liquid this loss is less marked but nevertheless exceeds 90%.

From the above it follows that reception of sound vibrations of the air through a bony medium is practically impossible. On the other hand when the animal exists in water it can receive sound vibrations coming to it from the external medium through the medium of the dermal bones of the skull (up to 10% of the energy falling on them) if they lie at the surface of the skin itself.

From the above it follows also that in the discontinuous medium of animal tissue distant transmission of sound vibrations is extremely difficult. In multiple successions of liquids and dense tissue substances almost all the energy is absorbed as a result of multiple reflections. Effective transmission of sound vibrations in an animal organism is accomplished only through a homogenous pathway: either through bones, when they are in close contact with each other, or through a continuous canal of liquid.

The latter possibility has not yet been considered in our examination of the problem of sound transmission mechanism in Amphibia. Nevertheless a broad potential for such sound transmission is present in the organism and it may be carried to a high degree of perfection. In particular it was utilized with complete success in the inner ear in all vertebrates.

Since the sensory cells of the otic papillae or Organ of Corti only perceive the movements of particles in a liquid (they could hardly perceive changes of pressure directly), it is then necessary for this action to have a clear directional aspect. In the approach from many sides of sound vibrations which come to the inner ear in practically the same phase (since the sound waves are of relatively great length), contrary vibrations would be absorbed, and as a result there would have arisen periodic fluctuations of pressure in the liquid medium of the inner ear. Only by a unilateral approach could sound vibrations have been perceived by particulate action. Sound vibrations must be brought in on one side by the canal and led out on the other side in a shielded space. All the remaining parts of the auditory organ must be inaccessible to sound vibrations from outside and must be securely isolated. Just this is accomplished in the inner ear of vertebrates, and is most prominently developed in the cochlea of mammals.

The cartilaginous or bony otic capsule itself is quite securely shielded from sound vibrations in an animal living in air. In addition, the otic capsule is shielded exteriorly by a padding of soft dermal tissue. In the otic capsule of the Amphibia there is one opening for the entrance of sound vibrations (the fenestra ovalis) and one or two openings on the opposite side for their exit along the perilymphatic canal into the well-screened, broad, and expanded lymphatic space of the braincase. In addition, in Amphibia there is still only one endolymphatic canal, terminating in the sacculus endolymphaticus in the skull cavity. In Amphibia there is a definite differentiated route for transmission of sound vibrations in the inner ear. Not all the perilymph is a suitable medium for sound transmission. The perilymph of the upper division of the labyrinth is arranged around the utriculus and the semicircular canals;

there is little need for this—it is pierced by a strand of loose connective tissue. The cysterna perilymphatica has become adapted as a special route for the transmission of vibrations from the membrane of fenestra ovalis, passing into the ductus perilymphaticus, enclosed in a cavity, and terminating in the sacculus perilymphaticus in the braincase (Fig. 121). Here a completely unobstructed transmission of vibrations in one direction is perfected: fenestra ovalis—to cysterna—to ductus—to saccus perilymphaticus. In the region of the perilymphatic duct only a very thin membrane separates the perilymphatic cavity from the endolymphatic cavity of the sacculus; at this point two auditory receptors are located, the macula neglecta (amphibiorum) and the macula basilaris.

D. Bony Sound Transmission from the Ground in Amphibia

The practical possibility of sound transmission from the ground is shown by its existence in snakes. In Amphibia such a form of sound transmission has been realized in the Apoda. In the latter case the auditory ossicle is completely ossified and rather bulky. It is connected directly to the quadrate, which is also completely ossified. There is nevertheless a loss of energy owing to the presence of an articulation between the auditory ossicle and the quadrate bone. The latter is firmly joined to the dermal bones of the anterior half of the skull through the squamosal bone. A similar articulation of the auditory ossicle to the quadrate bone was present also in some Stegocephalia. Rudiments of it, in the form of cartilaginous ligaments (Figs. 135 and 136) are present in some Caudata.

From the lower jaw the vibrations may be conducted through the quadrate, and the squamosal connected with it, to the auditory ossicle. In the Hynobiidae they pass in part a shock-absorbing cartilaginous cushion (Fig. 135). In other urodele Amphibia in place of this cartilage there is a ligament which obviously more greatly dampens all sound vibrations received. In other cases transmission of vibrations from the squamosal bone to the ossified walls of the otic capsule is possible. A layer of connective tissue lies between them, however, which should also hamper this transmission. Transmission from the quadrate bone to the ossified wall of the otic capsule is definitely possible; but there is only cartilaginous contact between them which again leads to some loss.

The transmission of sound vibrations from the ground along the bony pathway must be regarded, nevertheless, as being of little effectiveness in modern Amphibia. Comparison of Hynobiidae with other Urodela shows that sound transmission from the ground along a bony route obviously played a major role among them, but in modern urodele Amphibia it loses its significance more and more. In the evolution of urodele Amphibia osseus articulations between bones are replaced by cartilage and connective tissue. The cartilaginous packing between the auditory ossicle (stapes) and the quadrate is replaced by a ligament which increases the loss in this mode of sound transmission. There still remains, however, the possibility of sound transmission through liquid in a canal. Such a mechanism is developed by Amphibia in the aquatic phase of their life and then improved during life on land.

E. The Transmission of Water-Borne Sound Vibrations through the Venous System

The reception of sound vibrations in the water may be carried on by the whole body surface on which the sound waves fall. For their transmission to the internal ear, however, it is necessary that the vibrations be admitted to the fenestra ovalis of the otic capsule (or at the endolymphatic duct), since the wall of the otic capsule in terrestrial vertebrates is well shielded. If one thinks of liquid canals as possible sound transmitters in amphibian larvae living in water, then attention need not be called to the close association between the lateral head vein and the membrane of the fenestra ovalis. This connection is usually well developed not only in larvae, but also in adult urodele Amphibia of the family Hynobiidae (probably in Proteidae also). It is apparent to a lesser degree when the lateral head vein lies directly on the dorsal element of this membrane (Fig. 120). Such is the position of this vein in larvae

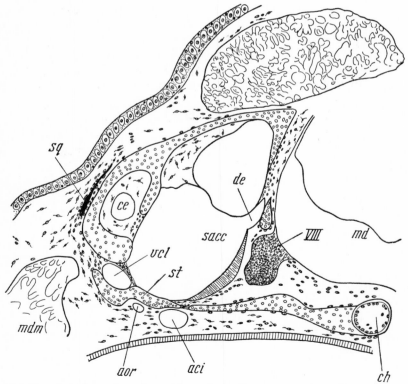

Fig. 120. *Hynobius keyserlingii* larva 20 mm long. Cross section through otic region. *aci*, Internal carotid artery; *aor*, orbital artery; *ce*, external semicircular canal; *ch*, notochord; *de*, base of endolymphatic duct; *md*, elongation of brain; *mdm*, m. depressor mandibulae; *sacc*, sacculus; *sq*, squamosal; *st*, stapes; *vcl*, lateral head vein; *VIII*, auditory ganglia.

of *Hynobius, Ranodon, Ambystoma, Pleurodeles, Triton, Salamandra*, and *Necturus*. In the Hynobiidae this connection is especially close and is accomplished by means of the auditory ossicle (stapes). In larvae of *Ranodon* the lateral head vein adjoins the dorsal side next to the anlage of the stapes. The latter partly covers this vein laterally. The ligament running from the stapes to the posterior edge of the squamosal bone (ligamentum squamosostapediale) encloses the lateral head vein from the laterodorsal side and thus fixes firmly its position on the free dorsal part of the membrane of the fenestra ovalis and partly on the dorsal section of the base of the stapes itself. In *Hynobius* the connection is found to be still closer (Fig. 120). From the anlage of the stapes there first develops a mesenchyme strand, enclosing the vein, and then a dorsal cartilaginous process which at a later stage, near metamorphosis, sometimes extends completely around the vein enclosing it in a canal passing through the base of the auditory ossicle. During metamorphosis this canal apparently disappears. However, the vein does not lose its close association with the stapes. By its branching the lateral head vein completely encloses the ossified auditory ossicle.

Usually the well-developed connection of the lateral cephalic vein with the base of the auditory ossicle or directly to the membrane of the fenestra ovalis prevents one from believing it to have much functional significance. It may be presumed that the lateral head vein is utilized in larvae and in some adults of urodele Amphibia as a fluid canal for transmission of sound vibrations which could be received on superficial veins of the head. The lateral head vein collects blood from various subcutaneous ramifications but especially from the direction of the vena temporo-orbitalis, carrying blood from the circumorbital venous ring and its many branches. The impact of sound waves on the surface of the head should produce pressure pulsations in the subcutaneous veins and, consequently, in the orbitotemporal and lateral head vein. Sound vibration pressure in the lateral head vein should be passed on to the membrane of the fenestra ovalis, and the latter then becomes the source of sound waves propagating further through the inner ear from the perilymphatic sac to the duct and the thin membrane of the sacculus endolymphaticus with its auditory papillae (Fig. 121).

As a canal for transmission of sound vibrations the lateral head vein system is of considerable advantage. This transmission is almost without any loss. Some reflection may definitely take place at the skin surface. The skin of the larvae is very thin, however, and quite suitable for the role of a receptive membrane. The venous vessels lying beneath it are thin-walled and through their ramifications present more surface for reception of sound vibrations (Fig. 123). The existence of the ramification of a sound-conducting canal creates no difficulty since its conductivity is determined by the sum of the sections of all its branches. From the standpoint of acoustic laws the venous canal sound transmission in larvae of Amphibia should be highly effective.

With metamorphosis, some of the advantage of the fluid canal sound transmission is lost. First, a thick dermis is developed, with a multilayered epidermis and a thick fibrous layer in which multicellular glands lie. This

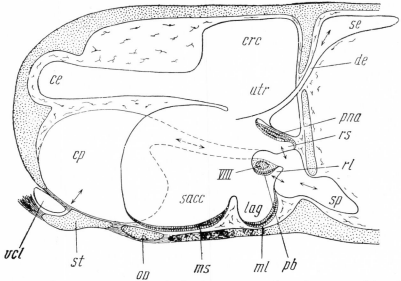

FIG. 121. Sound transmission in Hynobiidae (cross section through otic capsule) *ce*, Exterior semicircular canal (posterior pedicle); *cp*, cysterna perilymphatica; *crc*, common pedicle of vertical canals; *de*, endolymphatic duct; *lag*, lagena; *ml*, macula lagenae; *ms*, macula sacculi; *op*, operculum; *pb*, papilla basilaris; *pna*, papilla neglecta amphibiorum; *rl*, recessus lagenae; *rs*, recessus sacculi; *sacc*, sacculus; *se*, endolymphatic sac; *sp*, perilymphatic sac; *st*, stapes; *utr*, utriculus; *vcl*, lateral head vein; *VIII*, branch of auditory nerve.

dermis should considerably deaden the sound vibrations bearing upon it. In addition, transition of the animal from the aquatic to the aerial medium after metamorphosis immediately deprives the above sound-transmitting canal of its basic advantage. The sound waves from atomspheric air would be almost completely reflected upon impact of the dermal surface.

Yet all this does not mean that the described canal sound transmission completely loses it significance in terrestrial adult Amphibia. Almost all Amphibia spend a considerable part of their life, and especially the biologically important mating and reproductive periods, in water. For an animal committed to the water the canal sound transmission in some respects becomes even more essential since during metamorphosis a very ample net of dermal vessels is developed for the dermal respiratory system. This net of vessels is located immediately beneath the epidermis, and when the latter is of considerable thickness (*Cryptobranchus*), the capillaries penetrate even into the epidermis itself, which provides a greatly amplified surface suitable for reception of sound vibrations. Perhaps this system, while compensating to some degree for the loss of energy by reflection of sound at the skin of the animal, is capable of existing even on land.

In amphibian larvae there is also another canal capable of sound transmission, which is so strongly developed during metamorphosis that it evidently takes on a special importance in the adult animal. Even in larvae, sound vibrations received by the subcutaneous veins of the head pass along the lateral head vein, apparently not only to the otic capsule (to the stapes and fenestra ovalis), but also along its important branch, the median cerebral vein (vena cerebralis medialis), within the cerebral cavity, to the sacculus endolymphaticus which the main trunk of this vein and its numerous branches closely adjoin (Fig. 123). Sound vibrations can pass directly along the endo-lymphatic duct to the endolymph of the inner ear, particularly to the sacculus, just at the location of the principal auditory papillae, papilla neglecta (am-phibiorum) and papilla basilaris. In the Hynobiidae the sacculus endolym-phaticus is still small but is nonetheless enveloped by numerous branches of the median cerebral vein. In the Ambystomidae and Salamandridae the sacculus endolymphaticus is considerably enlarged and vascularized even in the larval stages of development (Fig. 122). During metamorphosis the sacculus endolymphaticus reaches even larger size. The median cerebral vein is completely broken up into a multitude of branches, completely en-veloping the surface of the sacculus and impressed in deep grooves on it. Simultaneously a net of venous vessels expands into the dermis itself, directly beneath the epidermis. This ample net of dermal vessels with thin walls and a large total surface area may well receive sound vibration pressure in the aqueous medium in the head region. Transmission of these vibrations through the veins to the sacculus endolymphaticus should also be highly perfected (Fig. 123). Finally, the position of the endolymphatic duct guarantees the transmission of vibrations directly to the auditory papilla. This whole system ought to be highly effective while the animal is in the water. Since almost all Amphibia spend the mating and egg-laying periods in the water, then perhaps the advanced development of this system of sound transmission is explained by the biological importance of this period for terrestrial forms.

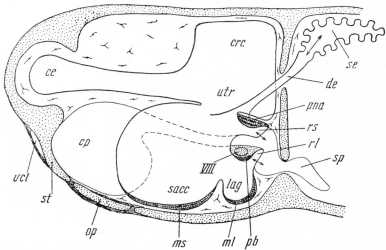

FIG. 122. Sound transmission in Salamandridae (cross section of otic capsule). Stapes joined to the wall of otic capsule; ligament formerly leading from it encloses the lateral head vein. Ab-breviations as in Fig. 121.

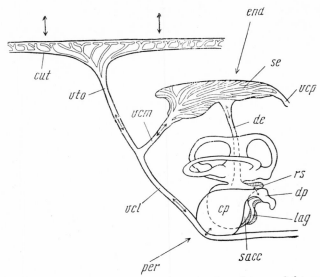

FIG. 123. Diagram of the connection of the inner ear of urodele amphibians with the venous system of the head. *cp*, Cysterna perilymphatica; *cut*, dermal veins; *de*, endolymphatic duct; *dp*, perilymphatic duct; *end*, endolymphatic pathway of sound transmission to macula neglecta; *lag*, lagena; *per*, perilymphatic pathway of sound transmission to papilla basilaris (reduced); *rs*, recessus sacculi; *sacc*, sacculus; *se*, endolymphatic sac; *vcl*, lateral head vein; *vcm*, median cerebral vein; *vcp*, posterior cerebral vein; *vto*, vena temporo-orbitalis.

However, the receptive surface of the dermal veins of the head after metamorphosis is so great, and the further transmission of vibrations along the fluid canal must be so perfected that to a certain extent it justifies posing the question of the possibility of sound transmission along the venous-endolymphatic system, even for animals committed to the aerial medium. Certainly in this case one must calculate a loss of less than 99.9% of the energy of aerial sound vibrations by reflection from the dermal surface.

The sacculus endolymphaticus is especially well developed in salamandrids and plethodontids, i.e., in the most terrestrial forms of urodele Amphibia. However, further development is attained by the endolymphatic apparatus of Anura. Its function still remains unknown for the most part.

What has been said of the possible role of the sacculus endolymphaticus in sound transmission definitely does not exclude other functions for it. It is very likely (Dempster, 1930) that the sacculus endolymphaticus has, incidentally, an excretory function. In drawing off a liquid secretion it actively reduces the osmotic pressure in the labyrinth (the high concentration of salts induces a continuous endosmosis therein toward the perilymph). Such a modest function hardly justifies the volume of this organ however; in any case it does not explain the vast discrepancy in its dimensions and blood supply in various Amphibia. Differences within lines may be correlated to differences in the biological significance of hearing.

Our assumption here is that the existence of canal sound transmission from the superficial veins of the head (Fig. 123) in larvae of Amphibia, and through the lateral head vein in Hynobiidae, to the membrane of the fenestra ovalis (with or without participation of the auditory ossicle), and in all urodeles through the median cerebral vein and the sacculus endolymphaticus directly to the inner ear, is the sole possible route of sound transmission, at least during the sojourn of these animals in the water. Unless one of these routes functions the urodele Amphibia in general do not perceive sound vibrations. It seems to me that the only doubts in this case exist with respect to the reception of sound vibrations in the air when the animal is committed to the land. Both canals for sound transmission, either venous-perilymphatic or venous-endolymphatic can definitely also serve for the transmission of vibrations from the soil surface. In this case, patches of thin dermis located below the angle of the lower jaw play a role and so also does the plentiful supply of branches of the venous vessels directly connected to the same lateral head vein at the very base of the auditory ossicle or directly to the membrane of the fenestra ovalis.

Apparently this same mechanism of sound transmission through dermal veins to the sacculus endolymphaticus functions in some cases in anuran Amphibia also. We cannot assume that the toad (*Bombina*) is deaf, since the sounds produced by it have great biological significance. Nevertheless the middle ear apparatus common to anuran Amphibia is reduced in the *Bombina* toad. In the larvae there is a definite connection of the lateral head vein to the membrane of the fenestra ovalis. In adult animals an extensive system of dermal respiration is established, with a very large median cerebral vein abundantly branching at the sacculus endolymphaticus. A broad endolymphatic duct provides a direct connection to the labyrinth of the ear. Apparently, in the toad (*Bombina*) the same mechanism of sound transmission along a fluid canal is utilized that is present in urodele Amphibia. Probably the same applies to the spadefoot toad (*Pelobates*). In other anurans the venous-endolymphatic route of sound transmission may only be an accessory and apparently operates only when the animal is in the water, i.e., mainly during mating. It is possible that in this way sound transmission from the ground through the skin beneath the lower jaw is also perfected in anurans.

F. AUDITORY RECEPTORS AND THE INTERNAL PATHS OF SOUND TRANSMISSION IN AMPHIBIA

In fishes the auditory receptors are the macula sacculi and its derivative the macula lagenae (in the herrings as an exception, it is the macula utriculi). The significance of the macula neglecta remains an open question.

In terrestrial vertebrates yet another receptor is segregated from the macula lagenae, lying in a special projection (recessus lagenae), the macula basilaris, which usually extends into the labyrinth as a papilla (papilla basilaris). Comparative morphological information indicates that this particular receptor, developing progressively in some amniotes, gives rise to the Organ of Corti, and the lagena itself, extending and curling spirally, gives rise to the cochlea of mammals. Therefore we should regard the papilla basilaris of Amphibia as a specific auditory receptor (Fig. 121). It is especially well developed in anuran Amphibia in which a quite typical membrana tectoria is present on it (it differs only in its attachment to a projection on the opposite wall). In all Amphibia, however, there is in addition a second receptor of similar structure (Fig. 121) with an exactly similar membrana tectoria, the papilla neglecta (amphibiorum). The position of this receptor is extremely distinctive; it lies within a special projection (recessus sacculi) on the septum separating the sacculus from the utriculus, directly on the edge connecting its foramen (foramen utriculosacculare) and immediately behind the descent of the endolymphatic duct.

We are obliged to leave open the controversial question of its homology to the macula neglecta of fishes and amniotes. The position of the fenestra, connecting the sacculi of the labyrinth, makes possible a movement of the macula neglecta from one sacculus to another. There is undoubtedly such a shift in fishes.

If it is believed that this receptor is homologous in the whole vertebrate series then it must be noted that during this time the macula basilaris was characteristic of terrestrial vertebrates only and in secondary aquatic life it is reduced (partially in most Urodela, completely in the psoteids and *Amphiuma*); the macula neglecta on the contrary, is characteristic of aquatic (fishes) and amphibiotic animals. It reaches maximum development in Amphibia and in totally terrestrial animals it is gradually reduced (completely in mammals). The stage of development and position of the macula neglecta is also associated with the gradual development of the endolymphatic duct and the existence of a connection of it with the external medium. In bony fishes the endolymphatic duct is reduced, and with it the macula neglecta is reduced. In Amphibia both the endolymphatic sac and duct system, and the macula neglecta (amphibiorum) reach the maximum level of development. In mammals the sacculus endolymphaticus and also the macula neglecta are reduced. Apparently there is a functional dependence between the endolymphatic duct and the macula neglecta that determines both the position of this receptor and the level of its development.

It seems to me to be a sufficiently well founded conclusion that the macula neglecta is a receptor specially adapted for reception of sound vibrations passed on to the sacculus of the labyrinth through the endolymphatic duct (directly from the external medium in cartilaginous fishes, and through a dermal venous system and the sacculus endolymphaticus in Amphibia).

On the other hand, the papilla basilaris is developed only in terrestrial vertebrates, along with the development of the middle ear as an apparatus for the transmission of aerial sound vibrations and their transformation at the membrane of the fenestra ovalis. This receptor is constructed according to another channel of sound transmission to the inner ear, from the membrane of the fenestra ovalis to the perilymphatic canal, to the cysterna and the duct, and thence to the basilar membrane in the recessus lagenae. With reduction of the middle ear in urodele Amphibia this route was originally used (in Hynobiidae and in larvae) for transmission of sound pressure vibrations in the lateral head vein (subcutaneous receptor veins).

Obviously the existence of two auditory receptors in Amphibia and two paths of sound transmission reflect their utilization of two habitat media, aerial and aquatic, with specific conditions for reception of sound vibrations. Thus in anuran Amphibia there is at the same time a middle ear, as an apparatus for transmission of sound vibrations of the air to the papilla basilaris, and the venous-endolymphatic apparatus, for transmission of sound vibrations in water to the papilla neglecta (amphibiorum).

In urodele Amphibia the middle ear is reduced and the perilymphatic canal is used initially (in Hynobiidae and in larvae) for the transmission of sound vibrations of the water through the venous system of the head. The fundamental apparatus of sound transmission in urodele Amphibia has become the venous-endolymphatic canal which is probably used by them not only in the water, but partly in the air. The latter is accompanied by considerable loss of energy so that urodele Amphibia may not possess as highly developed hearing as the anurans.

Both receptors in Amphibia are supplied with cuticular membrana tectoria; they take the form of convex papillae lying in special protrusions of the labyrinth (recessus). The latter possesses a very thin membrane on the opposite side, separating the process from the perilymphatic duct (Figs. 121 and 122). Equalizing of sonic pressure between the endolymph and perilymph produces vibrations in this membrane. The vibrations are passed on to the tectorial membrane of the auditory papillae. An especially refined analysis of sounds is hardly feasible by this system of reception of sound vibrations. However, the total sonic effect may nevertheless afford perceptible qualitative difference (frequency of dominant sound vibrations and their amplitude).

In our problems the following conclusions are of fundamental significance:

1. The existence of the fenestra ovalis in the wall of the auditory capsule in all Urodela, and also rudiments of the extracolumella, the tympanic cavity, and stapedial muscles in the Hynobiidae, proves that urodele Amphibia originated from forms having a normal apparatus for transmission of aerial sound waves typical of terrestrial vertebrates.

2. The reduction of the middle ear in urodele Amphibia is probably to be accounted for not in terms of a secondary aquatic life, but of a secretive, semi-burrowing way of life. An indirect indication of this is the existence in the Hynobiidae of remnants of the osseous system of sound transmission from the ground in the form of a direct connection of the otic capsule to the quadrate. This system, however, has definitely lost its significance in the life of modern urodele Amphibia.

The route of sound transmission from the ground along the bony pathway is fully realized only in the gymnophiones, as the result of complete ossification and direct contact of the quadrate and strapes.

3. The fairly bulky cartilaginous operculum is not part of any system of sound transmission. It perhaps plays the role of an accommodation apparatus along with the opercular muscles, but it has particular significance as a mechanism shielding the inner ear from sharp concussions during movements of the animal on land.

4. Corresponding to the two habitat media of Amphibia, aerial and aquatic,

there are two types of sound transmission apparatus and two auditory receptors. First, in anuran Amphibia, there is a tympanic-stapedial system of reception of aerial sound vibrations and their transmission to the fenestra ovalis, and also perilymphatic canal sound transmission to the membrane and to the papilla basilaris. This canal sound transmission is utilized only by means of the dermal veins of adult Hynobiidae and of the larvae of Amphibia. Second, in all Amphibia there is a dermal-venous system of reception and transmission of sound vibrations in an aquatic medium, and endolymphatic canal sound transmission to the papilla neglecta (amphiobiorum). This pathway becomes the sole route of sound transmission in adult urodele Amphibia and also in some anurans, in which the former apparatus is reduced (*Bombina* and *Pelobates*).

VI. THE DEVELOPMENT OF THE CHONDROCRANIUM

The development of the chondrocranium of the Caudata has been studied in detail only for its common representatives *Triturus* and *Ambystoma* (Stöhr, 1879; Gaupp, 1906, 1913), and *Necturus* (Platt, 1896a; Winslow, 1898). To some extent the development of *Salamandra* (Stadtmüller, 1924) and *Cryptobranchus* (Aoyama, 1930; Fox, 1954) was also studied. With regard to *Hynobius* there are only the accounts of Edgeworth (1923) and Fox (1959). Only in recent times have detailed researches been conducted on the devel-

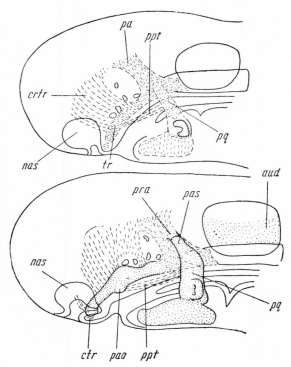

FIG. 124. Two stages in the development of the chondrocranium and mandibular arch in larvae of *Hynobius keyserlingii* 10–11 mm long. In the otic region the ectomesenchyme duct is visible leading to the crista trabeculae. *crtr*, Anlage of crista trabeculae; *ctr*, anlage of cornua trabeculae; *nas*, olfactory sac; *pa*, anlage of pila antotica; *pao*, anlage of antorbital process; *pas*, ascending process of palatoquadrate cartilage; *ppt*, anlage of pterygoid process of palatoquadrate cartilage; *pq*, palatoquadrate cartilage; *pra*, processus antoticus; *tr*, trabecula.

opment of the skull of *Hynobius* and *Ranodon* with very extensive material, including a complete series of successive stages (Regel, 1961, 1962, 1963).

Our description is based mainly on these latter investigations which were conducted under the direction of the author.

The chondrocranium of urodele Amphibia develops in the early stages in a manner generally similar to that of primitive bony fishes. There are combined anlagen of the parachordals and trabeculae in paired mesenchyme condensations running from the notochord forward beneath the base of the forebrain. The chondrification of these anlagen begins anteriorly and leads to the formation of definite trabeculae (Fig. 124). After this, cartilage appears lateral of the anterior end of the notochord giving the anterior parachordals. Thereafter, chondrification continues along the sides of the anterior ends of the parachordals so that the latter grow out to meet the posterior ends of the trabeculae and unite with them. The boundary between the two parts of the floor of the skull is still visible for some time in the form of a transitional region of newer cartilage beside the hypophysis. From the described experimental investigations (Platt, 1896a; Stone, 1926; Hörstadius, 1950; and others) it is known that the anterior parts of the trabeculae are developed from ectomesenchymal ganglion plates. During the later formation of the trabeculae, dorsal ridges (crista trabeculae) grow on them. This evidently occurs from an upward migration of ectomesenchyme cells from the preceding region in the space between the forebrain and the eye (Fig. 124). Thus the lateral walls of the cranium are developed, in which fairly large fenestrae persist at first. Gradually contracting, these fenestrae are transformed into exits for the optic nerve, the retinal artery, the oculomotor nerve, the orbital artery, and the pituitary vein (Fig. 125). Later these are sometimes further subdivided into three to five openings. The anterior parachordals extend backward along the notochord to the anlage of the occipital arch.

Lateral of the otic bulb, in the region of the anlage of the horizontal semicircular canal, the cartilaginous otic capsule (Fig. 125) is initiated, which then expands downward connecting with the basal plate parachordals through several commissures. The anterior and posterior basicapsular commissures are developed first, then the prefacial and basitrabecular commissures. The prefacial commissures are separated from each other by the ganglia of the facial and trigeminal nerves. Between the two basicapsular commissures there persists at first a fairly large basicapsular fenestra which gradually contracts, being transformed into the fenestra ovalis and serving for sound transmission from the columella (stapes) to the inner ear. Between the auditory capsules above a pair of small separate cartilages is initiated which then form commissures between the two capsules, the tectum synoticum.

Posterior of the otic capsules paired occipital arches are initiated on the notochord. The bases of these arches expand along the sides of the notochord, forming the posterior parachordals. In these cartilages, in Hynobiidae, traces of segementation are visible alternating with the muscle segments. In the corresponding three postotic myotomes (the first of which is rudimentary) projections of parachordal cartilages are visible in the myosepta (Fig. 126).

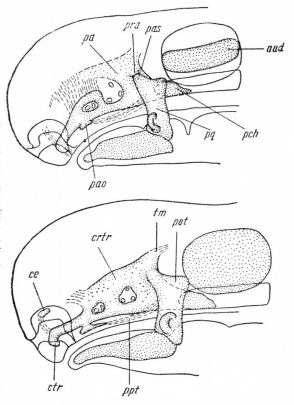

FIG. 125. Two stages in development of the chondrocranium and mandibular arch in larvae of *Hynobius* 11–12 mm long. Showing the chondrified connection of the crista trabeculae; mesenchyme duct, otic capsule, anlage of the ethmoid shaft and lamina antorbitalis, and processus ascendens joined to processus antoticus. *ce*, Anlage of columella ethmoidalis; *pch*, parachordals; *pot*, otic process of palatoquadrate cartilage; *tm*, anlage of taenia marginalis posterior; other abbreviations as in Fig. 124.

The two posterior projections correspond to the bases of the occipital and preoccipital arches. The anterior pair of protrusions lies in front of the first myotome.

The lateral elements of both occipital arches grow upward and join the otic capsule posteriorly, close to the exits of the vagus and glossopharyngeal nerves. Between the occipital and preoccipital arches openings persist for the exit of the occipital nerve. The anterior parachordals grow posteriorly and are fused to the posterior parachordals and the basicapsular commissures, forming the basal plate of the cranium.

The auditory capsule expands on the medial side leaving an opening for the exit of the otic nerve and an entrance for the endolymphatic duct. In the posterior wall of the capsule two openings remain for the perilymphatic canals.

The anterior ends of the trabeculae are curved outward forming the trabecula horns. Posteriorly the trabecula horns fuse to each other and provide a plate underlying the olfactory sacs, the planum internasale, bounded anteriorly by the large basicranial fontanelle of the cranium. The horns of the trabecula expand and thus develop the floor of the olfactory capsule and its lateral walls. Medial of the horns separate ethmoid bars are initiated, the columnae ethmoidales (Fig. 125). These give rise to the anteromedial walls of the capsules. The posterior wall is developed in part from an antorbital process. The precerebral plate is differentiated *in situ*. Sometimes there is a separate chondrification here.

The crest of the trabecula grows dorsally, especially posteriorly, where it passes to a thickening bounding a shaft, the pila antotica (Figs. 125 and 127). The upper end of the latter grows backward and produces a bridge—the taenia marginalis—connecting the anterior part of the skull with the otic capsule. The skull roof develops only posteriorly, into the tectum synoticum (Fig. 128), and anteriorly between the posterior elements of the olfactory capsules. Between the latter the internasal cavity persists anteriorly in which is located the intermaxillary gland. Posteriorly it is bounded by a plate, the planum precerebrale.

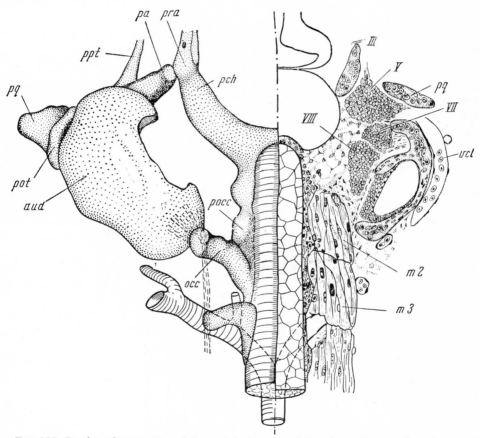

FIG. 126. Combined restoration of the occipital region of *Hynobius* of 13 mm length. Dorsal view; on the right side the occipital region is shown in section. *aud*, Otic capsule; *m2, m3*, occipital myotomes; *occ*, occipital arch; *pa*, ascending process of palatoquadrate cartilage; *pch*, parachordal; *pocc*, base of preoccipital arch; *pot*, otic process of palatoquadrate cartilage; *ppt*, pterygoid process of palatoquadrate cartilage; *pq*, palatoquadrate cartilage; *pra*, processus antoticus; *vcl*, lateral head vein; *III*, occulomotor nerve; *V, VII, VIII*, ganglia of trigeminal, facial, and auditory nerves. From Regel.

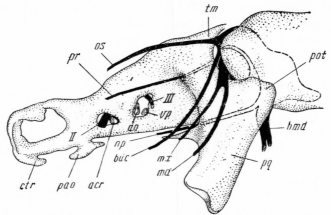

FIG. 127. Graphic reconstruction of the chondrocranium of *Hynobius* about 13 mm long. Lateral view. Variant showing passage of the ophthalmicus profundus nerve through a canal in the processus antoticus; pterygoid process chondrified. *acr*, Central retinal artery; *ao*, orbital artery; *buc*, facial nerve VII; *ctr*, cornua trabeculae; *hmd*, hyomandibular nerve VII; *md, mx*, mandibular and maxillary nerves V; *np*, palatine nerve VII; *os*, ophthalmicus superficialis VII; *pao*, processus antorbitalis; *pot*, otic process of palatoquadrate cartilage; *pq*, palatoquadrate cartilage; *pr*, ophthalmicus profundus nerve V; *tm*, taenia marginalis; *vp*; pituitary vein; *II, III*, nerves. From Regel.

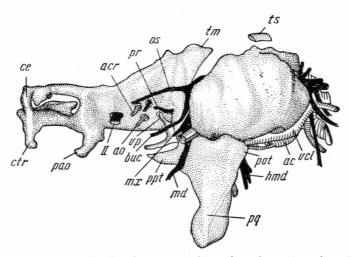

FIG. 128. Reconstruction of the chondrocranium of *Hynobius* about 16 mm long. Lateral view, showing anlage of tectum synoticum, exits of nerves and vessels. *ac*, Internal carotid artery; *acr*, central retinal artery; *ao*, orbital artery; *buc*, facial nerve VII; *ce*, columella ethmoidalis; *ctr*, cornua trabeculae; *hmd*, hyomandibular nerve VII; *md, mx*, mandibular and maxillary nerves V; *os, p*, ophthalmicus superficialis nerve VII; *pao*, processus antorbitalis; *pot*, otic process of palatoquadrate cartilage; *ppt*, pterygoid process of palatoquadrate cartilage; *pq*, palatoquadrate cartilage; *pr*, ophthalmicus profundus nerve V; *tm*, taenia marginalis; *ts*, tectum synoticum; *vcl*, lateral head vein; *vp*, pituitary vein; *II*, nerve. From Regel.

All this is very similar to that observed in primitive bony fishes and is especially similar to the development of the chondrocranium in *Polypterus*. It is obvious that the skull developed in the same way in crossopterygian fishes in which, however, the trabeculae were not fused to the parachordals and taeniae marginales were not developed, so that the orbital part of the skull did not fuse to the otic region and was connected to it by a movable articulation.

Essential changes ensue in Amphibia in connection with the development of the visceral skeleton which assumes new inter-relationships with the brain-case. The palatoquadrate cartilage develops initially as an independent formation in which the posterior part is the most bulky, bearing an articulation to the Meckel's cartilage (Fig. 124). From this part an ascending process (processus ascendens) develops anteriorly and upward, fusing to the pila antotica in the postorbital region. In the Hynobiidae a temporary articulation to a small process develops, the processus antoticus (Fig. 127), at the base of which there is sometimes a canal for n. ophthalmicus profundus passing into the orbit. This is interesting since such an articulation was characteristic of crossopterygian fishes in which a canal of the orbital nerve also sometimes passed into the processus antoticus (Fig. 21).

From the quadrate cartilage a mesenchyme strand develops anteriorly

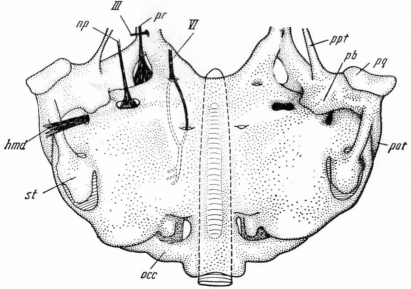

FIG. 129. Reconstruction of the notochordal section of the skull of *Hynobius* about 23 mm long. Ventral view, showing occipital arch: stapes and its connections: nerve exits. *hmd*, Hyomandibular nerve VII; *np*, palatine nerve; *occ*, occipital arch; *pb*, processus basalis of palatoquadrate cartilage; *pot*, processus oticus of palatoquadrate cartilage; *ppt*, pterygoid process of palatoquadrate cartilage; *pt*, ophthalmicus profundus nerve V; *pq*, palatoquadrate cartilage; *st*, stapes; *III, VI*, occulomotor and abducens nerves. From Regel.

connecting to the trabecula in the anterior orbital region. This strand chondrifies at each end, first anteriorly from the trabecula, and then posteriorly from the quadrate cartilage. Thus in the Hynobiidae there develops a continuous processus pterygoideus (Figs. 128 and 129). It persists briefly, however. The posterior part of the pterygoid process is strengthened, and in the anterior region the cartilage is resorbed. At the front end a laterally directed process is formed, the processus antorbitalis (Fig. 125). It is developed at the expense of the anterior end of the pterygoid process, but then enters into the composition of the posterior wall of the olfactory capsule.

At the base of the ascending process on the inner side of the palatoquadrate cartilage a small protrusion (the processus basalis) forms, connecting to a process at the base of the skull in the anterior part of the otic capsule. In the Hynobiidae a genuine articulation is formed here, the basicranial articulation, which is also well developed in adult Hynobiidae. This articulation was also present in both crossopterygian fishes and primitive Stegocephalia. It was also present in the Microsauria. In the Stegocephalia and Microsauria it supplemented the articulation of the dermal bones, the pterygoid and parasphenoid. This connection lost its movability and was replaced by a suture in the higher labyrinthodonts and Nectridia. In the Hynobiidae there is a definite primary connection in the form of a movable basicranial joint (Fig. 129).

Lastly, the upper part of the quadrate cartilage makes contact with the otic capsule by means of a small processus oticus. This is a new acquisition of terrestrial vertebrates, replacing the connection of the hyomandibula, which lost its significance. The processus oticus occupies a somewhat different position in larvae (Fig. 130) and in adult urodele and anuran Amphibia. The chondrified connection is established briefly, and only in late stages of larval growth.

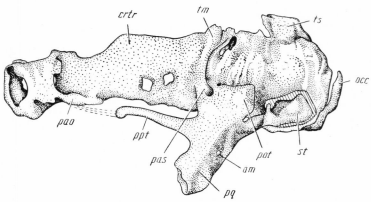

FIG. 130. Reconstruction of left half of skull of *Hynobius* about 26 mm long. Stage of maximum development of cartilage. Lateral view. *am*, Foramen of mandibular artery; *crtr*, crista trabeculae; *occ*, occipital arch; *pae*, processus antorbitalis; *pas*, ascending process of palatoquadrate cartilage; *pot*, otic process of palatoquadrate cartilage; *ppt*, pterygoid process of palatoquadrate; *pq*, palatoquadrate cartilage; *st*, stapes; *tm*, taenia marginalis; *ts*, tectum synoticum. From Regel.

A cartilaginous ligament from the processus oticus to the otic capsule serves as an attachment to the posterior part of the palatoquadrate. This became necessary after reduction of the temporal region of the skull roof, which gave support for the posterior section of the jaw arch in Stegocephalia. During metamorphosis it disappears again and the processus oticus adjoins the otic capsule only by a broad margin. In this case the cartilaginous articulation of the processus oticus replaces the bony articulation with the squamosal, which covers the posterior part of the palatoquadrate, expands over the otic capsule, and reaches to the parietal bones.

We have already given a description of the development of the sound transmission apparatus of the upper division of the hyoid arch. In urodele Amphibia, the lower division of the hyoid proper is very prominently developed in the form of a plate lining the oral cavity. This development is plainly connected with its significance in the pressure mechanism of aerial respiration. The branchial arches are developed in a total of four pairs in their lower divisions only, the ceratobranchials and the hypobranchials. The latter are normally present on two anterior arches and sometimes (as in the Hynobiidae) on a third arch also. This again is very similar to those present in *Polypterus*, in which the upper divisions of the arch were already reduced. Obviously the same was true in crossopterygian fishes also, owing to the gular type of respiration.

VII. THE BONY SKULL

In its composition the bony skull of urodele Amphibia is considerably more simple than the skull of most Stegocephalia. However, in the latter the number of bones in the skull was occasionally reduced markedly. It was the same in the line leading to anuran Amphibia. The same development occurred in lepospondylous forms (e.g., *Scincosaurus*) and partly in the microsaurs also. In the latter such characteristic stegocephalian bones as the tabular have disappeared, but by way of compensation there is a large supratemporal. In the palate a small ectopterygoid was still retained. In the skull roof the parietals, frontals, and nasals take predominant roles. Postparietals were usually present, however. In any case the cranium remained stegocephalian. In urodele Amphibia not only the tabulars but also the supratemporals, postparietals, postorbitals, and the jugals disappeared. In the reduction of all these bones the temporal region of the skull was exposed and covered externally by the maxillary musculature. In the palate the ectopterygoids disappeared and in the lower jaw only the dentary, angular, prearticular, and splenial were retained.

Study of the embryonic development of bones by the usual methods, up to the present, has not suggested the existence of any accessory anlagen. However, a modified method of *in vivo* alizarin staining made it possible to find several bones besides the usual ones (Lebedkina).

In *Hynobius* and *Ranodon* the earliest to be initiated are the premaxillae and the main bones of the skull roof, the frontals and the parietals. The frontal

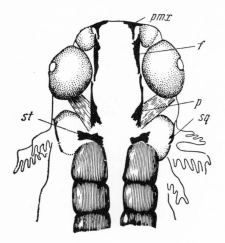

FIG. 131. Larva of *Ranodon sibiricus* 26 mm long. *In vivo* staining with alizarin, showing anlagen of skull roof bones. *f*, Frontal; *p*, parietal; *pmx*, premaxillary; *sq*, squamosal; *st*, supratemporal (+ postparietal?). From Lebedkina.

in *Ranodon* shows traces of complex origin of from three to four components. Immediately after these bones there is initiated posterior of them, in the rear portion of the otic region, a pair of transversely oriented bones to which a dorsal muscle is attached (Fig. 131). According to the position of the anlage directly behind the parietals they are comparable to postparietals. However, later on they expand laterally toward the squamosal and cover a major portion of the otic capsule, occupying a position characteristic of the supratemporals. Later they are fused to the parietals, forming a lateral ridge on their posterior part. This correlation is readily shown sometimes in the later stages also, when these bones may occasionally retain their distinctness for a long time (sometimes until metamorphosis, Fig. 133). In consideration of all this, it seems to me more likely that these bones represent supratemporals to which postparietals have perhaps fused.

Following these anlagen the nasals appear (Fig. 132). In both *Ranodon* and in *Hynobius* the nasal is developed from two anlagen, a medial one located medial of the ascending process of the premaxillary bone, and a lateral one lying outside it. At first the medial anlage is no smaller than the lateral

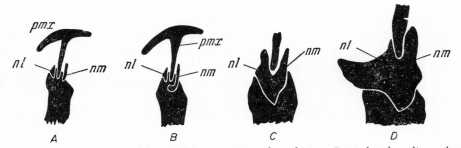

FIG. 132. Development of the nasal bones in *Ranodon sibiricus*. Lateral and median anlagen in larva 39 mm long (*A*); both anlagen in larva 42 mm long (*B*); union of anlagen in larva 84 mm long (*C*); gradual expansion of lateral portion in larva 101 mm long (*D*); *nl*, Lateral anlage; *nm*, median anlage; *pmx*, premaxilla and its ascending process. From Lebedkina.

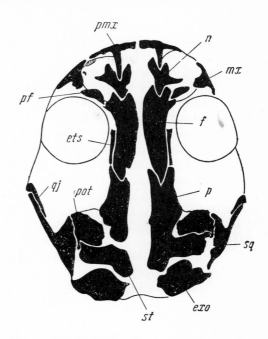

FIG. 133. Larva of *Ranodon* 93 mm long (variant). Skull roof bones; *in vivo* staining with alizarin; *ets*, Ethmosphenoid; *exo*, exoccipital; *f*, frontal; *mx*, maxilla; *n*, nasal; *p*, parietal; *pf*, prefrontal; *pmx*, premaxilla; *pot*, prootic; *qj*, quadratojugal; *sq*, squamosal; *st*, supratemporal (+ postparietal?). From Lebedkina.

one but is sometimes even longer. Later, the lateral anlage is more prominently developed. The two anlagen are fused to each other behind the ascending process of the premaxillary bone. The lateral portion develops considerably further and constitutes a large part of the nasal bone of the adult animal. In some anomalous forms the fusion sets in at later stages, or sometimes the medial bone fuses not to the lateral process, but to the ascending process of the premaxilla. It is possible that the medial anlage is homologous to the rostral element of crossopterygians, ichthyostegids, and *Megalocephalus*.

The last to be initiated is the maxilla (Fig. 133) and, in the skull roof, the prefrontal, lachrymal, and narial (septomaxilla). In the palate region the earliest to appear are solitary anlagen (1 to 2) of the vomerine and palatine teeth, and then at their bases dermal plates develop which are anlagen of the vomer and palatine bones. Medial of these anlagen primordia of succeeding teeth appear. The posterior end of the palatine bone is protracted into a process growing backward. Between it and the quadrate cartilage, in *Ranodon*, a separate anlage of the pterygoid appears which grows forward and is joined to the palatine bone. The pterygoid is sometimes laid down in the form of two primordia. Also, separate anlagen of the palatine and pterygoid are present in *Hynobius* and in *Pleurodeles;* however, merging occurs very quickly, and the distinctness of the anlagen is made out only with difficulty. Before metamorphosis the palatine portion of the pterygopalatine is reduced, the teeth fall out, and the bone is then resorbed. The pterygoid thereafter expands in breadth and shifts its position.

The development of the parasphenoid is most interesting. In all forms studied (*Ranodon, Hynobius, Ambystoma,* and *Pleurodeles*) it is initiated as two distinct ossifications. The anterior anlage appears very early in front of the hypophysis; following this, the posterior anlage arises at the anterior end of the notochord. The anterior anlage may be paired (as in *Ranodon* and sometimes in *Hynobius*) or unpaired (frequently in *Hynobius*, *Ambystoma*, and *Pleurodeles*). Later on a process grows backward from the anterior anlage, lateral to the hypophysis, to join with the posterior anlage. The development of the parasphenoid from three centers was recently established in reptiles and other amniotes. Jarvik (1954) stated the hypothesis that only the anterior anlage is homologous to the parasphenoid of crossopterygian fishes, which underlies the anterior division of the skull (ethmosphenoid). The posterior anlage of the parasphenoid is homologous (according to Jarvik) with the paired dental plates which underlie the otic region of the skull in crossopterygian fishes (*Eusthenopteron*). At the posterior end of the parasphenoid in crossopterygians there is an ascending process. In the larvae of urodele Amphibia the same ascending process is also developed in the rear portion of the anterior division of the parasphenoid. In addition, in the anterior part of the posterior division, a posterior ascending process also develops. Between the two ascending processes in the braincase the internal carotid artery passes and thus marks the boundary between the anterior (sphenethmoid) division of the skull and the posterior division (otico-occipital). The anterior ascending process extends to the basitrabecular process and partially underlies it. In this a remnant of the connection to the anterior division of the skull, on which this process lies in crossopterygian fishes, is manifested. The posterior ascending process underlies the anterior part of the otic capsule. This corresponds to Jarvik's hypothesis on the origin of the posterior portion of the parasphenoid from the infraotic dental plates of *Eusthenopteron*. At the time of metamorphosis the above processes are gradually smoothed over.

Thus, in the development of the parasphenoid in urodele Amphibia there were retained traces of the origin from the skull of crossopterygian fishes with its characteristic subdivision into two divisions. Let us recall that in the ichthyostegids also a suture was retained between the two divisions, and the parasphenoid underlies only the anterior division [another remnant of the division of the skull roof is, as we have said, the cleft between the parietal shield and the cheek region (squamosal) in the anthracosaurs].

In the lower jaw of the Hynobiidae the common dermal bones of the urodele Amphibia, dentary, splenial, angular, and large prearticular, are developed. The last is initiated from two portions. The significance of the upper anlage is uncertain so far.

The skull of adult *Ranodon* (Fig. 134), and also of *Hynobius*, is distinguished from the skulls of other urodele Amphibia only by the presence of separate lachrymal bones, which in other forms are obviously fused to the prefrontal bones.

In the skull roof, as in other Caudata, the parietal, frontal, and nasal bones are of dominant significance. The same is observed in the microsaurs and *Dendrerpeton*. The ascending process of the premaxillary bone lies on the surface of the nasal bone, the nasal bones adjoin by their rear edges to the frontal bones, and the latter adjoin the parietal bones farther on.

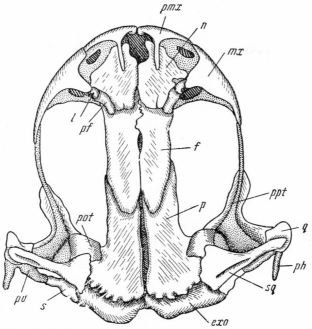

FIG. 134. Skull roof of adult *Ranodon* about 200 mm long; *exo*, Exoccipital; *f*, frontal; *l*, lachrymal; *mx*, maxilla; *n*, nasal; *p*, parietal; *pf*, prefrontal; *ph*, hyoid process; *pmx*, premaxilla; *pot*, prootic; *ppt*, pterygoid process of palatoquadrate cartilage; *pv*, processus ventralis stapedes; *q*, quadrate; *s*, stapes; *sq*, squamosal. From Lebedkina.

In comparison with the skull roof of the microsaurs, an expansion of the whole skull occurred in modern urodele Amphibia and there was a considerable increase in the size of the orbits, which shifting backward contacted the postorbital bones (postfrontal and postorbital), that does not occur in modern Amphibia.

In other respects simplification of the skull roof took place at the expense of reduction of the postparietal and supratemporal bones and their fusion to the parietal bones. This fusion can still be traced in the larvae of Hynobiidae and some other Caudata. The quadratojugal lies beneath the squamosal at the surface of the quadrate. This upgrowth of the quadratojugal under the squamosal has already been noted in the microsaurs.

The floor of the cranium and palatal region are also simplified by further development of the interpterygoid fenestra, again with increase of size and in adaptation to the shifting of the eyes.

The skull of adult *Ranodon* (Fig. 135) does not differ in this respect from other urodele Amphibia. The broad parasphenoid underlies almost the whole braincase. In front of it lies only the large vomer with the intervomerine cleft for the intermaxillary glands. The palatine bones are absent in adult Caudata (they are fused to the pterygoids and are reduced at metamorphosis).

The palate is simplified in comparison with the microsaurs owing to the reduction of the palatine and the transversa (ectopterygoid), which was de-

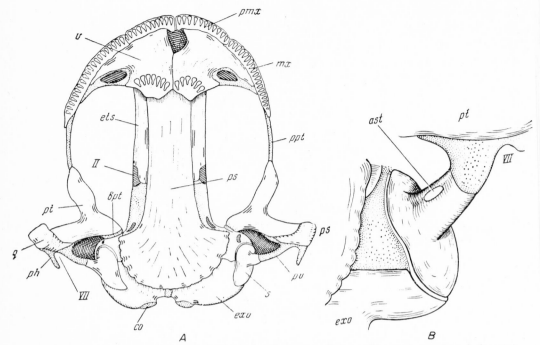

FIG. 135. Skull of adult *Ranodon* 220 mm long, from below (A) and stapes from below (B) variant. *ast*, Canal of orbital artery; *bpt*, basipterygoid articulation; *co*, occipital condyle; *ets*, ethmosphenoid; *ps*, parasphenoid; *pt*, pterygoid; *s*, stapes; *v*, vomer; *VII*, notch for hyomandibular nerve; *II*, foramen for optic nerve; other abbreviations as in Fig. 134. From Lebedkina.

termined by the increase of the interpterygoid fenestra. The reduction of the transversa was noted above in microsaurs and also in *Dendrerpeton.*

From a posterior view of the occipital region of the skull, the similarity of the Hynobiidae (and of *Ranodon* in particular) to some Stegocephalia and especially to the microsaurs is especially clear.

In Fig. 136 the skulls of *Ranodon* and *Dvinosaurus* are compared. In Fig. 137 the skull of the microsaur *Cardiocephalus* is shown in the same view. The position of the stapes posteriorly is especially similar. In the microsaurs the stapes lay in a very broad plate in the fenestra ovalis and was supported on the quadrate bone by a short columella. It was similarly situated in *Ranodon* in which, however, there is still a cartilaginous part of the columella (processus ventralis) adjoining the quadrate bone. In *Cardiocephalus* there is a large fenestra in the ossified otic capsule under the fenestra ovalis which was perhaps occupied by the cartilage of the operculum, as in modern Amphibia.

The similarity in structure of the otic region in Hynobiidae and *Dvinosaurus* is very interesting. An ossified stapes was present as a small dorsal process, and was obviously prolonged distally into a cartilaginous shaft (Bystrov, 1938, figures it in form of a ligament) running along the quadrate to the hyoid process. In the bony skeleton this shaft (processus ventralis stapedis) matches the cleft between the squamosal and the pterygoid. In place of a processus hyoideus there is an uneven surface marking the position of a cartilaginous extension. A similar structure was apparently present in the otic region of *Dendrerpeton,* as shown by a sharply defined depression

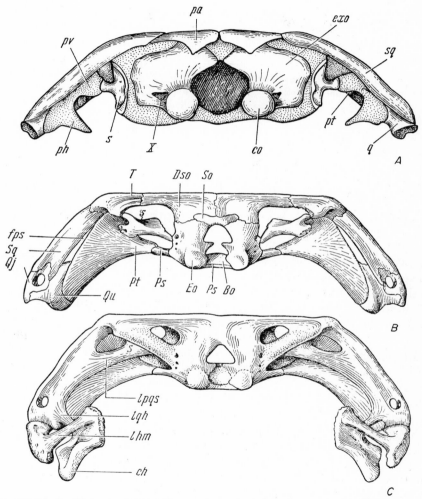

FIG. 136. Skull of *Ranodon* 145 mm long, posterior (A); from Lebedkina. Skull of *Dvinosaurus,* posterior (B); from Bystrov. The same with ligaments restored (C). *Bo,* Basioccipital; *ch,* hyoid; *co,* occipital condyle; *Dso,* postparietal bone; *exo, Eo,* exoccipital; *fps,* cleft between pterygoid and squamosal bones; *lhm,* ligamentum hyomandibulare; *lpqs,* ventral process of columella; *lqh,* hyoquadrate ligament; *pa,* parietal bone; *ph, pv,* processus hyoideus and processus ventralis stapedis; *Ps,* parasphenoid; *pt,* pterygoid; *Qj,* quadratojugal bone; *Qu, q,* quadrate; *s,* stapes; *so,* supraoccipital; *Sq,* squamosal; *T,* tabular; *X,* nerve.

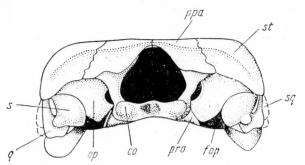

FIG. 137. Skull of *Cardiocephalus*, posterior view; *co*, Occipital condyle; *fop*, fenestra of the operculum?; *op*, opisthotic; *ppa*, postparietal bones; *pro*, pro-otic; *q*, quadrate; *s*, stapes; *sq*, squamosal; *st*, supratemporal. From J. P. Gregory *et al*.

lying above the quadrate on the edge of the squamosal along its boundary with the pterygoid, i.e., in the position of the cartilaginous shaft of the larvae of Hynobiidae. The cranium of *Cardiocephalus*, according to the position and associations of the auditory ossicle, is especially similar to modern gymnophiones (Apoda).

VIII. DEVELOPMENT OF THE VERTEBRAL COLUMN

The development of the vertebral column in the Hynobiidae begins with the appearance of rudiments of the neural arch in the form of accumulations of mesenchyme cells below the myosepta directly in front of the intersegmental vessels. Consequently the arches are initiated, as in other vertebrates, in the hindmost part of the primordial mesodermal segment. In these aggregations cartilage is soon differentiated. The cartilaginous arches are located directly on the notochordal sheath. Simultaneous with the development of the cartilage arches, the concentrations of mesenchyme corresponding to each mesodermal segment begin to form lateral to the notochord. These concentrations are especially clear in *Ranodon*, being of larger size and having a much greater number of cells in all the anlagen. The bilateral character of the anlage is clearly visible (Fig. 138).

The concentrations of skeletogenous blastema are most clearly developed on the ventrolateral surface of the notochord, where the nuclei are arranged in two or three rows. They are arranged in two rows dorsolaterally, in one row ventrally, and dorsally there is only one row of scattered cells. In the region of the myosepta the dorsolateral part of the perichordal layer is united to the base of the neural arch. The perichordal layer thickens and expands around the notochord; dorsally, however, it remains more compressed, and ventrally it is looser. In the layer adjoining the envelope of the notochord the nuclei are strongly flattened out. In the more superficial layers they take on oval shape, arranged transversely to the long axis of the notochord. In the middle part of the segment the cells are greatly elongated (especially in the surface layer) and acquire a rodlike form, enclosing the notochord.

These segmental concentrations of skeletogenous blastema on the noto-chord surface are, incidentally, the foundation for the later development of the intervertebral cartilages. In the perichordal condensations, however, almost all the skeletogenous blastema of the vertebrae have been concentrated They occupy the whole mesodermal segment area and are not interrupted between the segments. It would not be erroneous to say that in the perichordal condensations of mesenchyme, organically related with the bases of the arches, we have the anlage of the centra of the vertebrae (including the inter-vertebral cartilage which has no distinctive significance in urodele Amphibia). There is no doubt that these perichordal primordia are homologous with the perichordal cartilage or the primary centra of the vertebrae of reptiles. They are not only alike in origin but also in structure. We shall call them peri-chordal condensations, perichordal blastemas, and perichordal cartilages. The perichordal condensations pass first, at the hatching stage, into a later phase of tissue differentiation; they give rise to the protochondral net of basic material, and simultaneously features of surface ossification appear. In both cases the organizing role of the cartilage of the neural (and hemal) arches is clearly manifested.

The first indications of differentiation are manifested in the appearance of fine filamentous structures under the edge of the base of the neural arch in the region of its transition into the perichordal blastema. They are colored azure blue in Mallory stain and are clearly distinguished only in large numbers.

These processes of differentiation proceed very rapidly so that among larvae at the hatching stage, identical with those in which no intercellular structure is noted, larvae of a certain size and external appearance occur in which there are already unmistakable anlagen of the ossified vertebral centra. In the anlage of the latter the nature of the fibrous structures (above) is changed; they are flattened, more deeply colored and have a more definite orientation, lying in a thin sheet. Above all they are easily observed on the

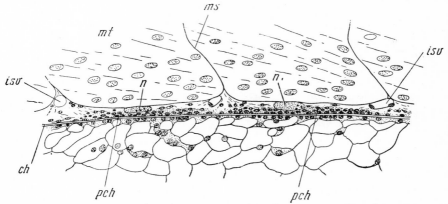

FIG. 138. Frontal section through a larva of *Ranodon sibiricus* 22 mm long showing segmental condensation of skeletogenous mesenchyme on lateral surface of the notochord. *ch*, Notochordal sheath; *isv*, intersegmental vessel; *ms*, myosepta; *mt*, myotome; *n*, spinal chord; *pch*, peri-chordal blastema.

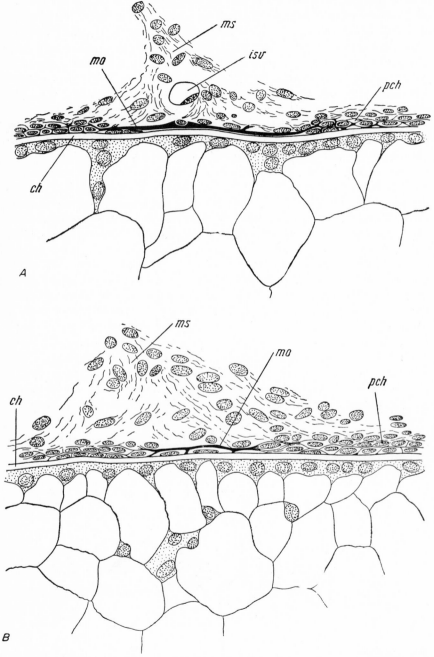

FIG. 139. Frontal section through a rudiment of a centrum of a larva of *Ranodon* 23 mm long, directly below the base of the neural arch (A), and in the lower part of the notochord (B). *ch*, Notochordal sheath; *isv*, intersegmental vessel; *mo*, osteoid membrane of centrum; *ms*, myosepta; *pch*, perichordal blastema.

posterior, and partly on the anterior, edge of the hemal arch, since here a layer of perichordal blastema appears in which the forming plate lies. Closer to the middle this plate lies directly on the notochord (Fig. 139). Originating as a not yet ossified homogenous layer it serves, however, as a base for the development of the bony centrum of the vertebrae. Following the appearance of the dorsal bone anlagen, ventral centers of ossification also appear. Obviously they correspond to anlagen of the bony hypocentrae. In the caudal region they lie at the base of the hemal arch. Bone formation follows this with surprising speed over the whole length of the vertebral column; it is delayed a little only in the development of the bony centra in the caudal region (Fig. 140). On the other hand, the anlage of the cartilaginous arch runs in a craniocaudal sequence starting in the anterior part of the trunk and only passes into the caudal region after some delay. Therefore in the caudal region, where the development of both the neural and especially the hemal arches is much delayed, the connection between the process of chondrification of the arches themselves and the differentiation of the perichordal blastema is clearly evident.

In the caudal region the continuous transition of the new cartilage of the neural arch into the perichordal layer, which also develops in the arch region, i.e., intersegmentally (in the myosepta) although only one rank of cells constitute it here, is readily visible. Likewise, the perichordal sheath passes

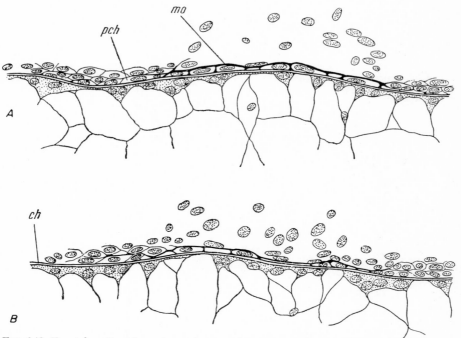

FIG. 140. Frontal section through a rudiment of a centrum of a larva of *Hynobius keyserlingii* 20 mm long, in the caudal region. Beneath the base of the neural arch (A); on a plane at the middle of the notochord (B). Abbreviations as in Fig. 139.

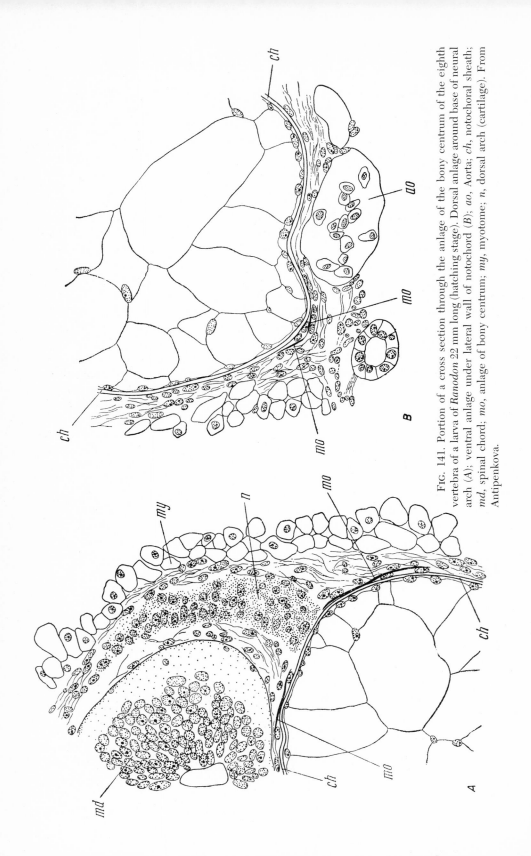

FIG. 141. Portion of a cross section through the anlage of the bony centrum of the eighth vertebra of a larva of *Ranodon* 22 mm long (hatching stage). Dorsal anlage around base of neural arch (A); ventral anlage under lateral wall of notochord (B); *ao*, Aorta; *ch*, notochoral sheath; *md*, spinal chord; *mo*, anlage of bony centrum; *my*, myotome; *n*, dorsal arch (cartilage). From Antipenkova.

without any interruption into the protochondral primordia of the hemal arch. All these formations comprise a single unit. They also comprise a single unit in tissue differentiation. In comparison with reptiles one may clearly speak of the formation of primary centra of vertebrae in the caudal region. These centra are connected intervertebrally, as in reptiles, and in *Hynobius* they form a distinct continuous perichordal cylinder (Fig. 140).

The first indications of ossifications appear, as described above, at the bases of the neural arches in the form of a homogeneous layer on the surface of the perichordal blastema (Fig. 141). This layer rapidly spreads from the base of the arch, both in a dorsal direction over the upper wall of the noto-cord, and in a ventral direction. Expanding below, it joins the ventral ossified hypocentra and soon encloses the notochord, first by a lateral half-ring (Fig. 142), and then is converted into a complete ring around the notochord dorsally and ventrally. Thereafter in the center of the neural arch yet another peri-chordal and quite distinct ossification (Fig. 142C) develops which later fuses to the centrum of the vertebra. The separate ossification of the neural arch obviously reiterates their separation into the adelospondylous vertebrae of the microsaurs.

The above discussion indicates that tissue differentiation leading to the anlagen of the vertebral centra begins from the base of the neural arch in the form of the appearance of fibrous intercellular structures at first, followed by a homogeneous layer organically connected to the cartilage of the neural arch. The primordia of the vertebral centra thus develop in the form of mem-branes differentiated from the base of the arch on the surface of the peri-chordal blastema (in the posterior half of the caudal region) or directly on the surface of the notochord (in the trunk and the anterior part of the tail). Following this a ventral ossification occurs on the surface of the notochord, which in the caudal region is associated with the base of the hemal arch. The perichondral ossification of the neural and hemal arches is inseparably linked to the primordia of the vertebral centra from the very start. Bone formation is a uniform process here, ranging around the notochord on the one hand, and over the cartilage of the neural and hemal arches on the other hand.

On the surface of the notochord lie extremely flattened cells in the form of a thin perichordal syncytium, not only intersegmentally, but also in the future intervertebral regions. These cells frequently fall under the developing bone membrane, usually staying above it. In any case, after the appearance of the bone membrane, a layer of extremely flat cells which are difficult to find—only rarely occurring as a very protracted (in section) nuclei in a sag-ittal section—are to be found on its surface. In tangential section, however, they form an almost continuous layer of cells with large, circular, weakly staining nuclei (since they actually are only disks). Evidently the flat cells on the surface of the bone membrane are osteoblasts.

The developing ossification originally did not penetrate the space between the base of the arch and the sheath of the notochord (Fig. 143). The cartilag-inous arches, as in the early stages of development, are located directly on the sheath of the notochord. Ossification begins to penetrate gradually under the bases of the arches, extending deeper and deeper and completely sepa-

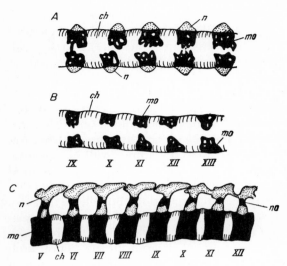

FIG. 142. Paired anlagen of bony centra in a larva of *Ranodon* 27 mm long; whole preparation after *in vivo* staining with alizarin; cartilage of neural arches indicated by dots. Dorsal view of vertebrae IX to XII (*A*); the same, ventral view. (*B*) Larva of *Ranodon* 30 mm long, similar preparation; lateral view of vertebrae V to XII; showing independent perichondral ossification of the middle parts of the neural arches. *ch*, Notochord; *n*, neural arches; *mo*, bone rudiments of centra; *no*, ossified neural arches. From Lebedkina.

rating the cartilaginous arch from the sheath of the notochord by a thin layer of bone. This process, occurring rather slowly in *Ranodon*, is accomplished even in the early stages of ossification of the vertebrae in *Hynobius* (and probably in most other Urodela).

While the first phase of the origin of the bony vertebral centrum, in the form of narrow intersegmental rings, is clearly related to the organization of the neural arches and hypocentra (also connected with the hemal arches in the tail), the second phase of development of the centra is characterized by the formation of a definite perichordal blastema. While in the first place a thin membrane originates in the form of a thin ring enveloping the notochord only in the region of attachment of the hyosepta, in the second phase this ring

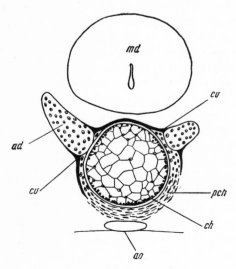

FIG. 143. Cross section through posterior margin of second vertebra of a larva of *Ranodon* 25 mm long (orientation not precise). *ad*, Neural arch; *ao*, aorta; *ch*, notochord; *cv*, edge of centrum; *md*, spinal chord; *pch*, perichordal sheath.

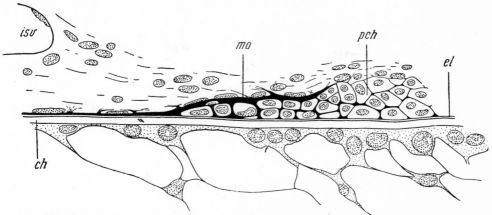

FIG. 144. Frontal section through rudiment of centrum of a larva of *Ranodon* 24 mm long showing development of posterior portion of centrum at the surface of the perichordal sheath (protochondria). *ch*, Fibrous sheath of notochord; *el*, elastic sheath; *isv*, intersegmental vessel; *mo*, osteoid membrane; *pch*, perichordal sheath (protochondria).

first becomes thicker anteriorly (in the posterior half of the preceding segment) and posteriorly (in the anterior half of the succeeding segment) (Fig. 144). These elements of the centra lie on a thicker layer of perichordal tissue and are therefore raised above the notochordal surface, forming an expansion of the ends of the vertebral centra. Bone formation occurs on the surface of the perichordal blastema in close association with its protochondral net. The osteoid layer is differentiated on the superficial membrane of protochondral alveoli (Fig. 140). Later on, however, growth in thickness occurs exteriorly as a result of the activity of the superficial layer of osteoblasts, and osseous tissue is later clearly distinguished in its staining and structure. In Fig. 144 the start of the inclusion of cells within the bony layer is visible at high magnification. The beginning of the predominance of the protochondral net of perichordal tissue in the more prominent lamination of the basic substance is also visible. Later on coarsely alveolar, but nonetheless genuine, hyaline cartilage develops here (Fig. 145). In the region between succeeding vertebral centra the cells, being elongated at right angles to the long axis of the notochord, take a rodlike shape, and the new cartilage acquires a seemingly fibrous character.

The perichordal blastema passes into an annular cartilaginous formation which is usually called intervertebral cartilage. However, it could with equal justification have been called vertebral cartilage since (to a small degree) it underlies the anterior and posterior thirds of the vertebral centra. In some cases it expands under the middle section of the centrum of the vertebra (*Cryptobranchus*); in any case it forms a continuous layer under the vertebral centra in the posterior part of the caudal region.

The perichordal cartilage is principally the foundation on which the centra of the vertebrae are perichondrally developed, to a lesser degree in the an-

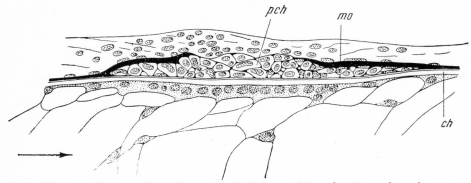

FIG. 145. Frontal section through notochord of a larva of *Ranodon* 24 mm long showing start of chondrification of perichordal blastema and bone formation of anterior and posterior parts of adjacent vertebrae on their surfaces. *ch*, Fibrous sheath of notochord; *el*, elastic sheath; *isv*, intersegmental vessel; *mo*, osteoid membrane; *pch*, perichordal sheath (protochondria).

terior and posterior thirds of the centra (Fig. 145). In the middle section of the cartilage between the successive centra a microcellular zone of newer tissue is differentiated, plainly serving as the growth zone, at the expense of which elongation of both the individual vertebrae and the vertebral column as a whole occurs. Just after metamorphosis the articulation is differentiated in the perichordal cartilage. Thus we come to the inevitable conclusion that the perichordal cartilage of urodele Amphibia is the basis for the formation of vertebral centra (by perichondral ossification) which also are perichordal cartilage, as it is for the primary centra of reptile vertebrae. The only difference is that this cartilage is interrupted intersegmentally, i.e., in the middle of the centrum, in urodele Amphibia.

We suggest that this interruption is the result of a secondary reduction (in the posterior section of the tail in *Hynobius* the original continuity is still retained). In each segment, in the posterior third of the centrum of the preceding vertebra and the anterior third (of the centrum) of the succeeding vertebrae, this cartilage is developed (Fig. 145). The middle section of the centrum of each vertebra is developed earlier intersegmentally, and is initiated in organic association with the bases of the neural arches (Figs. 139 and 140) directly on the surface of the notochord, and also ventrally, enveloping the notochord from below (the hypocentra). In the caudal region the latter ossification is associated with the hemal arches.

However, in the caudal region in which a thicker perichordal layer of skeletogenous blastema is developed (especially ventrally), the middle section of the vertebral centrum is developed not on the sheath of the notochord but on that of the blastema (Fig. 140). In the anterior part of the caudal region it is retained only ventrally and sometimes forms a real hypochordal cartilage, continuously linked with the cartilaginous hemal arches. The ossified vertebral centra are here clearly linked to the bases of the hemal arches. Thus ventrally, between the arches, the bony layer lies not on the notochordal sheath, but on this hypochordal cartilage.

A. The Perichordal Cartilage and the Problem of Its Origin

Of the facts which have been presented concerning ontogenetic development, the following are of great significance (Schmalhausen, 1957c).

1. The perichordal cartilage is formed from paired segmental anlagen of
skeletogenous material. This supports the belief that in its construction,
material of the paired skeletal formations connected to the notochord (i.e.,
the arches of the spinal column) are utilized.

2. The perichordal cartilage is the foundation for the development of the
vertebral centra, which to a considerable extent are formed on it as the result
of perichondral ossification (Fig. 145). In this a similarity to the development
of the centrum in reptiles, and also in anuran Amphibia, is manifested. At any
rate it does not contradict the hypothesis of the origin of the perichordal
cartilage at the expense of the vertebral arches.

3. The perichordal cartilage connects sections belonging to different
vertebrae. Evidently this connection is the result of secondary (purely pro-
visional) merging of adjacent elements of the skeleton which occurs in anuran
Amphibia and in reptiles (also only in ontogenesis).

4. Since in the Stegocephalia the hypocentra come first in the original
organization of the centra, and other elements, the pleurocentra, are inserted
later, it may be presumed that in lepospondylous Amphibia the centra were
developed from the same elements which in this case fused together early.

Therefore we may conclude with some certainty that the perichordal
cartilage of urodele Amphibia results from the merging of the cartilaginous
bases of the main elements of the vertebral column of the Stegocephalia, i.e.,
the hypocentra and pleurocentra. Further evidence may be advanced in favor
of this conclusion. The ancestors of modern urodele Amphibia were, notwithstanding their close biological association with water, terrestrial animals. We
have no grounds to presume that modern forms arose from secondarily aquatic
forms. In terrestrial vertebrates, more or less perfect articulation developed
between the centra. This articulation is always established midway in the
muscular segments, i.e., between the points of attachment of the myosepta.
Such an attachment favors maximum utilization of the musculature in the
flexing of the vertebral column. In the dual centra of embolomerous labyrinthodonts the main articulation is always developed between the anterior
centrum (pleurocentrum) and posterior centrum (hypocentrum) of the same
mesodermal segment. Conversely, the neighboring centra of different mesodermal segments are joined to each other more firmly in the vicinity of the
myosepta. In the embolomerous Stegocephalia the strengthening of these
connections was favored by the formation of sutures at the bases of the neural
arches which were wedged between the centra of the various segments
(Fig. 50). Thus the two centra belonging to different mesodermal segments
were firmly connected to each other, and formed one functional whole in the
middle of which the myosepta were attached and to which the ribs were
attached. Later, in the evolution of the vertebral column the firmness of the

vertebrae is enhanced by formation of the single integral vertebral centrum. In some rhachitomous labyrinthodonts it originated as the result of predominant development of the anterior section of the vertebra (the hypocentrum) and the suppression of the posterior section (the pleurocentrum), the significance of which has been reduced to the level of small intervertebral bodies (Fig. 146).

In some reptiles the same increase in solidity was attained as the result of the reverse process, predominant development of the posterior section of the embolomerous vertebra, i.e., the pleurocentra, and the suppression of the anterior section, i.e., the hypocentra which originally were still retained in the form of small wedges between the ventral sections of the centra (Fig. 146) and then eliminated altogether so that the lower hemal arches are freely articulated between neighboring centra in reptiles.

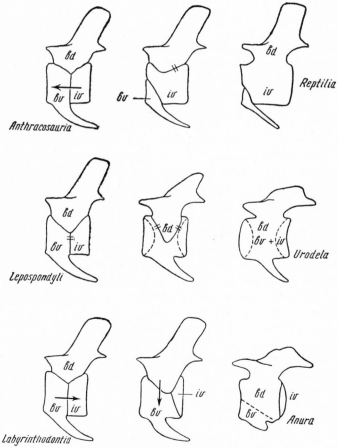

FIG. 146. Diagrams showing the origin of centra in a series of reptilomorphs, lepospondylous amphibians, and labyrinthodont and anuran amphibians. *bd*, Base of neural arch; *bv*, hypocentra; *iv*, pleurocentra.

Notwithstanding these differences in the mode of evolution, in different branches of terrestrial vertebrates the same intervertebral articulation—between the pleurocentrum of the preceding vertebra and the hypocentrum of the succeeding vertebra—was always retained. Only a secondary departure from this is possible, through a specially reduced pleurocentrum (intervertebral body) capable of fusion not only with the preceding vertebra, but sometimes with the succeeding one, with which it has a common origin. This occurred in some anuran Amphibia in which, incidentally, the centrum itself was transformed by secondary expansion of the dorsal elements and the suppression of the ventral elements (Fig. 146).

In all primitive terrestrial vertebrates the intervertebral articulation lay within the mesodermal segment, i.e., between the pleurocentra of the preceding vertebra and the hypocentra of the succeeding one. This necessarily follows from the functional correlation between the elements of the skeleton and the muscle segments. Therefore we have no grounds to suppose that in the ancestors of lepospondylous Amphibia this could have been otherwise. One cannot presume that the position of the articulation has been altered. The latter would be impossible if only because in the ancestors of lepospondylous Amphibia whole centra appeared very early.

A natural conclusion from the above discussion is the recognition that the articulation, developing in the perichordal cartilage in urodele Amphibia, occupies its original position between the pleurocentra of the preceding vertebra and the hypocentra of the posterior one. In this case the perichordal cartilage is not a separate element of the vertebral column, but is the result of a secondary embryonic merging of two elements, the pleurocentra of the preceding vertebra and the hypocentra of the succeeding one. Such a merging is not peculiar to urodele Amphibia. It is seen also in anuran Amphibia and in reptiles. The boundary between the elements of the two adjacent vertebrae is always distinguished by its structure; in both urodele Amphibia and in reptiles it is marked by a zone of rod-shaped cells, clearly indicating the location of the future articulation.

From the historical priority of the intervertebral articulation we may assert with complete confidence that the perichordal cartilage of urodele Amphibia was formed from the cartilaginous precursor of the pleurocentra anteriorly and of the hypocentra posteriorly.

Indisputably, formation of true centra originated much earlier, in the ancestors of lepospondylous Amphibia (Fig. 65). We have no evidence to suggest that the formation of the true centra in this case preceded the preliminary phase of the suppression of one element by another. If the true centrum was formed by early fusion of its elements, then there is no basis for such suppression in the ontogenesis of later forms. Highly perfected for its time, the spinal column of lepospondylous Stegocephalia, so it seems to me, could readily have been derived from the embolomerous type. In such a case it may be presumed that in the construction of the "primordial" centrum, i.e., of the perichordal cartilage of urodele Amphibia, approximately equal portions of the cartilaginous basis of both the hypocentra and pleurocentra participated.

B. The Problem of the Origin of the Centra of
   Urodele Amphibia

The formation of the bony centrum in ontogenesis in the form of a complete osseous cylinder is not proof of its origin from only one element. In bony fishes the centrum likewise develops first in the form of bony cylinders around the notochord although their origin from separate sections is proved in many instances by paleontological evidence and is sometimes supported by facts of ontogenetic development also (the merging of half-vertebrae in *Amia calva*; Schauinsland, 1906).

In fishes, as in lower terrestrial vertebrates, the centra are not developed only as independent formations surrounding the notochord. Ossification of the centrum is always associated with ossification of the arch bases (Fig. 141). An osseous membrane extends around the notochord (Fig. 142) starting at the base of the arch and, in fishes as in lower terrestrial vertebrates including the urodele Amphibia, it surrounds the bases of the arches. The osseous membrane was not originally present beneath the bases of the arches (Fig. 143). The latter, are located directly on the notochord. Only later does ossification penetrate under the bases of the arches, between them and the sheath of the notochord. Dorsal and ventral ossifications obviously corresponding to the basidorsals and the basiventrals (i.e., the hypocentra) fuse to each other and form paired half-rings enveloping the notochord laterally (Fig. 142). The presence of the paired anlagen of bony centra fully agrees with the theory of their origin from the bases of neural and hemal arches. Centra in the form of paired half-rings also occur in rhachitomous Stegocephalia. Thus ontogenetic, as well as paleontological, records indicate the origin of osseous centra from elements of the vertebral arches. Urodele Amphibia are not exceptional in this regard.

In the Hynobiidae (especially *Ranodon*) the organizing role of the bases of the neural arches in the ontogenetic development of the centra is clearly defined. Hence the processes of histogenesis in the perichordal blastema (formation of protochondral structure) commence early and the bone formation process begins. From the bases of the neural arches a thin bone membrane is spread over the notochord surface in both dorsal and ventral directions. This would lead to the conclusion that in urodele Amphibia the expanding bases of the neural arches play a definite role in the formation of the centra. This is not unexpected since even in the embolomerous labyrinthodonts the bases of the neural arches are wedged between the hypocentra and the pleurocentra, establishing a firmer connection between the latter.

In the rhachitomous labyrinthodonts, beginning with *Dendrerpeton* and *Eugyrinus*, the bases of the neural arches expand further along the surface of the notochord and in *Miobatrachus* (*Amphibamus*, Fig. 50) and anuran Amphibia they give rise to a larger portion of the centrum. In reptiles the enlarging portions of the bases of the neural arches are likewise visible in the development of the centra (the pleurocentra are homologous only to the "primary" centra which later overgrow the bases of the neural arches).

In urodele Amphibia the primary source for the development of osseous vertebra is undoubtedly the bases of the neural, and in part the hemal, arches. However, later on in the development of the centrum and in the process of its elongation, the arches take no part. Bone formation continues on the surface of the perichordal cartilage (protochondral). Thus the anterior and posterior thirds of each centrum (Fig. 145) are developed to a lesser degree. While the perichordal cartilage represents the cartilaginous basis of the original elements of the vertebra, the parts of the centrum developing on it by means of perichondral ossification should be regarded as hypocentra and pleurocentra, merged in each vertebra by means of the neural arches (basidorsalia) wedged between them.

The position of the median part of the centrum in the myosepta (Fig. 139) directly corresponds to its position between the hypocentra anteriorly and pleurocentra posteriorly (in embolomerous Stegocephalia). If we consider the development of the perichordal blastema on the surface a decisive criterion, then one may regard the whole middle third of the centrum, developing on the notochord surface, as the product of fusion of the bases of the neural arch with the hypocentra. One would imagine, however, the absence of perichordal cartilage in the middle of the vertebra to be the result of secondary reduction and that the layer of osteoblasts on the notochord is its last remnant. In such a case the role of the neural arch in the formation of the centrum would be very insignificant, and would reduce mainly to a limited role in ontogenesis as a center of early differentiation. Be that as it may, the basic elements entering into the composition of the centra of urodele Amphibia are, obviously, the hypocentra and the pleurocentra.

Thus we come to the probable conclusion that lepospondylous vertebra originated as the result of the early fusion of the elements of the embolomerous vertebra (Fig. 146).

C. Transverse Processes and Ribs

Urodele Amphibia occupy an apparently isolated position among terrestrial vertebrates not only with respect to the origin of the centra, but also in peculiarities of the structure of the transverse processes and the position of the ribs. The transverse processes of urodele Amphibia have a dual structure and one is not able to see in them the result of fusion of the diapophyses and parapophyses. On the other hand, in contrast with the latter they are located dorsal of the vertebral artery and consequently could hardly be regarded as the result of a simple shift of the parapophyses from the centrum to the neural arch. The peculiar position and also the development of the transverse processes precludes the special designation "rib bearer" ("Rippenträger;" Göppert, 1896). Nevertheless Göppert saw in them the result of the dorsal expansion of the parapophyses.

According to descriptions by recent investigators the transverse processes of urodele Amphibia, like the ribs themselves, are developed independently of the arches at the expense of myoseptal material (Gamble, 1922; Emelyanov, 1925; Mookerjee, 1930), but no definite conclusions were drawn from this. For this reason the problem of the origin of the ribs of urodele Amphibia cannot be regarded as solved. Following the work of Göppert it was generally accepted that the ribs of all terrestrial vertebrates are homologous with the dorsal ribs of fishes. Emelyanov regarded the ribs of amniotes as ventral ribs which had moved into the deep abdominal musculature. In his opinion however, the ribs of urodele Amphibia are not homologous to the ribs of amniotes, but are actually dorsal ribs. However, the paleontological record contains no indication of the existence of two types of ribs in ancient terrestrial vertebrates, although the ribs of lepospondylous Amphibia in some respects are unique.

D. Development of the Transverse Processes of the Vertebrae

After the anlage of the cartilaginous neural arch in the embryo of urodele Amphibia, a condensation of skeletogenous mesenchyme is formed in the proximal area of the transverse myosepta, beginning at the abdominal cavity and passing to the upper half of the neural arch. The lower part of the condensation lies lateral to the notochord and is prolonged into a small process above the abdominal cavity. It obviously represents a rudimentary anlage of the hemal arch that quickly disperses. The upper part of the mesenchyme condensation closely adjoins the neural arch and is greatly flattened in its lower part. From this a process forms passing downward lateral to the vertebral artery. In the anterior part of the trunk this protrusion sometimes curves around the vertebral artery and extends downward to the notochord. From the same mesenchyme condensation, penetrating in a lateral direction deep into the myosepta cavity, there is a band of flattened mesenchyme representing the anlage of a rib. A mesenchyme condensation adjoining the neural arch is soon differentiated and forms a fairly large, flat mass of prochondral tissue that may extend to the notochord in the area of the first vertebra (Fig. 147). In this continuous prochondral mass chondrification then sets in. The latter starts in two places: first, at the base of the lateral process closely associated with the cartilage of the neural arch, the anlage of the transverse process, i.e., "a rib-bearer" (Figs. 147 and 148); and second, in the myoseptum itself the cartilaginous rudiment of the rib (Fig. 148). The position of the anlage of the rib is determined particularly by the vertical myoseptum. It

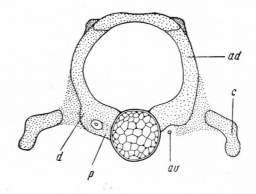

FIG. 147. Second vertebra of larva of *Hynobius* 20 mm long. *ad*, Neural arch; *av*, vertebral artery; *c*, rib; *d*, rudiment of diapophysis; *p*, cartilaginous parapophysis merging at the end with the rudiment of the diapophysis.

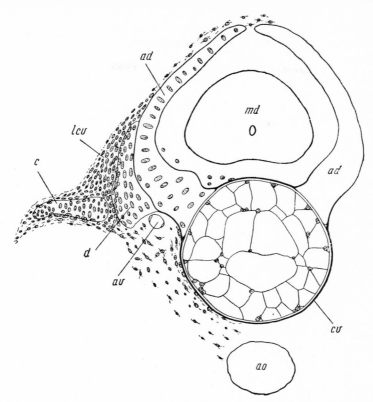

FIG. 148. Section through vertebra from anterior part of trunk of a larva of *Hynobius* 25 mm long. *ao*, Aorta; *ad*, neural arch; *av*, vertebral artery; *c*, rib; *cv*, centrum; *d*, rudiment of diapophysis; *lcv*, rudiment of rib-vertebral ligaments; *md*, spinal chord.

corresponds only approximately to the position of the horizontal septum, since only the lateral part of the latter is present. We affirm that in the early stages of development, not just in the stage of mesenchyme concentration, but also in the prochondral stage, in *Hynobius*, and *Ranodon*, there is complete continuity of the anlage. The chondrified anlagen in the trunk region follow quite normally, i.e., starting at the transverse process they continue distally from the vertebra as the anlagen of the ribs. Only in the first vertebrae is this sequence definitely changed, in relation to a change in the function of these ribs.

Part of the mesenchyme, and then the prochondral concentration, passing down to the notochord below the vertebral artery, is the anlage of the parapophysis. As we have said, these anlagen are observed only in the anterior part of the trunk (and at the end of the caudal region), and then only occasionally. Nevertheless genuine cartilage parapophyses are usually developed in the first vertebrae, on either one or both sides (Fig. 147). Cartilaginous processes are not developed in the trunk region in Hynobiidae (in contrast to *Necturus*). Comparison of different variants however, compels one to see in

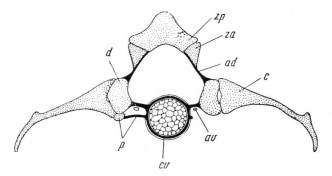

FIG. 149. Sixth vertebra (variant) of a larva of *Hynobius* 32 mm long. *ad*, Neural arch; *av*, vertebral artery; *c*, rib; *cv*, centrum; *d*, diapophysis; *p*, parapophysis; *za, zp*, anterior and posterior sygapophysis.

the above-mentioned ventral processes in the septal concentrations lying lateral of the vertebral artery, anlagen of the distal parts of the parapophyses which were merged with the primordia of the transverse processes (Figs. 148 and 149). The proximal part of the parapophysis is not usually developed. Cartilage anlagen are only observed early in the vertebrae, and then not always. Cartilaginous parapophyses ossify later, but in addition bony para-pophyses are developed directly where there were no cartilage anlagen. Thus early in the vertebrae well-developed bony parapophyses which are distally connected with bulky cartilaginous lateral processes are formed (always on both sides of the vertebrae). However, bony parapophyses are developed only in the anterior section of the trunk.

As we have seen, the anlage of the transverse process of urodele Amphibia is quite peculiar. It is developed on the upper arch, not at the expense of this arch, but from skeletogenous material concentrating at the base of a transverse myoseptum, and is prolonged into a rudiment of a rib. This mate-rial forms a seemingly extraneous development on the neural arch (Fig. 148). Such an impression is maintained by the fact that although the chondrification of the transverse process ("rib bearer") begins from the neural arch, these processes are nevertheless distinguished by a characteristic structure and consist of newer cartilage (Fig. 148). Moreover, the perichordal ossification of the arch begins earlier and therefore the thin, bony (or osteoid) membrane is sometimes found under the newer cartilage of the transverse process and yet very sharply limiting it. All this clearly shows that in the transverse proc-esses of urodele Amphibia we have a new formation genetically associated with the base of the ribs, i.e., constructed in ontogensis from the same source.

In the anlage of the transverse processes numerous variations are seen in the position, volume, and shape of the anlage, and the degree of separation from the arches as correlated to the rudiments of the ribs and to the rudiments of the parapophyses. All this obviously indicates that the new formation has not yet acquired a stable form-regulating mechanism. The proximal parts of the parapophyses in the vicinity of the median and posterior sections of the trunk have been completely reduced. The distal part of the parapophyses have obviously fused to the transverse processes and entered into their formation. This material seems to be completely incorporated into the mass of septal material of the transverse processes. In the later stages of development, however, and particularly at the start of the process of ossification, the dual nature of the transverse process is quite clearly manifested. A dichotomy is noted in the growth of the blood vessels and the resorption of the cartilage in the distal part of the process and the base of the rib. From here the enchondral ossification of both formations commences. A double bony process is developed which occasionally appears as a fusion of the parapophyses and diaphyses. Simultaneously a forked rib is developed (Fig. 150).

The peculiar anlagen and structure of the transverse processes of urodele Amphibia have impeded their interpretation as special "rib bearers." Göppert and other authors presumed that they were the result of expansion of the parapophyses (i.e., elements of the hemal arches) in a dorsal direction from the centrum under the vertebral artery to the neural arch. This hypothesis is not supported by the facts. The main bulk of the transverse process develops as a new formation. However, material of the distal section of the parapophysis takes part in its development. This material is wholly merged with septal material; it has lost its capacity for independent modification in the chondri-

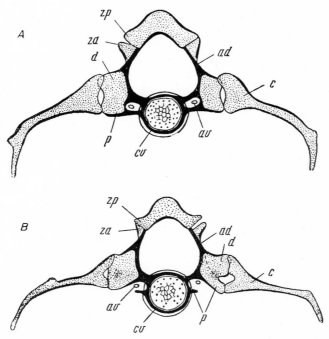

FIG. 150. Sixth (A) and seventh (B) vertebrae of a larva of *Hynobius* 35 mm long. *ad*, Neural arch; *av*, vertebral artery; *c*, rib; *cv*, centrum; *d*, diaphysis; *p*, parapophysis; *za*, *zp*, anterior and posterior zygapophyses.

fication stages (in the distal part), but it has retained some individuality in the processes of ossification. Thus, notwithstanding the loss of individuality of its anlage, the distal part of the parapophysis is clearly seen in the bony transverse process of the vertebra of urodele Amphibia, as its anteroventral fork.

Thus we come to the conclusion that the transverse processes of urodele Amphibia ("rib bearers") have a dual origin: they are neomorphs, arising at the base of the ribs at the expense of septal mesenchyme, and they are also the distal elements of the former parapophyses, inherited from fishes. The duality of origin is clearly stamped in the structure of the adult animals.

Light is shed upon the origin of the new elements of the processes, i.e., the diapophyses, which first appear only in terrestrial vertebrates, by further facts concerning their ontogenesis in urodele Amphibia. The mesenchyme concentration at the base of the transverse myosepta closely adjoins the neural arch and has the same characteristic structure—all the cells are protracted in a dorsoventral direction along the surface of the upper arch. This structure is retained at the protochondral stage and even in the new cartilage, as a consequence of which it is definitely separated from the cartilage of the arches proper, in which the cells have the opposite, transverse, orientation (Fig. 148). During chondrification of the rudiments the "rib bearers" are specially distinguished by the elongated cells in the dorsal part of the concentration that passes laterally into the dorsal surface of the rib. This is the anlage of the ligament connecting the rib to the dorsal surface of the transverse process (Fig. 148). The resemblance of the characteristic structure of the whole rudiment of the transverse process to the anlage of the ligament leads one to the thought that, in general, the whole transverse process was developed from a ligament suspending the rib from the neural arch. The latter obviously arose in terrestrial vertebrates in connection with an increase in the load on the ribs upon emergence of the animal onto land (the abdominal musculature supporting the viscera is attached to the ribs, so that all the organs in the abdomen hang individually on the ribs, especially in those forms which have no pectoral framework, i.e., in urodele Amphibia).

E. Development of Ribs in the Hynobiidae

In the early anlage the rib has the form of a concentration of mesenchyme in the vertical myoseptum, and at its boundary with the horizontal myoseptum it is directly connected to the neural arch. In the later prochondral stage of development, this transverse connection to the cartilagenous neural arch is retained. However, in the anlagen of the first three ribs the distal ends are much expanded and this creates the impression of distal-proximal growth (*Hynobius*, 14 mm; *Ranodon*, 23-24 mm). Following this, chondrification in these three ribs starts at the distal expanded end of the rib (*Hynobius*, 16 mm).

After chondrification the ribs become connected to the neural arch at the intermediate section of the prochondral tissue. This mass of prochondral tissue later on builds up and is transformed, as described above, into a transverse process—the rib bearer (Rippenträger)—which remains sharply set off from the neural arch for some time after chondrification. The ribs initiate, as above, in the myosepta between the muscle segments and extend the full length from the vertebra to the outer body wall in these septa. The rib does not extend laterally directly to the side of the body wall from the place of its attachment to the diapophysis; it bends downward to the ventral side (Figs. 149 and 150). Therefore the distal section of the rib is found in the vicinity of the hypaxial musculature to which it becomes attached. The end of the rib curves down below the horizontal septum, marked here by the lateral nerve (n. lateralis X), and lies beneath m. rectus lateralis which definitely belongs to the hypaxial musculature.

The base of the rib and its connection to the transverse process merits special consideration. After the formation of the cartilaginous rib it is found to be set on the transverse process by means of a much expanded base (Fig. 149). The long axis of this expansion is not quite vertical—the lower part is slightly anterior and the upper part is shifted backward. The upper part of the base of the rib consists of newer cartilage. It envelops the diapophysis posteriorly and is closely bound to the developing vertebral rib posteriorly. Correspondingly the transverse process is set somewhat at an angle. This position reflects the dual origin of the latter, the parapophysis lies below and anterior to the diapophysis. Later, as the result of the processes of ossification the ends of the transverse processes are divided, as described above. The same separation occurs at the base of the rib. Ingrowth of vessels and resorption of cartilage occurs here at the midpoint. As a result, simultaneous with ossification, the characteristic bifurcation of the base of the rib develops (Fig. 150).

The bifurcate formation, i.e., the dual attachment of the rib to the vertebra, is characteristic of all terrestrial vertebrates in some form or other. It is obviously linked to the new function of the rib which, upon emergence of the animal onto land, took the whole weight of the internal organs suspended by the abdominal muscles from the ribs. The vertical load required strengthening of the attachments to the vertebral column, and the first reaction to this requirement was a differentiation of the ligaments at the base of the vertical myosepta. These ligaments pass from the dorsal surface of the rib to the lateral surface of the dorsal arch. At the ends of these ligaments new processes were then formed, the diapophyses, on the dorsal arches and the dorsal arm, i.e., the "tuberculum," at the base of the rib.

In urodele Amphibia the thoracic framework which supports a major part of the viscera in the amniotes is lacking, and the vertical load on the ribs is especially great. Correspondingly the ribs are strengthened, not only at the vertebral column but distally in the superficial fasciae of the lateralis muscles by special dorsal processes (Figs. 149 and 150), which have been compared to the processus uncinatus of the amniotes.

A special and somewhat different load is supported by the first three ribs. To their distal parts is attached the serratus muscle by means of which the whole body is suspended on the pectoral girdle. In this the stout second rib takes a fundamental role.

F. The Question of the Homology of the Transverse Processes. The Parapophyses and Diapophyses

The developmental history of the transverse processes in the Hynobiidae gives a clear picture of the origin of these processes. However, for the final decision concerning the question of their homology with the processes of other vertebrates it is still necessary for us to make comparisons with both the higher fishes and with other terrestrial vertebrates—the Stegocephalia and the amniotes. In fishes the ribs are articulated to the lateral processes of the centra of the vertebrae, i.e., to the parapophyses, which are derivatives of the hemal arches. In terrestrial vertebrates the ribs were shifted dorsally and acquired a second attachment to the neural arches. Concerning the transitional position of the ribs in the ancestors of terrestrial vertebrates one must judge by the rib articulation in crossopterygian fishes and in ichthyostegids. Unfortunately, in both cases the rib articulation is known only for the base of the caudal region.

In *Eusthenopteron* the rib had a short base by which it was attached to the posterior edge of the centrum (hypocentrum) directly below the neural arch, closely adjacent to its base. In *Ichthyostega* the rib had the same broad base and was articulated to the rear edge of the centrum (hypocentrum) and to a small tuberculum at the base of the neural arch. Between the centrum and the neural arch an opening is left under the base of the rib, through which the vertebral artery passed. The small tuberculum at the base of the neural arch (in the caudal region) is a vestigial diapophysis and the corresponding part of the rib base is its tuberculum. Even from this it is clear that the diapophyses do not originate as the result of the shift of any process from the centrum to the arch; they were formed *de novo* at the base of the neural arch in connection with the acquisition of a new dorsal articulation of the rib. This dorsal rib articulation was acquired as the result of a gradual expansion of the rib base and the shifting of its upper edge from the centrum to the neural arch. The broad base of the rib covered over the vertebral artery at the boundary between the centrum and the neural arch. Reduction of the median part of the rib base then led to the separation of two heads, ventral (the capitulum of the rib), and dorsal (the tuberculum). This division usually is scarcely noticeable in the Stegocephalia. In *Benthosuchus* a definite bifurcation is present only on the cervical ribs; in the trunk region the capitulum and the tuberculum are indistinguishable, but the proximal end of the rib is much expanded. Expansion of the rib base was definitely related to the expansion of the region of the rib attachment to the centrum and to its neural arch. Correspondingly, in addition to the small parapophysis or articulation surface on the centrum, a more or less definite diapophysis was developed on the neural arch. This diapophysis is a new progressively developing acquisition of terrestrial vertebrates, while the parapophysis, inherited from fishes, is reduced.

In lepospondylous Amphibia the parapophysis was retained in the form of a more or less prominent process which occupies a dorsal position in the anterior part of the vertebra. Dorsally and posteriorly of it, at the base of the neural arch, a diapophysis rises. Very often fusion of the two processes is seen. In modern urodele Amphibia as we have already seen, there is also a fusion together of the parapophyses and diapophyses; this is the principal peculiarity of the vertebral column in this group. The processes fuse together in their distal parts lateral to the vertebral artery, and therefore the latter often passes through the opening at the base of the "rib bearer" (Figs. 147 and 150). However, the duality is clearly retained in the structure of the transverse processes of the adult animals, indicating their origin from a fusion of the parapophyses and diapophyses. The proximal element of the rib is divided into two arms, corresponding to the two points of its attachment on the parapophysis and diapophysis. In the ontogenesis of urodele Amphibia traces of the history of movement of the rib and the dual development of its attachment were retained. The rib is initiated in the ventral section of the septal blastema and in its proximal part shows an articulation to the anlagen of the rudiments of the distal parapophyses (Figs. 147, 149, and 150). The dorsal articulation of the rib to the diapophysis develops later as the result of a secondary dorsal growth of the rib base. The rib is then attached to a transverse process by a very broad base (Fig. 149). During ossification the rib base bifurcates and forms the fork characteristic of urodele Amphibia (Fig. 150). In some urodele Amphibia the dorsal rib attachment shifts still farther upward along the neural arch. In the caudal region the rudimentary ribs retain the broad attachment to the transverse processes, having a clear dual origin. In the Stegocephalia and in higher terrestrial vertebrates the fork is usually not as prominently developed, but nonetheless it shows the homology of the upper fork of the rib of urodele Amphibia with the tuberculum of the amniotes. On the other hand, the parapophysis in Stegocephalia and amniotes was not moved dorsally and was not fused to the diapophysis. It remained in place on the centrum and was usually reduced so that the capitulum became attached directly to the centrum.

The diapophysis of the vertebra of labyrinthodonts and amniotes is obviously formed *de novo* as in urodele Amphibia. It may be presumed that the diapophysis is of uniform origin in all cases and that it is fully homologous in all terrestrial vertebrates. We may connect its origin, and also the origin of the rib tuberculum, to an increase of the vertical load on the rib with the emergence of the animal onto land. This led to differentiation of the ligament at the base of the vertical myoseptum in which the rib lies. The ligament connects the dorsal surface of the rib to the lateral surface of the arch and effectively supports the rib together with its load (Fig. 151). Corresponding to the place of attachment of the ligament, at the expense of its material, there developed a tuberculum, the rudiment of the diapophysis on the neural arch, and a rudiment of a protuberance at the base of the rib (Fig. 151). The parapophyses protruded, but very slightly. This led to the typical picture of rib attachment in the Stegocephalia and amniotes (Fig. 151). In lepospondylous Amphibia both processes, the parapophyses and the diapophyses, protruded prominently and converged terminally (Fig. 151). In some forms they were fused together and this led to expansion of the rib base and sometimes to a peculiar mode of rib attachment.

Fusion of the ends of the parapophyses and diapophyses occurred in some forms leading to urodele Amphibia. The ontogensis of the vertebra-rib articulation in urodele Amphibia allows one to reconstruct the history of its origin (Fig. 152). Parapophyses of considerable length were present in the ancestral forms. They extended in a dorsal direction lateral of the vertebral artery. The rib was reinforced by a ligament extending to the neural arch. The rib base was expanded along the length of the ligament, and with development of an opposing process the same ligament came into contact with the neural arch (Fig. 152). Thus arose the second process of the vertebra—the diapophysis. The rib acquired a still firmer support at the vertebra by the joining of the tips of the two processes, the parapophyses and diapophyses, which were merged together. With the transfer of all support to the neural arch the proximal part of the parapophysis lost its significance and it was reduced (Fig. 152). The deeper forking of the rib base, and also the transverse processes, was probably linked to the requirement of achieving maximum firmness of support for the vertical load on the rib with a possible lightening of the weight of the bony skeleton.

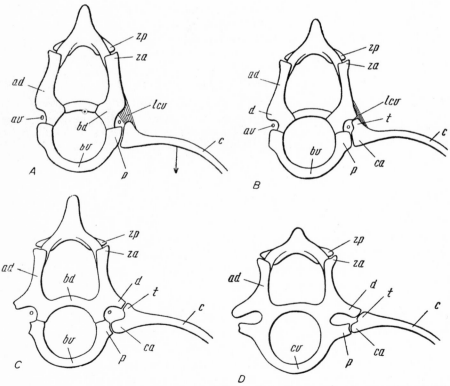

FIG. 151. Diagrams showing articulations of the rib to the vertebra in primitive terrestrial vertebrates. Hypothetical original form (A); ichthyostegids (B); Labyrinthodonts (C); Lepospondylous Stegocephalia (D). ad, Neural arch; av, vertebral artery; bd, base of neural arch; bv, hypocentra; c, rib; ca, capitulum of rib; cv, centrum; d, diapophysis; lcv, rib-vertebral ligament; p, parapophysis; t, tuberculum of rib; za, zp, anterior and posterior zygapophyses.

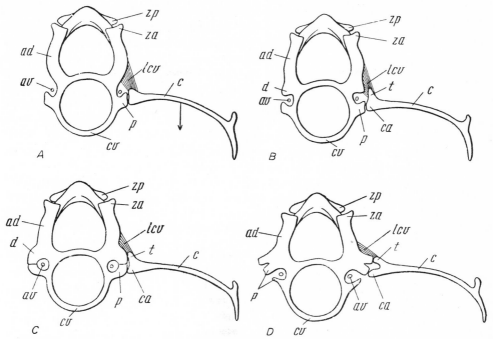

FIG. 152. Diagrams showing origin of transverse processes in urodele Amphibia. Stress on rib (indicated by arrow) and position of ligament (A); appearance of diapophysis and rib tuberculum at the place of ligament attachment (B); connection of distal parts of parapophyses and diapophyses (C); reduction of proximal part of parapophyses (D). *ad*, Neural arch; *av*, vertebral artery; *bd*, base of neural arch; *bv*, hypocentra; *c*, rib; *ca*, capitulum of rib; *cv*, centrum *d*, diapophysis; *lcv*, rib-vertebral ligament; *p*, parapophysis; *t*, tuberculum of rib; *za, zp*, anterior and posterior zygapophyses.

G. THE PROBLEM OF THE HOMOLOGY OF THE RIBS OF TERRESTRIAL VERTEBRATES

The question of the homology of the ribs of vertebrates arose after ribs in higher fishes had been described as occupying a different position in relation to the lateral muscles of the body. Since, in crossopterygians proper and also in dipnoan fishes, dorsal ribs have not so far been described, we have no grounds to presume the existence of dorsal ribs in terrestrial vertebrates. At the same time, if ribs of reptiles and vertebrates higher in origin are ventral ribs (Emelyanov, 1938), then we have no further basis to believe that there could be ribs of different origin in Amphibia.

Paleontological records show a complete homology of the ribs of Stegocephalia and reptiles. Therefore, if ribs of reptiles are ventral ribs, then ribs of Amphibia should be ventral ribs. Embryological evidence does not give grounds for relating ribs of modern Amphibia to dorsal ribs. In contrast to modern Amphibia, in all primitive Stegocephalia there were elongate ribs enclosing a major part of the trunk. Such ribs were also present in the ichthyostegids. There were elongated ribs in the embolomerous Stegocephalia (Anthracosauria) which passed to the reptiles. In the rhachitomous labyrinthodonts also there were still occasional elongate ribs. Since these ribs were not utilized by Amphibia for respiration they could be reduced, and this occurred in parallel in various phylogenetic lines. A shortening of the ribs took place in many labyrinthodonts (for example in *Trematops* and *Micropholis*). Short, straight, distally expanded ribs were present in Acanthostoma. There were short, straight ribs in the branchiosaurs and also in *Miobatrachus*. In the lines leading to anuran Amphibia further reduction of the ribs occurred.

Simultaneous with this shortening, the ribs acquired an almost transverse orientation and were naturally arranged in the medial section of the trunk musculature, i.e., approximately in the vicinity of the horizontal septa. Abbreviation of the ribs was accompanied by their shifting dorsally in the myosepta.

In the lepospondylous Amphibia there still were sometimes fairly long ribs; however, they were reduced and passed on to the urodele Amphibia in the form of relatively short, slightly curved elements which, in some cases, are almost completely reduced (e.g., in the secondarily aquatic *Amphiuma*).

It is quite evident that in primitive Stegocephalia there were the same ventral ribs as in crossopterygian fishes, and these ribs passed from embolomerous Stegocephalia to reptiles, in which the ventral tips of the ribs were joined to the sternum. In the rhachitomous labyrinthodonts the ribs were shortened and took a more horizontal position. The same process occurred also in the lepospondylous Amphibia. In all these cases, however, we are obviously dealing with one and the same thing—the ventral ribs.

The dorsal shift of the ribs is correlated to their peculiar function in terrestrial vertebrates, particularly in Amphibia. This function arose along with the emergence of the animal from water onto land, which brought about necessity of bearing the whole weight of the trunk proper. With elevation of the body on the appendages, all the internal organs are supported by the abdominal musculature which is attached only to the ribs. Therefore, the rib would become adapted for bearing a vertical stress. Hence there is the expansion of the base of the rib, the development of a firm ligament between the base of the rib and the neural arch of the vertebra, the development of the diapophysis and the rib tuberculum at the place of attachment of this ligament, and, in urodele Amphibia, the attachment of the distal section of the rib to the superficial fasciae of the lateralis muscles. Only with the development of the pectoral framework in the amniotes was the nature of the load on the rib modified since the whole thoracic system then served as a support for a major portion of the internal organs. The rib structure is also altered in correlation with the new respiratory function.

IX. THE DEVELOPMENT OF THE APPENDAGES OF URODELE AMPHIBIA

With the emergence of crossopterygian fishes onto land the load on the paired appendages increased extremely abruptly. This led to a gradual development of the limb girdles and particularly their primary skeleton since they served as the place for attachment of musculature.

Sometimes the full suite of the dermal bones of the pectoral girdle was retained in the position characteristic of crossopterygian fishes. In *Eogyrinus*, in addition to the clavicle and cleithrum common to Stegocephalia, there were also the supracleithral and post-temporal, by means of which (as in fishes) the pectoral girdle was attached to the skull roof (by the horn of the tabular bone). In other Stegocephalia only the clavicles were present in the ventral division of the girdle and the cleithra in the dorsal division (Fig. 153). In addition, there were still usually broader interclavicular bones. Usually the cleithrum enveloping the fore-edge of the scapula, was prolonged into a broad plate covering the suprascapular cartilage. The clavicles also lay along the fore edge of the scapulars and were prolonged in the form of a broad plate on the ventral side of the body. These bones were also present in lepospondylous forms, at any rate in the Nectridia. In the microsaurs there were narrow clavicles, interclavicular bones in the form of plates with posterior processes, and (sometimes?) a small cleithrum. In urodele Amphibia these dermal bones were completely reduced.

The primary skeleton of the pectoral girdle, very weak in all fishes, attained considerably more development in the Stegocephalia, but it had just a single scapular ossification (as in crossopterygians) which more or less incorporated the coracoid division forming a scapulocoracoid. A considerable part of the girdle, both dorsally and especially ventrally, remained cartilaginous (Fig. 153).

In this form the pectoral girdle passed to the urodele Amphibia. According to all the evidence the primary girdle of the latter is very similar in form to the girdle in Stegocephalia. The scapular and especially the coracoid divisions of the girdle were much expanded, and between the latter the cartilaginous plate of the sternum is placed posteriorly. As in the Stegocephalia also, however, there is only one relatively small scapulocoracoid ossification.

The pelvic girdle of the Stegocephalia was much more highly developed than in fishes. In addition to a broad ventral plate, there is a large ascending process, which in primitive forms has two forks, a shorter dorsal one and a

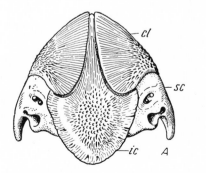
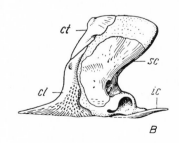

FIG. 153. Shoulder girdle of *Benthosuchus*, ventral view (A) and lateral view (B). *cl*, Clavicle; *ct*, cleithrum; *ic*, interclavicle; *sc*, scapular. Restoration by Bystrov.

long posterior one (Fig. 30). In *Eogyrinus* these forks of the iliac division of the pelvis lie free along the ribs, attached only by muscles (like the scapulae of the pectoral girdle). In other Stegocephalia a closer connection to the ends of a pair of sacral ribs is developed. In the pelvic girdle of primitive Stego-cephalia there were sometimes three ossifications—the pubis and ischium ventrally, and the ilium dorsally (Fig. 45). In the original forms these ossifica-tions were fused into one bone. In all later Stegecephalia there were de-veloped only two ossifications, ischial and pubic. The pubic portion remained cartilaginous. In the microsaurs all three parts were sometimes represented by a single bone. In urodele Amphibia the pelvic girdle has the same struc-ture as in the Stegocephalia, and the iliac bone is also connected to the ends of one pair of sacral ribs. The pubic part remains cartilaginous, and anterior of it there is frequently another cartilaginous process—the prepubis.

While we see here the great similarity in the structure of the primary girdles of the appendages in urodele Amphibia and Stegocephalia, this ap-plies to a still greater extent to the free appendages (Fig. 154). In the primi-tive forms such as *Cryptobranchus, Hynobius,* and especially *Ranodon,* the skeleton of the limbs is almost identical to the skeleton of the limbs of the labyrinthodonts in so far as they have been investigated. In *Trematops milleri* and *Eryops megalocephalus* (Fig. 154) the composition of the skeleton is the same as in *Ranodon.* The latter (like all modern forms) differ only in the fusion of the first two distal elements. In the lepospondylous Stegocephalia the skel-eton structure was somewhat simplified. It is likewise simplified in most modern Caudata also. In *Scincosaurus* the appendages were the same as in modern Ambystomidae and Salamandridae. In *Scincosaurus* a separate cen-trale, which is present in many modern forms, was not present. On the other hand, on its second and third digits there was one more phalanx than in urodele Amphibia. Also in *Trematops* there was one phalanx more on all digits than in urodele Amphibia. Altogether the similarity in structure of the

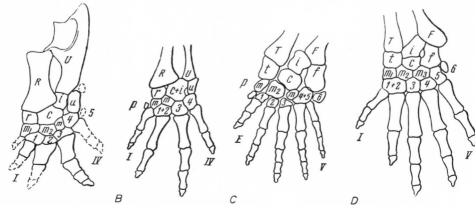

FIG. 154. Appendages of the Stegocephalians *Eryops* (A), *Trematops* (C), and the modern urodele amphibians *Ambystoma* (B) and *Ranodon* (D). c, Centrale; f, fibulare; F, T, tarsals; i, intermedium; m, m₁, m₂, m₃, mediales; p, prepollex; R, radius; r, radiale; T, tibiale; U, ulna; u, ulnare; 1–6, distal carpals; I–IV, digits.

appendages of primitive Caudata and Stegocephalia is so great that one cannot believe that they arose from different sources.

In the developmental history of the free appendages of urodele Amphibia, characteristics more primitive than in other Tetrapoda are also exhibited. In any case, in the Hynobiidae on the margins of the appendages there are rudiments of other radii, the prehallux and postminimus in the posterior appendages, and also rudiments of three or four medial elements along with the usual centrale. In addition, the primary radial arrangement of the elements of the carpus and tarsus is shown better than in other terrestrial vertebrates. The intermedium and ulnare (fibulare) in newly hatched larvae lie level with the end of the radius (tibia), in precisely the same position as the corresponding parts in crossopterygian fishes. Among the elements belonging to one ray, in the early stages there are the prochondral interconnections, especially clear in the series: tibia, tibiale, mediale, tarsale (+2), and the first digit; intermedium, centrale, mediale 2, tarsale 2 (+1), and the second digit; fibula, fibulare (mediale 3), tarsale 3, and the third digit; and also tarsale 4 and the fourth digit. Analogous joints are also developed in the anterior appendages. in addition to the prolonged radial joints transverse joints developed very early between the distal elements of the appendages (the tarsalia and the carpalia distalia). These joints are specific acquisitions of terrestrial vertebrates. They were brought about by the development of the supportive function of the sole of the foot, for which movable joints were differentiated at the base of ankle, and also at the base of the metapodium. The movability of the digits required firmer support in the distal elements of the basipodium. In urodele Amphibia this was developed only in the form of syndesmoses. In anurans there is usually seen complete fusion of the latter elements of the carpus (carpalia 3 + 4 + 5 together with the corresponding medialia).

In any case a definite relationship to all the Stegocephalia is found in the limb structure. It is one of the best testaments to the origin of the urodele Amphibia and the labyrinthodonts from a common ancestor.

X. Conclusions on the History of the Origin of Urodele Amphibia

The developmental history of primitive urodele Amphibia shows their fundamental relationship to forms derived from fishes, in particular the crossopterygian fishes.

The external larval gills are undoubtedly the result of accelerated development and transformation of the internal gills in the median area of the gill arches. In all likelihood such larval gills were present even in crossopterygian fishes, just as they are also present in the Dipnoi.

The developmental history of the blood vascular system gives a clear picture of the transformation of typical fish circulation into the transitional blood circulation of modern Amphibia. It reflects the prominent role of dermal respiration in the first terrestrial forms.

The seismosensory system, well developed in the larvae, was retained, namely in the arrangement of all the lines characteristic of crossopterygian fishes (and the Stegocephalia). In the development of the olfactory organ, features of the organization of fishes were retained and definite indications of movement of the nostrils, which led to the formation of the choana. In the development of the nasolachrymal duct the participation of the suborbital canal of the seismosensory organs is visible. In the auditory organ and in the sound transmission apparatus there is likewise clearly reflected the history of its origin. The suspensorial apparatus (hyomandibula) retained all the articulations characteristic of bony fishes. Complete continuity of the hyoid arch was also retained (in hynobiid larvae). In the development of the cartilaginous skull very primitive features are shown (in the segmentation of the occipital region) and also phylogenetic links to the crossopterygian fishes, particularly in the attachment of the palatoquadrate cartilage to the skull by the basitrabecular articulation and in the development of a temporary articulation of the ascending process to the postorbital region of the skull (processus antoticus). Urodele Amphibia are undoubtedly the most primitive of the terrestrial vertebrates.

All the preceding examinations of both paleontological and embryological materials show quite clearly the close relationship of urodele Amphibia and batrachomorphic Stegocephalia.

Undoubtedly the secondary loss of the tympanic cavity and of sound transmission from the air was accompanied by a reduction of the otic notch. This occurred in all lepospondylous forms. However, in both the Nectridia and in the microsaurs, there were still occasional rudiments of the otic notch. The rest of the skull structure, the structure of the appendicular girdles and the free appendages of lepospondylous Stegocephalia are quite similar to the labyrinthodonts. Simplification of structure of the skull roof occurred even in the lepospondylous group and led to the skull structure of urodele Amphibia. The sole clear and definite difference present is in the structure of the vertebral column. This difference is of the same order as that between Mesozoic and modern Amioidei. The developmental history of the spinal column of urodele Amphibia shows, however, the origin of the perichordal cartilage from paired anlagen, obviously corresponding to the merged cartilaginous primordia of pleurocentra (anteriorly) and hypocentra (posteriorly). As for the osseous centra, they are developed in the form of ossifications starting from the base of the neural arches and from independent ossifications on the sides of the ventral wall of the notochord, which in the tail are linked to the base of the hemal arch. Consequently, the primary bone formation indicates the participation of the bases of the neural arch above, and the hypocentra below, in the development of the osseous centrum. Later the growth of the bony cylinder continues perichondrally on the surface of the perichordal cartilage. This apparently indicates the participation of not only the hypocentra but also the pleurocentra in the formation of the bony centrum. Thus we come to the conclusion that lepospondylous vertebrae apparently arose as the result of early fusion of the base of the neural arch with the hypocentrum (anteriorly) and with the pleurocentrum (posteriorly). The original form could have had an embolomerous vertebral column in which the base of the dorsal arch was wedged between the hypocentra and pleurocentra and firmly united to them.

The embolomerous Stegocephalia known to us could not have given rise to the lepospondylous Amphibia, not only because they were contemporaneous, but especially because they were then reptilomorphs with angustotabular crania. Embolomerous batrachomorphs likewise probably could not have been ancestral forms; they had unique specializations such as the glands in the orbital region.

The embolospondylous Stegocephalia (Dendrerpetontidae), very primitive in all characteristics, were batrachomorphic and closest in skull structure to the lepospondylous forms, especially to the microsaurs. The tabulars are already reduced, and the supratemporals well developed. In the skull roof the parietals, frontals, and broad nasals dominate. There is an elongate lachrymal extending from the orbit to the nostril. The palate is very similar to the palate of the microsaurs. The interpterygoid fenestra was small, and the ectopterygoid small. The parasphenoid was much expanded posteriorly and on this expansion there were fine small teeth. This recalls the hypothesis of Jarvik (1954) concerning the origin of the posterior part of the parasphenoid from the dental plates of crossopterygians (*Eusthenopteron*). There was a basipterygoid articulation. In the lateral occipital bones there were small exits for the occipital nerves. On the squamosal, along the ascending fork of the pterygoid, starting from the quadratojugal upward above the quadrate, there is a depression which was probably filled by cartilage of the ventral process of the auditory ossicle (stapes), as in *Dvinosaurus*, and in the Hynobiidae.

In the vertebral column the neural arches rested on the notochord by means of much expanded bases. The hypocentra enclosed the notochord below and on the sides. The pleurocentra were present in the form of a complete ring around the notochord. The zygapophyses were strongly developed. The vertebral spines were very short. A broad scapular ossification and the usual dermal bones were in the pectoral girdle. In the pelvic girdle the ischium and the ilium were ossified. The appendages were well developed, with fairly long digits. According to all accounts they were terrestrial inhabitants of swampy localities.

According to all these characteristics the Dendrerpetontidae could well have been the original forms for lepospondylous Stegocephalia. However, the members of *Dendrerpeton* known to us belong to the Upper Carboniferous and consequently were contemporaries of the Nectridia and the microsaurs. Therefore, this can only indicate their close relationship and general derivation from more ancient forms. Nevertheless, the latter obviously differed but little from the more recent Dendrerpetontidae.

As for the more direct ancestral relationships of urodele Amphibia, they undoubtedly lead back to representatives of the Carboniferous microsaurs. There is an overall similarity in the skeleton as a whole, particularly in the skull (lacking otic notches), and in the sound transmission apparatus. In the lateral occipital bones of microsaurs there were as many as three openings, evidently for the occipital nerves. This is a very primitive characteristic, but in the larvae of urodele Amphibia at least two pairs of occipital nerves were found. The posterior of these nerves emerged through a special exit persisting between the occipital and preoccipital cartilaginous arches. The stapes, with a broad plate and short shaft which rested on the quadrate bone, was quite similar to the same elements in the primitive urodele Amphibia (and in the apodous gymnophiones). The appendages were also similar, but obviously somewhat weaker. This, along with the elongation of the body, indicates a semi-burrowing way of life. Probably the microsaurs are the direct ancestors of the Apoda and are related indirectly to the urodele Amphibia through a common source form. However, this link was undoubtedly very close. This is most evident in the structure of the vertebral column, especially in the differentiation of its anterior section. The first vertebra in the microsaurs bore a pair of articular depressions for the lateral condyles of the occipital atlas, and between them was an "odontoid" process, the tuberculum interglenoidale, fitting into the ventral depression at the base of the basioccipital bone. The first vertebra in most urodele Amphibia is just as well constructed: *Crypto-branchus, Amphiuma, Onychodactylus, Hynobius, Ranodon* (Fig. 155), and

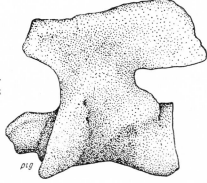

FIG. 155. First vertebra of *Ranodon*. Lateral view (compare with Fig. 70); *pig*, tuberculum interglenoidale.

many Salamandridae and Plethododontidae. In *Proteus* it is rudimentary; in the Apoda it is absent. This peculiar structure is not developed in other Stegocephalia and links to the urodele Amphibia only through the microsaurs. It is irrefutable proof of their close relationship. In both external aspect and in way of life the microsaurs were very similar to modern urodele Amphibia. *Cocytinus* and *Lysorophus* which Huene (1956) puts in Urodelidia, and Romer (1950a) puts in the Microsauria, approach them even more closely morphologically. They were, however, actually secondarily aquatic neotenics, and correspondingly simplified forms with reduced appendages—undoubtedly a specialized side branch.

17

The Fate of the Amphibia in the Mesozoic and the History of the Urodele Amphibia

With the appearance of reptiles, i.e., more active animals feeding on the same food and inhabiting the same biotope at the same time, the Amphibia encountered a difficult situation. They could not survive competition with insectivorous reptiles on land, and were obliged to feed in the water. With the appearance of predatory reptiles they reverted completely to aquatic life. This occurred in all lines—the labyrinthodont as well as the lepospondylous Amphibia. Some reptiles, however, also entered a secondarily aquatic life. With this the fate of the Stegocephalia was decided: as less active forms they did not survive the competition for food, and being completely unprotected they were subject to intensive extermination. They were very quickly supplanted by reptiles everywhere. On land this took place during just one geological period (the Permian). In water, however, the Amphibia disappeared during the Triassic.

In low temperature regions there was no such predominance of reptiles, as was of great significance in hot and warm temperate climates. At low temperatures the activity of reptiles falls off sharply; it also declines in the Amphibia. However, reptiles expend considerable muscular energy for respiratory movements, and for Amphibia in these conditions oropharyngeal respiration was quite sufficient, not requiring extra energy, and dermal respiration was accomplished without any expenditure of energy (we have seen that in many modern mountain Amphibia the lungs were reduced). The lack of food (insects) was combined with this, which again affected the reptiles more than the Amphibia since increased metabolism also required increased feeding. Meanwhile all free energy was expended in seeking prey, and this latter perhaps proved to be inadequate for covering basal metabolism. Amphibia probably require less food, and their expenditure of energy is less since they do not seek out and pursue prey, but lie in wait for it, remaining quite passive.

259

Moreover, the Amphibia can always feed in the water which may be rich in animal foods (molluscs and insect larvae), and the water temperature is more stable.

In addition, the mode of reproduction is of even more significance in this case. Reptiles deposit large eggs on dry land; their development is direct and naturally more prolonged. The short summer season may prove to be insufficient for development to be completed. Development is possible over two seasons with embryos wintering in the eggs. In a cold climate, however, this undoubtedly resulted in mass mortality by freezing. Moreover, for newly hatched young, food-seeking in a cold climate was much more difficult than for adults.

On the other hand, Amphibia reproduce in the water. Their eggs are of small size and develop very rapidly; the larvae, hatched from the eggs in good feeding conditions (the heated summer water leads to rapid reproduction of Crustacea, and benthos are also abundant), develop very quickly. If by the end of the season the larvae have not reached the stage of metamorphosis they are in no way threatened since waters usually do not freeze to the bottom.

Thus, in a cold climate reptiles not only lose their predominance, but even give way to Amphibia, both in the adaptation of adults and in the development of young. Therefore, in modern times the Amphibia as a rule penetrate farther north than reptiles. We can obtain some idea of the modern dispersal of Amphibia and reptiles in the climatic zones of the USSR from the following table (from the account of Terentev and Chernov, 1949) showing the number of species occurring in various zones.

Zone	Amphibia	Reptiles
Tundra zone	3	0
Kamchtka and northern Kuriles	1	0
Western forest zone	13	7
Eastern forest zone	4	5
Transcarpathia	16	7
Steppes of Transbaikal	5	5
Caucasus	12	49
Mountainous area of east Central Asia	3	24
Desert area of Central Asia	3	49

This series reflects approximately the successive increase of summer temperatures and the lengthening of the warm season of the year. From this it is evident that only the Amphibia penetrate far northward. In the forest zone the Amphibia predominate. Likewise, the Amphibia still predominate decidedly in Transcarpathia. In the steppe zone some preponderance is found on the reptile side. In the Caucasus the number of species of reptiles exceeds the number of amphibian species by 4 times, and in the desert areas of Central Asia, by 16 times! Undoubtedly these differences would be multiplied many times if we calculated not only the number of species but also the number of individuals. To this should be added (among the Amphibia) the grass frog, the sharp-nosed frog, the hiberian frog, and the Siberian angletooth (*Hynobius*) which extend north to about the 67th parallel (on the Kolsk Peninsula) and to the 70th parallel in Scandinavia, and even occur beyond its borders. In European USSR the viviparous lizard extends to this latitude (to the northeast the boundary of its distribution lies farther south). Of other reptiles only the common viper passes beyond the 60th parallel limit [in the west European territory of the USSR the common grass snake (*Tropidonotus natrix*) ascends a little higher]. This was undoubtedly favored by a semiaquatic feeding and mode of life. We cannot but call attention to the fact that the sole representative of the reptiles penetrating farther northward than the others is a viviparous form. In this case the eggs are not only protected from cold but are also borne on the maternal body for heating in the sun.

Since viviparity is a more recent acquisition, we may affirm that in the Paleozoic there were as yet no viviparous reptiles and that reptiles could not have penetrated into countries having a colder climate.

Thus it is very probable that almost all Amphibia were supplanted and frequently exterminated by reptiles in all environments of the temperate and warm climatic zones. Only in colder climatic conditions, to the north or in mountainous localities, did Amphibia find for themselves areas of distribution still not penetrated by reptiles. In temperate and warm climatic zones only a few more specialized forms of Amphibia could be preserved. This applies in some degree to the small labyrinthodonts, giving rise to anuran Amphibia. Another group of Amphibia which survived the critical period comprises the lepospondylous forms which gave rise to modern urodele Amphibia and the Apoda. Being less active on land, they took up a cryptic mode of life, burrowing moss, under fallen leaves, and hiding under rocks. They came out to hunt at night, feeding partly on land, partly in water. Some of them sought food only under cover and transferred to a burrowing way of life. These were the caecilians (Apoda) which at present live only in tropical countries. Others maintained a closer relationship to the water where they not only bred but occasionally fed. Adult members of this group were protected by their inconspicuous way of life; however, their larvae were eaten by both fishes and reptiles.

Urodele Amphibia did not become abundant in the southern hemisphere since the small overgrown waters in which they usually bred were occupied by dipnoan fishes, the larvae of which are biologically quite similar to the larvae of urodele Amphibia. Therefore, Urodela were confined to the north and to mountain areas of the northern hemisphere where they escaped to some extent from both reptiles and from fishes also. The larvae of these urodele Amphibia were concealed in coastal aquatic vegetation, and also among rocks of mountain streams and lakes.

The adults (Fig. 156) led a secretive life on land. Here, mainly in montane

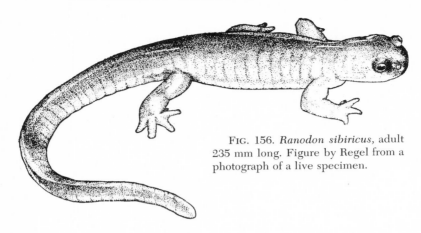

Fig. 156. *Ranodon sibiricus*, adult 235 mm long. Figure by Regel from a photograph of a live specimen.

localities, they survived throughout the Mesozoic as inconspicuous not very numerous forms probably similar to modern *Hynobius* and *Typhlotriton*. Afterward, as the majority of reptiles died out, the urodele Amphibia could again attain wider distribution in temperate and warm climates. From montane areas they proceeded to move out into the lowlands, mainly keeping to environments free of competition with fishes. The small reptiles that survived transferred to inhabiting more and more sunny, arid localities, and the urodele Amphibia remained in wet localities, utilizing drying-out fishless waters mainly for breeding. There was no especially keen competition from mammals, since most of the latter were vegetative or predatory feeders, and the urodele Amphibia were content with the small invertebrates on which they preyed, both on land and in the water. The food resources of standing waters during the Paleozoic were considerably augmented by an abundance of mosquito larvae which locally became the chief food for larvae of urodele Amphibia. Montane localities thus served as reservoirs in which Amphibia, especially urodeles, could survive the difficult (for them) Mesozoic era. As reptile dominance ended, the urodele Amphibia emerged anew into a broader arena, but as specialized forms in small shallow waters occupying a limited ecological zone of amphibiotic life in which they were not competing with fishes and did not conflict with mammals.

The larval development of urodele Amphibia is the least specialized (Fig. 157). It is similar to that characteristic of Stegocephalia, as is shown by fossil remains of the larval forms of Branchiosauria, *Tungussogyrinus*, and others, and also in the structure of neotenic forms such as *Dvinosaurus* (Bystrov, 1939). It apparently repeats in some measure the larval development of the original crossopterygian fishes in which external gills were probably also developed. One may even assert with some authority that in the larvae of crossopterygian fishes there were external gills on four branchial arches, since rudiments of four external gills are found in urodele Amphibia (in *Ranodon*; also traces in *Hynobius*; Schmalhausen, 1955b).

In the embryonic and larval development of *Ranodon* in general, relatively more primitive characteristics were retained (Schmalhausen, 1917b, 1953b, 1955b, 1956b), even more than in *Hynobius* although the latter should be considered, from the organization of the adult animal, as an earlier form. This is explained by the fact that *Ranodon* has large eggs with bigger yolk supply, which provides for a slower and more complete process of embryonic development (including the early stages of larval development). In *Hynobius*, which has small eggs, the development proceeds faster and is therefore shorter and more direct. However, the very fact of retention of primitive characteristics in the ontogenesis of *Ranodon* (development of the stapes with an opening for the art. stapedia, rudiments of an m. stapedius, remnants of the tympanic membrane, and others) shows that large eggs are not acquired secondarily but are inherited from distant ancestors. On the contrary, the small eggs of *Hynobius* and many other Urodela are newly acquired. If the large eggs of *Ranodon* were developed secondarily from small ones, then this could not be attributed to a restoration of ancestral characters lost through curtailment of development. What else explains the diversity in egg size and rate of development in different members of the Urodela?

The vast majority of urodele Amphibia live in mountainous areas. In mountain areas they find necessary moisture and good cover among stones and in moss. The larvae find good cover among the rocks in lakes and streams. The comparatively low summer temperature of the waters is accompanied by a high oxygen content, especially in mountain streams with rapid currents. Competition with fishes is slight, even in the streams. Favorable conditions facilitated the preservation of primitive Amphibia in mountainous localities.

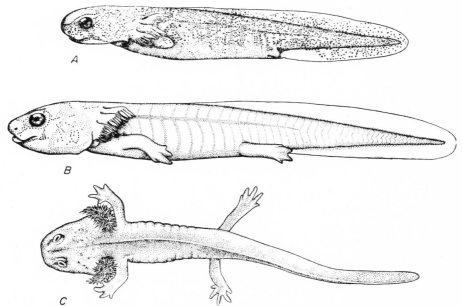

FIG. 157. Larvae of *Ranodon:* 23 mm long at hatching stage (A); 35 mm (B), and about 70 mm (C). Figures by Regel, the last from a photograph of a live specimen.

Of the most primitive family of Amphibia, the Hynobiidae, the vast majority belong not only to montane but even to high montane forms; among these are *Ranodon* (Fig. 156) and *Onychodactylus,* breeding in mountain areas of Asia (see Fig. 158). *Cryptobranchus japonicus (Megalobatrachus)* inhabits mountain streams of Japan and China (Fig. 158). *Cryptobranchus alleghaniensis* is distributed in the rivers of mountainous localities of North America. Only one species, *Hynobius keyserlingii,* mainly inhabiting mountainous localities, is also ranged in the west Siberian lowlands and at present is increasing its range of distribution, invading westward even into the European territory of the USSR. There are also many forms in the family Ambystomidae that survive in mountainous localities. In mountain streams of North America *Rhyacotriton* and *Dicamptodon* breed. Members of the family Salamandridae are more widely distributed, inhabiting all the northern hemisphere. However, most of the species are dispersed in mountainous areas. The most primitive member of the family is a mountain form, **Tylotriton,** living in the eastern Himalayas and south China. The range of the salamanders proper— *Salamandra*—is also confined to mountain country. Only the tritons are more widely dispersed. They are represented by the typical European montane forms of *Euproctus,* and also by the montane and plains members of the genus *Triturus* in Eurasia and North America. The whole family Plethodontidae originated from forms living in high montane areas. The most primitive members, *Gyrinophilus* and *Pseudotriton,* at the present time survive in mountain streams of North America. Thus, most urodele Amphibia, and particularly the more primitive of their representatives, inhabit mountain areas. Therefore,

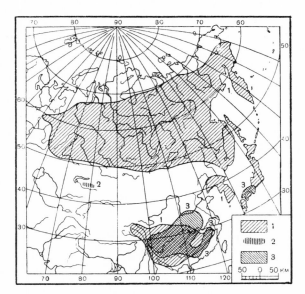

FIG. 158. Map of distribution of Hynobiidae and Cryptobranchidae in Asia. 1, Species of *Hynobius;* 2, *Ranodon sibiricus;* 3, *Cryptobranchus (Megalobatrachus) japonicus.* From Terentev and Chernov (1949).

we must regard the larger sized eggs of montane Urodela as a primitive characteristic.

The mode of egg deposition favors the mountainous origin of urodele Amphibia. Primitive urodele Amphibia of the families Hynobiidae and Cryptobranchidae lay spawn in the form of paired egg sacs which are attached to rocks or plants so that they are freely bathed on all sides by running water. Other Amphibia deposit the eggs singly or in strings or small bundles which also are sometimes firmly attached to underwater rocks or plants. This mode of egg deposition favors good aeration, gives some protection, and at the same time prevents the eggs from being washed away.

If the deposition of single eggs (by tritons) is advantageous in standing water, egg cases have a definite advantage in running water and in all cases where there is a good oxygen supply. The plains country *Hynobius keyserlingii* probably inherited its mode of egg deposition from mountain forms living in cold waters under conditions of abundant oxygen supply. At the same time the whole organization of the larvae with protruding external gills, the presence of balancers, and also the deposition of eggs in small clusters observed in many forms, suggest that even in mountain localities the urodele amphibians essentially restricted themselves to standing water or quiet overgrown creeks.

18

The Embolomerous Stegocephalia and the Origin of the Reptiles

Among the more ancient Carboniferous Stegocephalia one group of very primitive forms is distinguished which, although typically labyrinthodont in all respects, nevertheless shows certain characteristics of the path toward evolution of the reptiles. These are the anthracosaurs which are characterized primarily by the embolomerous structure of the vertebral column (which occurs also in other primitive labyrinthodonts). In this case the hypocentra and pleurocentra are equally developed, and envelop the notochord as complete rings. In each segment there are thus two centra, between which the bases of the neural arches are wedged in from above. Typical members have been described by Watson (1919): *Eogyrinus* (*Pteroplax*) and *Paleogyrinus*, fairly large aquatic animals that were piscivorous predators. Their skulls, generally constructed the same as those of other primitive labyrinthodonts, comprised a complete set of dermal bones in the skull roof, palate, and lower jaw. The skulls were fairly high and relatively narrow. There was one occipital condyle and the otic notches were deep. There was a movable basipterygoid articulation. The interpterygoid fenestra was small. The braincase was fully ossified as one unit. In the parietal region, in addition to the supratemporal, there was also an intertemporal. In the palatoquadrate arch there was a separate epipterygoid. All these are primitive characteristics occurring also in other labyrinthodonts. In addition we note, however, that the parietal shield (parietal, supratemporal, intertemporal, postparietal, and tabular) was separated by a suture from the facial region of the skull (squamosal). This is undoubtedly the remnant of that cleft which in crossopterygian fishes separates the posterior division of the skull (otico-occipital plus parietal shield) from the anterior division (the sphenethmoid plus frontal shield and cheek region). In this respect the anthracosaurs were more primitive than the ichthyostegids (in which there was also no intertemporal). In addition, in *Eogyrinus* the typical piscine connection of the pectoral girdle to the skull roof (tabular horns) by a special supracleithral and post-temporal was still

266

retained. In this respect also the anthracosaurs were more primitive than the ichthyostegids. The connection of the pelvic girdle to the vertebral column was equally primitive. The processes of the iliac bones were not articulated and only overlay the ribs. At the same time there is yet another feature distinguishing the anthracosaurs from the general body of labyrinthodonts, including the ichthyostegids. The relatively larger tabulars have a broad contact with the parietal bones, while in other labyrinthodonts the smaller tabulars are widely separated and do not touch the parietal bones (the supratemporalia are wedged between them). The "angustitabular" structure of the skull roof, one would think, is a small difference, but it is the characteristic distinction of reptilomorphic forms from the batrachomorphic forms in which the skull roof is "latitabular." *Eogyrinus* and *Palaeogyrinus* were aquatic animals with very weak, definitely reduced appendages. Another member of the Carboniferous embolomeres, *Diplovertebron* (Fig. 159), sometimes assigned to the seymourians, was evidently a terrestrial form, having very well-developed appendages with five digits on each, and in all respects approached the reptiles. Although the spinal column still had an embolomerous structure, its elements were not yet fully equal. The principal elements in *Diplovertebron* were the pleurocentra. The hypocentra formed incomplete rings around the notochord and were open above.

We assign all these forms to the Amphibia. In the Lower Permian, however, very similar forms appear, the position of which is quite intermediate between amphibians and reptiles. These are the seymourians, which many authors assign to the Stegocephalia. In the skull roof, *Seymouria* is indistinguishable from the anthracosaurs (Fig. 160). Their characteristic intertemporal was also present. The palate was very primitive, and the palatine and vomerine tusks common to the Stegocephalia were present. The occipital condyle was unpaired, as in the primitive labyrinthodonts. In the lower jaw there was a complete set of the bones characteristic of labyrinthodonts. The sound transmission apparatus was the same as in the labyrinthodonts. Corresponding to this there were otic notches into which the shaft of the auditory ossicle extended. There was also the alveolar structure of the dermal bones,

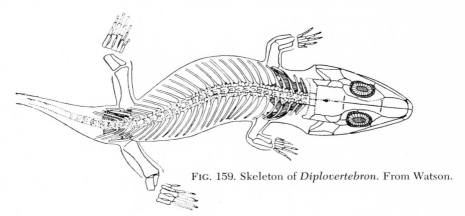

FIG. 159. Skeleton of *Diplovertebron*. From Watson.

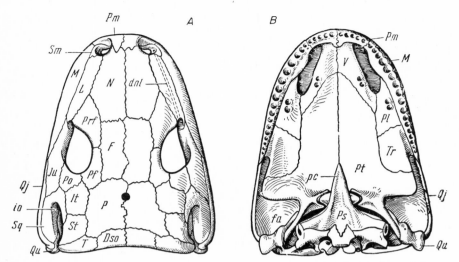

FIG. 160. Skull of *Seymouria*, from above (*A*) and below (*B*). *dnl*, Nasolachrymal duct; *Dso*, postparietal; *F*, frontal; *fa*, fenestra for jaw muscles; *io*, otic notch; *It*, intertemporal bone; *Ju*, jugal; *L*, lachrymal; *M*, maxillary; *N*, nasal; *P*, parietal; *pc*, anterior process of parasphenoid; *Pf*, *Prf*, pre- and postfrontal bones; *Pl*, palatine; *Pm*, premaxilla; *Po*, postorbital; *Ps*, parasphenoid; *Pt*, pterygoid; *Qt*, quadratojugal; *Qu*, quadrate; *Sm*, septomaxilla; *Sq*, squamosal; *St*, supratemporal; *T*, tabular; *Tr*, ectopterygoid (transversum); *V*, vomer. From Bystrov.

typical of the Stegocephalia. The teeth were folded as in the labyrinthodonts. In addition, larval development evidently took place in water in *Seymouria* and they underwent complete metamorphosis as did the Amphibia. In any case, in *Discosauriscus*, similar to *Seymouria*, there were external gills. In all these respects they were genuine Amphibia as accepted by Sushkin (1927), Romer (1945), and others.

On the other hand, however, there were typical features of reptilian organization. With the transition to terrestrial life reconstruction of the organs of movement, that is, of the postcranial skeleton, becomes of predominant significance. In this feature in particular the seymourians were actually reptiles. The appendicular girdles were well ossified and the appendages themselves were much more highly developed than in the Stegocephalia. The phalangeal formula of the digits, 2, 3, 4, 5, 3(4), is characteristic of reptiles. There were separate coracoid ossifications (fusing to the scapula). The iliac bones were expanded dorsally, as in reptiles. Although they were usually attached to one sacral rib, a dual attachment sometimes occurred. In the humerus of *Seymouria* there was a foramen entepicondyloideum as in primitive reptiles.

Not without reason do paleontologists ascribe special significance to the structure of the vertebral column. In the present case the spinal column had a composition characteristic of reptiles. The hypocentra, already smaller in *Diplovertebron*, were converted to "intercentra" in *Seymouria*, wedged ventrally between the vertebral centra formed of the pleurocentra on which the neural arches grew (Fig. 50). The ossified hypocentra were definitely reduced; however, over them, between the centra, there were fairly large interspaces in which cartilaginous prolongations of these same hypocentra evidently lay. If these parts are reconstructed then the vertebral column is shown to have a definite embolomerous structure. In the caudal region the hemal arches form a unit with the hypocentra and consequently do not rest on the centra but lie between them. The bicipital ribs are articulated with the capitulum on the hypocentrum, i.e., between the centra of the vertebrae, and the tuberculum on the broad transverse process on the neural arch.

Even more significant is the reconstruction of the first vertebra. Here, for the first time in terrestrial vertebrates, the movable arrangement of the first two vertebrae in the form of the atlas and the epistropheus appears. The neural arch of the atlas rested on the hypocentrum, and the pleurocentra (with an opening for the notochord) lies posterior of and adjoined directly to the centrum, i.e., the pleurocentra of the second vertebra—the epistropheus (Fig. 161).

In this characteristic, and in the present case it is of decisive significance, seymourians were genuine reptiles. This view has significance even if *Seymouria*, like *Discosauriscus*, bred in water and had larval development and metamorphosis like the Amphibia. Perhaps some seymourians, such as *Kotlassia*, reverted to fully aquatic life. Such secondary transitions to life in water occurred repeatedly in later reptiles. While the seymourians were amphibian in their biology, nevertheless they were still reptiles in structure. This indicates that the transition to full terrestrial life was as prolonged a process as the emergence of the crossopterygian fishes into the aerial medium.

Not only the ichthyostegids but also the Lower Carboniferous Stegocephalia were still fully aquatic animals; they both bred and fed in the water. The primitive reptiles likewise were not yet separated from the water and in all likelihood bred and developed in water. They undoubtedly moved about on dry land much better than the Amphibia, however, going out farther from the water basins, and they fed on terrestrial animals and later on vegetation also. We do not know when reptiles changed over to breeding on land and to laying large eggs protected by complicated envelopes. However, the Permian cotylosaurs are recognized as genuine reptiles by all paleontologists.

FIG. 161. First vertebra of *Seymouria*, lateral view. *ha*, Hypocentrum of first vertebra (centrum of atlas); *pas*, pleurocentrum of first vertebra (odontoid process of epistropheus); *he*, hypocentrum (intercentrum) of second vertebra; *pe*, pleurocentrum, i.e., centrum, of second vertebra (epistropheus). From Bystrov.

In the cotylosaurs had the same complete skull roof as the Stegocephalia and the seymourians; its composition, however, was somewhat simplified (Fig. 162). The intertemporal was eliminated and the tabular was shifted to the occipital region; the postparietals were merged and formed an unpaired dermosupraoccipital. The otic notches disappeared and the tympanic membrane, if present, was located lower, in the vicinity of the quadrate bone. The skull roof was more completely ossified than in the Stegocephalia. All the occipital bones were present including the supraoccipital. On the sides of the opisthotic, larger paroccipital processes were formed. There was also an ossified basisphenoid. The dermal bones of the pectoral girdle were more weakly developed than in *Seymouria*. The iliac bones of the pelvis were articulated to two or three sacral ribs.

The cotylosaurs are not a homogeneous group and at present are divided into the Captorhinomorpha (Fig. 162) and Diadectomorpha. The former come nearer the later pelycosaurs and consequently to the trunk of the theromorphic forms. The second are more similar to other branches of typical reptiles (chelonians, lepidosaurs, and archosaurs).

Loss of the tympanic membrane is characteristic of the captorhinomorphs. The auditory ossicle, fairly bulky, rested directly on the quadrate bone. It is difficult to find any other explanation for this than to suggest that the ancestral forms led a semi-burrowing existence. Perhaps they obtained their food under the ground. The relatively primitive *Limnoscelis* was an aquatic predator. The no less primitive Lower Permian *Romeria* was apparently a burrowing insectivore. Also, in species of *Captorhinus* the premaxillary bones were curved downward; evidently they also obtained their food by digging up insect larvae of which there were undoubtedly some very large forms at that time.

All these observations lend weight to our suggestion concerning the reduction of the system of aerial sound transmission and the gradual development of sound transmission from the ground, which could have been of great value in finding burrowing larvae in the ground. To this we must add that in the primitive captorhinids there were still rudiments of the otic notches and consequently, tympanic membranes (in *Romeria*, and traces in *Limnoscelis;* Huene, 1956).

A theory of the origin of captorhinomorphs from microsaurs (Tatarinov, 1958) is excluded in view of the quite separate differentiation of the spinal column and its cervical division (the first vertebra with an odontoid process as in urodele Amphibia).

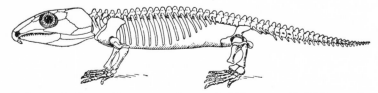

FIG. 162. Skeleton of a Lower Permian cotylosaur, *Labidosaurus*. By Williston, from Huene.

The presumption of the independent origin of the ichthyosaurs is more fundamental. The embolomerous vertebral column of the older Eotriassic forms, latitabular skull, folded teeth, and some other characteristics, link them directly to the labyrinthodonts. On the other hand, both groups of cotylosaurs are sufficiently different to bring up the question of the possibility of diphyly in the origin of other reptiles. The diversity among their primitive members is negligible, and it is fully explained by a difference in way of life and different nutrition. Both groups are quite similar to the seymourians and it is impossible to deny their relationship. Let us keep in mind the radiation of the typical differentiation of the vertebral column from the anthracosaurs to *Diplovertebron* and beyond to the seymourians. We note also the appearance in the latter of the characteristic structure of the first cervical vertebrae, the atlas and the epistropheus (Fig. 161), which progressed in the cotylosaurs and passed from the latter to all the higher vertebrates. It is difficult to conceive of the convergent development of such a specific system. In addition, the similarity in the embryonic membranes of all Amphibia also favors their origin from a single common root. On the other hand, there is the profound divergence of the cotylosaurs in their later evolution which cannot be doubted. The differences deepened and extended in the lines leading from the captorhinomorphs to the pelycosaurs, theromorphs, and mammals on the one hand, and in the branches leading from the diadectomorphs to the chelonians, squamate reptiles, archosaurs, and birds on the other hand.

Since the seymourians were still very much like the Amphibia, and the cotylosaurs probably had not yet abandoned the aquatic medium (*Limnoscelis* was an aquatic predator), the retention of some amphibian characteristics in the branches leading to the mammals is explained. The skins of mammals is rich in glands, as is the skin of Amphibia. The tongue was fleshy and also rich in glands. The hyoid and the remnants of the gill arches (the laryngeal cartilages) were relatively well preserved. In the embryonic skull of mammals postparietals are initiated, fusing later with the occipital bones. The fairly primitive structure of the appendages with some central ossicles was retained. The specializations of theromorphs and mammals developed in quite different directions from those of sauromorphs. It is sufficient to note that division of the bloodstream led to the retention of the left aortic arch in mammals and the retention of the right arch in the higher reptiles and birds, and also to differences in the evolution of the central nervous system which was accompanied in mammals by gradual development of a new cortex of the cerebrum. The same is also indicated by the development of quite diversified systems of sound transmission.

All of these differences were accumulated in the process of divergent evolution and cannot serve as a basis for acceptance of a polyphyletic origin of the higher terrestrial vertebrates, the amniotes.

19

Monophyletism versus Polyphyletism in the Origin of Terrestrial Vertebrates

The problem of the origin of terrestrial vertebrates may now be regarded as having been solved. All terrestrial forms, Stegocephalia and modern Amphibia, arose from primitive crossopterygian fishes. However, a disagreement has arisen regarding the question of single versus multiple origin of forms (i.e., the question of monophyletism versus polyphyletism) in the origin of terrestrial vertebrates, in particular, of the Amphibia. The position of the modern urodele Amphibia is the most uncertain. The Swedish school of paleontologists believes that the latter are of altogether independent origin and are not allied in close relationship either to the higher terrestrial vertebrates or even to other Amphibia.

The source of these views was the work of Holmgren (1933) who approached the problem through study of the development of the limbs of modern Amphibia. Holmgren justifiably affirms the great difference in the structure of the appendages of urodele and anuran Amphibia. This is undoubtedly the result of the extreme specialization of the latter (in adaptation to locomotion by saltation). The appendages of anuran Amphibia differ equally from the appendages of both the Stegocephalia and all other terrestrial vertebrates. On the contrary, the appendages of urodele Amphibia are not placed by Gegenbaur at the base of his structural plan of tetrapod appendages by accident. They are very similar to the appendages of primitive reptiles, and even to the appendages of mammals. The structural plan of anuran appendages advanced by Holmgren (1933; Fig. 56) is the result of embryological research and generalizations. It portrays the structure of the primitive appendages of terrestrial vertebrates in general and essentially repeats the Gegenbaur plan. On the other hand, the plan worked out by Holmgren for urodele Amphibia (1933; Fig. 37) not only fails to represent their specific limb structure but in general does not correspond to any other terrestrial vertebrate appendages. In this scheme special significance is given to the axis of the limb skeleton set between the first and second digits. The sole basis

272

for the identification of this axis was the presence in the larvae of *Hynobius*, in the early stages of development, of a small purely dermal web between the first two digits. This was, undoubtedly, a purely larval adaptation for support and locomotion of the young larva over the soft, muddy ground of shallow waters. Furthermore, in the quite artificial pattern of Holmgren, a second conclusion is drawn from the similarity of the appendages of Dipnoi (especially *Ceratodus*) having a central articulated axis in the fins, to the limbs of urodele Amphibia, as if they were constructed on the type of the biserial archipterygium; and from this the further conclusion of a diphyletic origin of Amphibia is drawn. Anuran Amphibia, like the Stegocephalia and higher terrestrial vertebrates, arose from crossopterygian fishes, maintaining a pattern of dichotomous branching in the skeleton of the paired appendages; urodele Amphibia arose, it would seem, from fishes similar to the Dipnoi, having fins built on the type of the biserial archipterygium.

Conclusions regarding the diphyletic origin of terrestrial vertebrates are thus constructed solely on the basis of the study of the limbs, and with considerable stretching of the point at that. In reality the skeleton of the urodele limb is very similar in its composition to the skeleton of primitive reptiles and mammals, and in particular it is almost identical to the limb skeleton of the Stegocephalia. The structure of the limbs not only cannot be utilized for constructing a hypothesis of diphyletic origin of terrestrial vertebrates, but on the contrary it gives us the best proof of their monophyly (Schmalhausen, 1958e).

The views of Holmgren were adopted by Swedish paleontologists, and most notably by Säve-Söderbergh (1934, 1935, 1936). The latter particularly asserts the affinity of anurans to labyrinthodonts. The anurans form only an extremely specialized terminal branch of a distinct line of evolutionary development represented by the series: Ichthyostegalia—Labyrinthodontia—(Phyllospondyli)—Anura. Urodele Amphibia are in some respects the result of a divergent development. This is manifested in the complete reduction of the anterior part of the palatoquadrate cartilage which rarely maintains contact with the ethmoid region of the skull. With this is associated also a reduction of the anterior palatine fork of the pterygoids (and the expansion of their posterior part), and also the reduction of the palatine bone. In the structure of the palate, in the large olfactory capsules, and in the broad hyoids (ceratohyals) of urodele Amphibia the author sees some similarity to dipnoan fishes. However, in the Dipnoi the anterior part of the pterygoid bears stout palatine teeth, and the olfactory capsules come together and form an internasal septum, i.e., they are not built as in urodele Amphibia but, on the contrary, are more similar to the olfactory capsules of labyrinthodonts, anurans, and other terrestrial vertebrates.

A comparison of urodele Amphibia with the Dipnoi gives so little support to the hypothesis of a diphyletic origin of terrestrial vertebrates that at present it is not used as justification of it. Moreover, Jarvik (1942) showed that the Dipnoi differ from terrestrial vertebrates and from crossopterygian fishes not only in advanced and unique specializations but also in the absence of real choanae. Correspondingly, Jarvik recently modernized the hypothesis of diphyletic origin of terrestrial vertebrates, utilizing differences in the structure of two groups of crossopterygian fishes—the Porolepiformes and Osteolepiformes.

As a basis for this he made an especially detailed study of the olfactory region of the skull. This investigation showed fairly large divergences between the two groups. In the main these differences narrow down to the following structural peculiarities: (1) In the Osteolepiformes the olfactory sacs are close together and are separated from each other by an internasal partition; in the Porolepiformes the olfactory organs are widely spreading and between the two olfactory capsules there are paired spaces (cavum internasale). (2) In the Osteolepiformes in the anterior part of the palate between the premaxillary bones and the vomers there was a small depression (fossa apicalis) in which intermaxillary glands were probably located. Posteriorly the depression sometimes ended in a pit under the front edge of the vomers (the intervomerine pit) and passed to a canal opening in the palate between the two vomers (intervomerine canal). In the Porolepiformes at the site of the depression there were also deep paired depressions, the internasal cavities mentioned above, in which large intermaxillary glands evidently lay. (3) In the Osteolepiformes the parasphenoid was narrow, tapering anteriorly; in the Porolepiformes it was wide and rounded anteriorly. (4) In the Osteolepiformes there was, lateral of the external nostrils, the typical dermal bone— the rostrale laterale—homologous to the septomaxillare of terrestrial vertebrates. In the Porolepiformes these bones are absent. In all these characteristics the anurans in particular, and the higher land vertebrates as well as the labyrinthodonts, are found to be similar to the Osteolepiformes, and the urodele Amphibia appear closer to the Porolepiformes.

In connection with these similarities it should be noted, however, that to a considerable extent they are concerned with the general shape of the head and the extent of development of the intermaxillary glands which were evidently present in all crossopterygian Rhipidistia and in all Amphibia. The expansion of these glands between the olfactory capsules (as paired masses in the Porolepiformes, unpaired in urodele Amphibia) may have led to a general convergent similarity in the structure of the olfactory region in Porolepiformes and in Urodela. Although *Megalichthys* belongs to the Osteolepiformes it has olfactory organs as widely separated as those in the Urodela. The same also applies to other forms with broad heads (*Panderichthys* and *Platycephalichthys;* Vorobjerva-Blokhina, 1959, 1962). Separation of the olfactory capsules along with reduced development of the organs of vision, the secondary flattened platybasic skull with a lowered cerebrum, led to an expansion of the parasphenoid. In the anurans the intermaxillary gland is of relatively smaller size and it expands anteriorly of the olfactory organs without entering between the olfactory capsules. At the same time, anurans have larger eyes. All this led to preservation of the nasal partition and a narrower parasphenoid. With respect to the septomaxilla, the conclusion of Lapage (1928) which was taken up by Jarvik (1942) has been found to be erroneous

(Schmalhausen, 1958b). The septomaxilla of urodele Amphibia is a quite typical dermal bone in its development, as in other terrestrial vertebrates.

Jarvik also points out other less significant differences, such as the branching of n. profundus V, the position of the terminal branch of n. buccalis VII, the position of n. palatinus VII and the development of the system of blood vessels of the orbital region. Differences are observed, however, within the limits of one order of modern Amphibia. Thus, for example, n. buccalis in the Hynobiidae passes medial of the choana and the olfactory capsules (as in the Porolepiformes, according to Jarvik, 1942), and in the Ambystomidae it breaks down into separate branches lateral of the choana and the olfactory organs (as in the Osteolepiformes; Schmalhausen, 1957a). The development of the system of blood vessels in the orbital region also varies; it is associated with their importance in the general dermal respiration of a given form. According to Kulczycki (1960) the difference between primitive Osteolepiformes and the Porolepiformes is very slight.

All these observations show that on the whole there is not sufficient evidence for a conclusion favoring the diphyletic origin of all Amphibia. However, Jarvik goes much farther; he accepts the broadest overall polyphyletism in the origin of terrestrial vertebrates.

According to the concept of Jarvik, the Ichthyostegalia, although very primitive (they have retained the suture between the anterior division of the braincase, the sphenethmoid, and the posterior otico-occipital, as a remnant of the crossopterygians, dividing the skull into two parts), are nevertheless a specialized blind alley, since they have the exceptionally unusual location of the anterior nostrils on the edge of the upper jaw. The older labyrinthodonts seemingly could not have arisen from the Paleozoic labyrinthodonts known to us, since they show peculiar specializations connecting them directly to certain Osteolepiformes, in particular, *Eusthenopteron*. Particularly, in these and others the fossa apicalis is well developed, and it passes backward into the intervomerine pit and intervomerine canal. The anuran Amphibia arose as an independent branch of primitive Osteolepiformes. They also inherited the typical septomaxilla. In addition, the higher terrestrial vertebrates, the Amniota, are of independent origin from these same Osteolepiformes. To this must be added that in this scheme each of the above groups is shown originating not from one form but from several (in particular it is considered likely that even the Ichthyostegidae and the Acanthostegidae arose independently from the Osteolepiformes), and the family "tree" is completely converted into a "lawn."

All these conclusions obviously rest upon an overestimation of the importance of miscellaneous specialized characters regarded as static, none of which are dynamic. It is presumed that specialized characteristics may not be lost (e.g., position of the nostrils in the Ichthyostegidae) and may not originate anew (e.g., the intervomerine pit). This position is not reliable in the present case. The anterior nostril is also located at the edge of the upper jaw in some crossopterygian fishes and in some labyrinthodonts (*Megalocephalus*). In other labyrinthodonts it has undoubtedly been shifted dorsally. Its position in *Ichthyostega* should not be regarded as a specialized but primitive characteristic (for Tetrapoda). With the presence, in all forms compared, of the recess (fossa apicalis) for the intermaxillary gland, it can alter its form depending on the expansion of this gland. On expansion backward it pushes between and under the vomers up to the fore-end of the parasphenoid. This process took place in some crossopterygians (*Eusthenopteron*) and the same, definitely and quite independently, occurred in the Triassic labyrinthodonts. The same process may also be traced out in modern urodele Amphibia. Their large intermaxillary gland is located in the internasal cavity. However, the excretory duct opens into a pit lying in the cleft between the vomers. In higher forms (in newts and Plethodontidae) the vomers cover the posterior part of the glands and are united at a suture, leaving only an opening for the excretory canals. Thus there arose the same intervomerine canal as in higher labyrinthodonts. This definitely could not serve as the basis for the conclusion of an independent origin of higher urodele Amphibia from crossopterygians close to *Eusthenopteron*.

At the conclusion of a critical review I must note that in some cases I do not deny the special position of urodele Amphibia which show, along with retention of very many features of primitive organization, quite definitely specialized characteristics also. From their very origin, terrestrial vertebrates have a history of sharply marked divergence; they show excellent examples of adaptive radiation of forms conquering new ecological zones.

Jarvik presumes, and it forms the foundation of his theory, that crossopterygian fishes reached such a level of evolutionary development that the transition to terrestrial life could have occurred without any essential alterations in internal organization. Therefore, it could have been accomplished repeatedly in various representatives of the crossopterygian fishes. It is indisputable that the organization of crossopterygian fishes was seemingly prepared for such a transition, but this transition was, however, undoubtedly a prolonged and complicated process (Schmalhausen, 1957d). Those forms which first surmounted the difficulties of the transition from water to land took a predominance in the struggle for existence. Forms which lacked this adaptation, or which participated in later attempts, came upon an already occupied ecological zone in which they could not compete with the already adapted first colonizers. Of decisive significance in this matter are not the theoretical discussions, however, but certain facts the importance of which we will attempt to assess.

I. The Divergence in Skeletal Structure

Paleontologists quite justifiably attribute much importance to the structure of the vertebral column which required considerable reconstruction for the transition from aquatic to terrestrial life. Differences in the composition of the vertebrae are found to be highly significant and characteristic of certain phylogenetic lines. This circumstance also tests the polyphyletic concepts of some paleontologists.

The spinal column of crossopterygian fishes, relatively well studied in *Eusthenopteron*, consisted of a persistent notochord with arches resting on it and central elements. The composition of the vertebrae of the primitive stegocephalian Ichthyostegidae is essentially similar. The spinal column of the rhachitomous labyrinthodonts, in which there were more or less well-developed pleurocentra (Fig. 50), is of about the same structure. In the embolomerous labyrinthodonts both the hypocentra and the pleurocentra formed complete bony rings around the notochord, between which the bases of the neural arches were wedged dorsally. The lepospondylous Stegocephalia had, from the very beginning, cylindrical ossified centra, forming a unit with the neural arches. Concerning the composition of the centrum one judges in this case only by the continuity of their union with the neural and hemal arches.

In some characteristics, urodele Amphibia are close to the lepospondylous Stegocephalia. Until recently it was believed that the centrum in urodele Amphibia arises first in the form of a thin osseous cylinder over the notochord surface. Thus, it seemed that the centrum of urodele Amphibia, and consequently of lepospondylous Stegocephalia, arose independently of the arches and belongs to a quite peculiar structural type (the pseudocentral vertebra).

In the study of the embryonic development of the vertebral column in the most primitive urodele Amphibia, namely in the Hynobiidae, there could be established, however, some new facts permitting a comparison of our understanding of the structure of lepospondylous vertebrae with other types of amphibian vertebrae (Schmalhausen, 1957c, 1958a,b). First, the "intervertebral" cartilage arises segmentally in the form of paired anlagen on the sides of the notochord. The anlagen then extend around in the form of rings. In the posterior part of the caudal region in *Hynobius* they are merged into a continuous perichordal cylinder. The bases of the cartilaginous arches of the vertebrae pass without any discontinuity into the adjacent perichordal cartilage. Therefore, participation of the latter, as well as the material pertaining to the arch, cannot be denied. Between the adjacent centra an articulation is developed by the formation of an articular cleft within the perichordal cartilage. Since the intervertebral articulation that formed could hardly have been replaced by another, it is evident that the articular cleft passes, as in other Amphibia, between the pleurocentrum of the anterior vertebra and the hypocentrum of the posterior vertebra. The cartilaginous vertebra, i.e., the perichordal cartilage, should consist of these two elements at least. In the middle part of the centrum, i.e., intersegmentally, the cartilage is reduced, however, and here the osseous centrum is developed very early. The latter is clearly developed as a perichordal ossification at the base of the arch. In the caudal region a similar ossification begins at the base of the hemal arch. In the trunk region, aside from the dorsal ossification originating from the base of the neural arch, there also appears a small ossification under the notochord. While the dorsal ossification shows the predominant role of the bases of the neural arches in the development of the osseous centra, the presence of the ventral ossification shows that some part in their formation was also taken by the hemal arches (the hypocentra). Further growth of the bony centra occurs perichondrally on the surface of the perichordal cartilage, as in the reptiles. Finally, it has been established that besides ossification of the bases of the neural arches there is also independent ossification of the more distal parts of the arch which then merge with the proximal ossifications of the arches, and subsequently with the osseous centrum, as one unit.

Collectively, all these facts show that there are no major differences in the composition of the vertebrae of lepospondylous urodele Amphibia and of labyrinthodonts. Undoubtedly in the formation of the centrum, ossifications growing out from the bases of the upper arches predominated, as in *Miobatrachus* (Fig. 50) and also in urodele Amphibia. This shows the parallel course of specialization in the branchiosaurs and in urodele Amphibia. Lastly, the presence of a separate perichondral ossification in the distal part of the neural arch (which is also seen in reptiles) is undoubtedly a primitive characteristic, uniting the lepospondylous and adelospondylous types of vertebrae (in which the suture between the neural arch and the centrum was retained. Thus, while the lepospondylous vertebra is also the result of sharply divergent evolution, it was developed from the same foundation as in other Amphibia. The spinal column of reptiles is derived, as is well known, from the embolomerous type of vertebra of primitive reptilomorphic Stegocephalia (through reduction of the hypocentra).

Perhaps lepospondylous vertebrae were developed from the embolomerous type by early fusion of its elements to the neural arches.

Evidently the vertebrae of all terrestrial vertebrates were derived from one root, from the primary rhachitomous type of vertebrae of primitive Stegocephalia which in turn are similar to the vertebrae of crossopterygian osteolepids.

The diversity occurring in the structure of the first vertebra is especially interesting. In the labyrinthodonts the first vertebra differed from the following ones only in the presence of an articular depression for articulation with the occipital condyle or, in higher forms, two articular depressions corresponding to two condyles. In the reptiles, beginning with the seymourians, the first vertebra retains the same structure that it had in the labyrinthodonts: the neural arches interlock below through the hypocentra and thus form a ring around the notochord. The first vertebra—the atlas—bears only an articular depression for articulation with the occipital condyle. The second vertebra is considerably transformed: the pleurocentra of the first vertebra are linked and later fused to the pleurocentrum of the second vertebra and form the odontoid process around which the atlas may rotate.

Another line of specialization leads from the microsaurs to the urodele Amphibia. Here the first vertebra is transformed: between the articular facets on it, entering the depression in the lower part of the occipital condyle or between both occipital condyles (Fig. 68), the tuberculum interglenoidale is developed. This structure passed on to the urodele Amphibia (Fig. 153). In this respect we have a typical divergence between the labyrinthodonts, reptiles, and the line of lepospondylous Amphibia leading to the urodele Amphibia.

The spinal column of terrestrial vertebrates was developed divergently

and the greatest divergence is between the Amphibia and the higher vertebrates, beginning with the reptiles. However, these types of vertebrae were
developed from one particular primary rhachitomous type of the primordial
terrestrial vertebrates, i.e., from one root. Therefore no conclusions in favor
of a polyphyletic origin of terrestrial vertebrates can be drawn from the structure of the vertebral column.

The braincase of crossopterygian fishes consisted of two separately ossified divisions, an anterior one (sphenethmoid) and a posterior one (otico-
occipital) which were normally connected by a well-defined joint behind the
hypophysis. The parasphenoid underlaid only the anterior division of the
braincase. In terrestrial vertebrates the braincase comprises one unit and as
a rule is made up of a large number of ossifications. It is then all the more
interesting to note that in the ichthyostegids the transverse suture between
the anterior and posterior divisions of the braincase was preserved posterior
of the hypophysis. As in the crossopterygians the parasphenoid was narrow
and underlay only the anterior division of the braincase.

In the embolomerous Stegocephalia, as described by Watson (1926b), both
divisions were already merged together and the parasphenoid was spreading
backward under the otic region of the skull. In more recent labyrinthodonts
a more or less extensive part of the skull in the olfactory region, and also between the orbital and otic regions, remained cartilaginous. In the anterior
part of the braincase the sphenethmoid was retained as a basic ossification
to which, in the hypophysial region, the basisphenoid was sometimes adjoined, and it usually fused with the parasphenoid. In the posterior part of
the braincase several separate ossifications were developed, the pro-otic and
sometimes the opisthotic in the walls of the otic capsules, and a typical basioccipital, exoccipitals, and supraoccipital in the occipital region. In all later
Amphibia, in labyrinthodonts, anurans, and also urodeles, these bones were
progressively replaced by cartilage and the number of ossifications was reduced. In modern Amphibia there are only the sphenethmoid (paired in
urodele Amphibia), pro-otic, and exoccipitals. The latter bones are often fused
together (Fig. 163).

Characteristic of all terrestrial vertebrates is the greatly expanded anterior
division of the skull, in particular the olfactory region. In the earlier Stegocephalia, as in the crossopterygian fishes, there was an interorbital septum,
and the forebrain with its olfactory lobes and olfactory nerves lay in cavities
and canals above this partition. In all later Amphibia there is a characteristic
gradual flattening of the skull and expansion of its base (Fig. 163). The cerebrum became lower, and the cavity of the braincase was pushed down to the
expanded interorbital partition. Thus the tropibasic skull of crossopterygian
fishes and early Stegocephalia was converted into the platybasic skull of the
labyrinthodonts, anurans, and urodele Amphibia.

We have grounds to suppose that the flattening and expansion of the amphibian skull is associated with the gradual development of a force mechanism of pulmonary respiration and the growing importance of the intermandibular pump as its main element (Schmalhausen, 1957d).

The above processes in the transformation of the original skull occurred

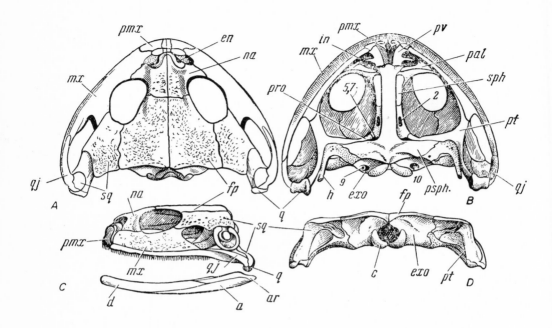

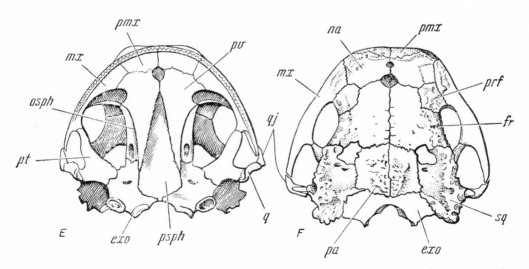

FIG. 163. Skull of *Calyptocephalus*, from above (A), from below (B), lateral view (C) and posterior view (D). Skull of *Tylotriton*, from below (E) and above (F). *a*, Angular; *ar*, articular; *c*, occipital condyle; *d*, dentary; *en*, nostril; *exo*, exoccipital; *fp*, frontoparietal; *fr*, frontal; *h*, hyoid; *in*, choana; *mx*, maxilla; *na*, nasal; *osph*, orbitosphenoid; *pa*, parietal; *pal*, palatine; *pmx*, premaxilla; *prf*, prefrontal; *pro*, pro-otic; *psph*, parasphenoid; *pt*, pterygoid; *pv*, vomer; *q*, quadrate; *qj*, quadratojugal; *sph*, sphenethmoid; *sq*, squamosal; 2, 5, 7, 9, 10, nerve exits. From Goodrich.

in parallel in the ancestors of anuran and urodele Amphibia and led to very similar shapes (Fig. 163). These forms of the skull were derived from the structure of earlier Stegocephalia, and there is no basis for the assumption of an independent course of transformation from various representatives of the crossopterygian fishes. The same may also be said of the dermal bones of the skull.

The skull roof of primitive Stegocephalia is of the same composition as in crossopterygian Osteolepida. The latter are distinguished only by the presence of the bones of the branchial operculum (remnants of which occur in the ichthyostegids), and a large number of bones in the olfactory region instead of the lone pair of larger nasal bones of terrestrial vertebrates. The floor of the skull is lined by the same bones as in crossopterygians. In some of the more specialized Stegocephalia, however, there occurred a further reduction in the number of bones. Primarily, in the batrachomorphic Stegocephalia the intertemporal disappears (it is probably fused to the supratemporal); it is present only in some Loxommoidea and in some primitive Rhachitomi.

In the reptilomorphic Anthracosauria and Seymouriamorpha the intertemporal is retained. This marks one of the first divergences between the Amphibia and the reptiles. Later divergences are of a gradual nature. In the batrachomorphs expansion of the braincase, especially posteriorly, occurred, dividing the tabulars which lost contact with the parietal bones; the vomers were expanded, and lateral of the parasphenoid the interpterygoid fenestrae opened out. In the reptilomorphs the braincase increased in height; the tabulars retained contact with the parietal bones; the vomers were narrow and elongated; the choanae were expanded and convergent. The otic notches dwindled and disappeared. Both lines begin with the appearance of small differences in the group of embolomerous Stegocephalia. Their evolution is definitely of a divergent character.

Further reduction of the number of dermal bones of the skull occurred in the branch leading from the labyrinthodonts to anuran Amphibia. In this branch, aside from reduction of the intertemporal bones, there also occurred an early reduction of the supratemporal, postparietal, and tabular bones (Figs. 60 and 62). In addition, in modern anurans all the bones surrounding the orbits (lachrymal, pre- and post-frontal, postorbital, and zygomatic) disappeared, and the frontal bones fused to the parietals (Fig. 163). All this is the result of very marked specialization in one of the branches of labyrinthodonts.

Similarly, although less significantly, simplification of the structure of the skull roof also occurred quite independently in the lepospondylous Stegocephalia. In the most primitive forms the construction of the skull roof is complete (Fig. 66). As in most other Stegocephalia there are no separate intertemporal bones. The supratemporal bones disappeared early and after them the tabulars and postparietals (Fig. 66). Correspondingly the otic notches also disappeared. The orbits were expanded; correspondingly, the interpterygoid fenestra of the skull base was enlarged and the palatines were reduced. All these modifications occurred in a series of lepospondylous forms and consequently give a clear picture of divergent development within a group of primitive Stegocephalia. As is evident, the specialization of the ancestors of urodele Amphibia occurred extremely early (in the Carboniferous). Nevertheless, in the ontogeny of modern forms some traces of the origin of the skull roof from the stegocephalian skull were retained as shown in the complexity of its composition (generally it even retained considerably more primitive structure than the anurans). First, in adult Caudata there are usually prefrontals (Fig. 163), and above these, in the Hynobiidae, lachrymals also (Fig. 134). By *in vivo* staining of the alizarin method there can be established in larvae of urodele Amphibia (Figs. 131 and 133) the existence of a quite distinct supratemporal which later fuses to the parietal bone. While the septomaxilla is also reduced in many modern Caudata, it is present in the Hynobiidae, Ambystomidae, and Plethodontidae. This bone is especially well developed in *Onychodactylus*, in which it is equipped with a typical medial process such as is present on this bone in the osteolepids on the one hand, and in lower labyrinthodonts, anurans, and primitive amniotes on the other hand.

The anterior part of the palatoquadrate division of the maxillary arch is reduced in all terrestrial vertebrates. It is manifested most fully in the Stegocephalia, in which it is very similar to the palatoquadrate part of the maxillary arch of crossopterygian fishes and is characterized by similar connections to the braincase. In contrast to crossopterygian fishes, in which all of this division is ossified, in all Stegocephalia, as in modern Amphibia, the anterior part of the palatoquadrate remained cartilaginous. Only the posterior part of the quadrate bone was ossified, and in the Stegocephalia (and amniotes) there is sometimes even an epipterygoid bone in the preotic region. In modern anurans the palatoquadrate cartilage is fully retained. In urodele Amphibia its anterior end is reduced. Only remnants are retained in Hynobiidae (Figs. 130 and 135) and Cryptobranchidae. The reduction of the anterior end of the palatoquadrate cartilage leads to reduction of the dermal bone—the dermopalatinum. The ectopterygoid is absent in modern Amphibia; however, it is present in the reptiles. It is interesting to note that the palatoquadrate cartilage to some extent retained all the typical connections to the braincase present in crossopterygian fishes. In some form or other it is present in modern Amphibia.

In the lower jaw of crossopterygian fishes, Stegocephalia, and reptiles there was a large number of fully homologous bones. The number of these bones was reduced both in the series leading to anuran Amphibia and in lepospondylous forms. In this respect, as in the composition of the skull roof, the anurans are more specialized than urodele Amphibia. In crossopterygian fishes the whole of Meckel's cartilage is sometimes ossified. In the Amphibia only two isolated ossifications are developed in it. One small ossification at the fore-end of the lower jaw (os mentomandibulare) is fused to the dermal dentary bone (dentale) in almost all Amphibia. Another ossification (os articulare) is developed in urodele Amphibia at the posterior end, in the vicinity of the jaw articulation. Among anurans it is found only in *Xenopus*.

The upper division of the hyoid arch, the hyomandibula of fishes (crossopteryians in particular) underwent the most profound transformation in the transition from aquatic to terrestrial life. Information on its structure in the Stegocephalia is unfortunately too limited, since a considerable part of it remained cartilaginous and could not be completely restored. In all Stegocephalia, however, it was undoubtedly of small size, and took the role of an apparatus for transmitting sound from the external medium (usually through the tympanic membrane lying in the otic notch of the skull roof) to the inner ear. Notwithstanding the sharp divergence in structure of this apparatus in terrestrial vertebrates, it is fundamentally a single structure, present in some primitive Stegocephalia (*Megalocephalus, Eryops,* and partly also the neotenic *Dvinosaurus,* in which the tympanic membrane, as in modern urodele Amphibia also, was absent). Until recently it was believed that in this respect only the urodele Amphibia occupy a special position, in which the apparatus conducting the sound is built on another principle. Study of the history of the ontogenetic development of the middle ear of the most primitive urodele Amphibia, the Hynobiidae, has shown, however, along with exceptionally primitive characteristics, definite features of modification in this same direction, as in the labyrinthodonts (and anurans and reptiles also), and gives undisputed evidence of a later secondary simplification of the whole system of sound transmission (Schmalhausen, 1956a,b, 1957b).

In the Hynobiidae, the larval structure of the auditory ossicle (stapes) and the elements associated with it (Fig. 112) shows a remote similarity to the hyomandibula of fishes. Here the whole hyoid arch can be demonstrated as a unit and all the characteristic connections of the hyomandibula. On the other hand, remnants of the tympanic cavity and temporary rudiments of the stapedial muscle show that the stapes (columella) served earlier for sound transmission from the air, as in the Stegocephalia. This function was lost and replaced by a system of sound transmission from the ground, probably in connection with the cryptic life of urodele Amphibia. This apparatus was also reduced in modern Urodela, however, and was supplemented by a system of sound transmission through the dermal veins of the head (Schmalhausen, 1957b).

The second transmission apparatus was a new structure developed only in terrestrial vertebrates. In crossopterygian fishes the hyomandibula still partly played the role of a jaw suspensor and linked the latter to the branchial apparatus. With the transition to terrestrial vertebrates there arose a complete change of function. If terrestrial vertebrates had arisen from different roots, then the system of sound transmission, even in the most general parallelism of evolution, could not have been based on one and the same structure. The evolution of the middle ear in terrestrial vertebrates ran divergently from the very beginning; the structure of the sound transmission apparatus in urodele Amphibia and the complex history of its transformation is one of the best proofs of this divergence. The diversity in the composition of the middle ear in various reptiles and mammals gives us further examples of divergent evolution in connection with variation in the way of life in these forms.

The hyoid proper and the gill arches with external gills retained the same structure in the larvae of urodele Amphibia that they had had in the larvae of the labyrinthodonts (this is evident in the structural peculiarities of the branchial skeleton of *Dvinosaurus* and impressions of the external gills in *Tungussogyrinus*). This, like the fate of the upper division of the hypoglossal arch (hyomandibula), shows the close relationship of urodele Amphibia to the labyrinthodonts, and consequently speaks in favor of their monophyletic origin from one and the same Osteolepiformes.

In bony fishes the anterior fins as a rule are more highly developed than the posterior. Correspondingly, the pectoral girdle is also much more strengthened and more complex in structure than the pelvic girdle. The anterior girdle is bounded anteriorly by the branchial cavity and is attached to the skull roof by a series of dermal bones. In terrestrial vertebrates this connection is lost and the head becomes movable. A remnant of it is retained only in *Pteroplax* (*Eogyrinus;* Watson, 1926b) in the form of a connection of the supracleithral through the post-temporal to the rear end of the tabular bones of the skull. In the Stegocephalia strong dermal armor with a broad pectoral section (clavicles and interclavicular bones) was retained on the pectoral girdle. Beneath this armor the cartilaginous girdle gradually developed. There was just one scapular ossification which sometimes enveloped the nearest part of the coracoid area (*Eryops*). The dorsal part of the scapular division remained cartilaginous, as did a large part of the ventral division of the primary girdle also. In some labyrinthodonts the dermal bones of the pectoral girdle were reduced, especially in terrestrial forms. In modern urodele Amphibia the pectoral girdle is undoubtedly very similar to the original girdle of the Stegocephalia; however, the dermal bones have disappeared without trace. The pectoral girdle of anuran Amphibia is different in form. Here, besides the scapular ossification there is still a distinct coracoid. In anurans, moreover, of the main dermal bones of the Stegocephalia, a clavicle on the ventral section of the girdle and a small cleithrum on the scapular were also retained.

Posteriorly, the pelvic girdle is markedly strengthened in comparison with the girdle of crossopterygian fishes, in accordance with the increased usage of the posterior appendages upon emergence of the animal on land. The ventral part of the girdle was expanded and the iliac process was very strongly forked, only connecting with the axial skeleton in terrestrial vertebrates, and the ribs were at the boundary between the thoracic and caudal region. In the early Stegocephalia the iliac section of the pelvic girdle was prolonged into a long posteriorly directed process which lay on two to three ribs (*Ichthyostega, Eogyrinus, Cricotus*, and *Pholidogaster*). A similar process was also present in the Microsauria. In later Stegocephalia a firmer connection to the ends of one pair of sacral ribs was established. This particular relationship passed on to modern Amphibia, to both urodeles and anurans. In the pelvic girdle of the Stegocephalia there were two to three ossifications: in the dorsal division a large iliac bone (os ilium); in the ventral division, posteriorly, the ischial bone (os ischium), and anteriorly (less constant) a pubic bone (os pubis). The pelvic girdle of urodele Amphibia retains the same form as in the Stegocephalia; however, the ossification is more weakly developed. In urodele Amphibia the iliac bone ossifies and there is an ossification in the ischial region. In anurans the form of the pelvic girdle is more unusual and shows an extreme degree of specialization. As a rule the long iliac division and the short ischial division ossify. Only in *Xenopus* was the ossification in the pubic section retained. On the whole the appendicular girdles of the urodele amphibians are quite similar to the primary girdles of the Stegocephalia while the girdles of anurans show features of marked specialization. The reptiles inherited the same girdle structure that occurred in the labyrinthodonts. This applies in even greater degree to the structure of the free appendages. Without going into details, there should first be noted the general similarity in the plan of skeletal structure of the appendages of the crossopterygian fishes, the Osteolepiformes (*Sauripterus* and *Eusthenopteron*), and the labyrinthodonts (*Eryops* and *Trematops*), and second, the exceptional similarity in the plan of the same structures in primitive urodele Amphibia (*Hynobiidae* and *Cryptobranchidae*) to the appendages of labyrinthodonts (Fig. 154). The structure of the appendages of the lepospondylous Stegocephalia, as far as is known (*Scincosaurus*), is identical to the structure of the typical appendages of modern urodele Amphibia. In both cases the modern forms differ only in a slight reduction in the number of phalanges of the digits. On the other hand, the appendages of anuran Amphibia may serve as an example of extreme specialization. They differ in structure from the appendages of labyrinthodonts to a greater degree than, for example, the appendages of mammals.

In the present case we are speaking of organs radically modified in comparison to the fins of fishes. It must be said that the pentadactyl appendages of terrestrial vertebrates were newly developed in accordance with the supporting function in transporting the body over a solid substrate in air. Corresponding to the differences in this substrate, the mode of locomotion, and the way of life, the appendages of terrestrial vertebrates underwent sharply divergent evolution. This evolution undoubtedly proceeds from only one stock. The original structure of the appendages of all terrestrial vertebrates is manifested in the appendages of the primitive Stegocephalia. If terrestrial vertebrates had arisen polyphyletically from such a form, then the similarity to the original structures would have been impossible. If urodele Amphibia had arisen not from Osteolepiformes with "dichotomous branching of the limb skeleton," but from Porolepiformes with bicipital branching, then in any case it could not have led to the almost identical structure in the appendages of primitive Urodela and the labyrinthodonts. One cannot conceive of convergent similarities with such large and sharp differences as in the Osteolepiformes and Porolepiformes, and with such differences in functional requirements as in the heavy labyrinthodonts (*Eryops*), on the one hand, and the light urodele Amphibia (*Hynobius* and *Ranodon*) leading secretive lives, on the other. With such a different functional load we would in fact expect much more pronounced divergences.

The limb structure of the urodele Amphibia and Stegocephalia indicates in the most emphatic way their monophyletic origin. The structure of the limbs of reptiles, which in their primitive forms are quite similar to the appendages of the labyrinthodonts, also argues in favor of this.

II. THE RESPIRATORY AND FEEDING MECHANISMS IN LOWER TETRAPODA

In fishes both respiration and ingestion are accomplished by a single mechanism of the visceral apparatus. In terrestrial vertebrates they were separated. On the one hand, a firmer attachment of the jaw to the braincase was established, and on the other hand, the hypoglossal-branchial apparatus was segregated from the jaw apparatus and became more mobile. This mobility was used, however, not only for respiration, (branchial or aerial) but also for taking in food with the tongue and for swallowing.

Although there were choanae in crossopterygian fishes and probably lungs as auxiliary organs of respiration, they did not have a special mechanism for pulmonary respiration. This must have arisen only after the emergence of the animals onto land. This was achieved with some difficulty (Schmalhausen, 1957d), and therefore the first mode of aerial respiration on land was dermal and then oropharyngeal. This mode of respiration remained the basic one in modern Amphibia also. Pulmonary respiration on land was established later, originally with the assistance of a force-pump mechanism developed through modification of the mechanism of branchial respiration. The suction mechanism of pulmonary respiration was developed later and only in the reptilomorphic branches.

The early development of dermal respiration in the Stegocephalia seems remarkable since the skin of the primitive forms was covered with scales. Meanwhile it has been shown that an abundant network of dermal blood vessels was developed even on the surface of the thick cranial armor (Bystrov, 1947). Both dermal and the oropharyngeal aerial respiration are new acquisitions of terrestrial vertebrates. Nevertheless, similar forms of dermal and oropharyngeal respiration were established in both urodele and anuran Amphibia. Evidently they were inherited from a common ancestral form, i.e., from primitive Stegocephalia. Some divergence exists in both the system of dermal respiration and the mechanism of oropharyngeal respiration. It is manifested particularly in the great specialization of the anurans.

The feeding mechanism also had to be reconstructed with the transition to terrestrial life (Schmalhausen, 1957d). Ingestion by the jaws became difficult and was supplemented by action of the tongue as a movable glandular organ. This type of tongue was a new acquisition of terrestrial vertebrates. The history of the development of the tongue in modern Amphibia shows it to have its origin from different sources. The basis of it is present in the anterior prominence of the hypoglossal apparatus—the primary tongue of fishes. In front of it, in the forepart of the floor of the oral cavity, there is developed in the larvae of Amphibia a thick glandular fold (Fig. 164). At metamorphosis,

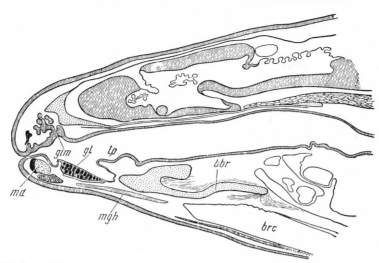

FIG. 164. Sagittal section through head of a larva of *Hynobius* 34 mm long showing anlagen of tongue. *bbr*, Body of sublingual cartilage; *brc*, branchial cavity; *gim*, intermaxillary gland; *gl*, glandular field of tongue; *lp*, primary tongue; *md*, lower jaw; *mgh*, geniohyoid muscle.

muscle fibers from the geniohyoideus muscle grow under this fold and then this layered formation merges with the primary tongue as one unit. Similarly the tongue of the higher terrestrial vertebrates is developed from two different rudiments. Later evolution of the tongue not only differs to a considerable extent in various reptiles, birds, and mammals, but is also highly diversified within the modern urodele Amphibia and in various anurans. As a rule, the tongue is most specialized in the anurans. However, in urodele Amphibia also their development was extremely specialized (for example the boletoid tongue of *Spelerpes*). Thus we have examples of typical development and of sharp divergence. This diversity stems from a single primary structure, how-ever, developing in various ways (the primary tongue of fishes; the glandular fold of the larvae of urodele Amphibia; and the musculus geniohyoideus). All this demonstrates monophyly in the origin of terrestrial vertebrates. An organ so complex in origin could hardly originate independently and convergently from different crossopterygian fishes. It is all the more unlikely that all further evolution of the tongue would then be typically divergent.

The teeth have been reduced in modern Amphibia. In urodele Amphibia they are occasionally well developed on the palate (vomerine teeth, and on the parasphenoid in higher forms). In anurans the jaws often lacked teeth al-together. Undoubtedly this is correlated with the role of the tongue as an organ for taking food and, sometimes, for passing it directly to the pharynx.

III. MODIFICATIONS IN THE SENSE ORGANS

The greatest changes in the transition to terrestrial life occurred in the organ of hearing. Here there arose a new apparatus for transmitting sound vibrations from the air to the inner ear. As we have seen before, the sound transmitting apparatus was developed from the same source and had a uniform primary structure in both Amphibia and reptiles. In further evolution it underwent diverse reconstruction during the adaptive radiations of terrestrial vertebrates. The evolutionary transformations were considerable even within the bounds of the urodele Amphibia.

In the Amphibia, both urodeles and anurans, there is a peculiar organ regulating the pressure on the inner ear—the operculum—connected to special muscles which are usually isolated bundles of m. levator scapulae. In other terrestrial vertebrates this organ is absent (apparently, however, an operculum rudiment is present in the chelonians). The uniqueness of this apparatus and the great similarity of its structure in urodele and anuran Amphibia could only be explained by their common origin from primitive Stegocephalia. Such a structure could not have arisen independently, and from two identical sources moreover (the wall of the otic capsule at the posterior edge of the fenestra ovalis and the muscles elevating the scapula), in two different phylogenetic lines.

Remarkable modifications also occurred in the inner ear. In all terrestrial vertebrates from the otic patch of the lagena of fishes there was segregated a new patch of sensory cells—the macula basilaris—as a special receptor of sound vibrations. Moreover in the Amphibia there was segregated yet another similar, undoubtedly auditory region (with a similar membrana tectoria), the macula neglecta amphibiorum. Although the macula basilaris in urodela Amphibia is reduced, both of these patches are present in both anuran and urodele Amphibia. Independent acquisition of two such specialized organs, one of which (macula neglecta amphibiorum) is a characteristic feature of the Amphibia, must be regarded as completely unlikely. Evidently these receptors were developed in the common ancestors of terrestrial vertebrates, in primitive Stegocephalia.

In the organ of vision, terrestrial vertebrates also have new acquisitions such as the new ciliary accommodation apparatus and the auxiliary glands. In this respect the two lines of modern Amphibia are similar. The mechanism for elevating and lowering the eyes by means of m. levator bulbi (derived from the jaw musculature, m. levator palatoquadrati) and m. retractor bulbi (derived from the oculomotor muscle, m. rectus externus) is also common to them. The first of these muscles is characteristic only of the Amphibia and is present not only in anurans but in urodele Amphibia also. The higher terrestrial vertebrates sometimes also possess a mechanism for elevating the eyeball; this, however, is attained in them by other means. Obviously the muscle elevating the eyeball was acquired by modern Amphibia from common ancestral forms, the primitive Stegocephalia (with a movable eyeball, correlated with the flattened shape of the skull and the development of the interpterygoid fenestra in all Amphibia).

In the olfactory organs the characteristic new acquisition of terrestrial vertebrates is the Jacobson's organ. This organ is present in both anuran and urodele Amphibia (Fig 103) and in reptiles, which also favors their monophyletic origin.

The nasolachrymal duct is a new acquisition of terrestrial vertebrates. It was apparently developed from part of a canal of the seismosensory system (Schmalhausen, 1958c,d), at the base of the posterior external nostril of crossopterygian fishes. This proves, among other things, the organic relationship (Fig. 103) and the dependence in development (in urodele Amphibia) of two typical canal bones, the septomaxilla and lachrymal, which are present not only in the Stegocephalia (and primitive reptiles and mammals), but quite typically in primitive urodele Amphibia also. Thus, the nasolachrymal duct of terrestrial vertebrates has apparently a complex origin. In this case the assumption of an independent origin in two distinct phylogenetic lines is quite incredible.

All these facts taken together point only to the monophyletic origin of terrestrial vertebrates, and all Amphibia in particular, from one group of primitive Osteolepiformes. This in itself is not contradicted by the fact that the urodele Amphibia represent the earliest segregated branch of primitive Stegocephalia.

If one considers modern Amphibia, then they definitely are diphyletic the Anura arose from batrachomorphic labyrinthodonts; and the Apoda and Urodela arose from lepospondylous Stegocephalia. The latter were differentiated very early, and so far it has not been possible to trace their history from fossil remains. However, the main divergence in the composition of the vertebral column, as shown before, is not as great and is mainly a matter of the early fusion of the elements. In urodele Amphibia ossification of the centrum begins at the base of the dorsal arches. The same is also observed in anurans. The latter stem from among primitive rhachitomous forms close to *Eugyrinus*. These forms are very close in skull composition to *Dendrerpeton*. In the latter the spinal column had an embolomerous structure; however, the bases of the neural arches were highly developed, and were saddle-like on the notochord. In this the start of those modifications which are present also in the branchiosaurs and lead through *Eugyrinus* and *Amphibamus* to anuran Amphibia, are visible.

On the other hand, an organization similar to that of *Dendrerpeton* could also have issued from the microsaurs. The skull structure is very similar, and the embolomerous vertebral column with firm neural arches set with expanded bases on the notochord, with stout zygapoophyses and very short neural spines would seem to lead directly to the microsaurs, and through them to urodele Amphibia. If the Dendrerpetontidae are not the common ancestors of Anura and Caudata, then in any case they diverge but little from them. Although modern Amphibia are diphyletic, they are nevertheless genetically related forms. This explains the many parallelisms in their organization. Urodele Amphibia were differentiated much later and underwent a rather complicated evolution.

The modern reptiles are likewise definitely polyphyletic. However, fossil representatives of the cotylosaurs (diadectomorphs and captorhinomorphs) are not so diverse that diphyletic origin of this group could be affirmed. The seymourians are possibly not the common ancestors but they are equally as close to them as to the Stegocephalia. On the other hand, particularly in seymourians, a vertebral structure appears which sharply distinguishes all reptiles from all Stegocephalia. This structure is fundamental to all higher vertebrates (reptiles, birds, and mammals) and these are, obviously, of common origin. Of the fossil forms only the ichthyosaurs are of independent origin.

IV. CONCLUSION

All theories of the polyphyletic origin of terrestrial vertebrates are founded on an over-estimation of certain, usually a very few, specialized characteristics. In consideration of the whole organization, insofar as is permitted by the available material, a pattern of divergence, i.e., of adaptive radiation of terrestrial vertebrates in the very earliest stages of their evolution, is clearly revealed. While among the Stegocephalia of the Carboniferous period there were already clearly established lines of development leading to the Amphibia and to the amniotes (in the form of the batrachomorphic and reptilomorphic Stegocephalia) yet this must be credited to very small divergences from common ancestors, probably close to Devonian ichthyostegids.

The lepospondylous Amphibia from the very first only show decided specialization in the structure of the axial skeleton. In this respect they are similar to modern urodele Amphibia. In the latter, however, the individual developmental history shows the origin of the centra to be from the same elements that enter into their composition in other Amphibia. The predominating role of the neural arches in the development of the bony centra is an example of parallel evolution in the phylogenetic lines leading to the branchiosaurs, to anuran Amphibia, and to the urodeles.

Parallelism is also seen in the modifications of the skull shape (expansion and flattening) in all Amphibia which is obviously correlated to the common mechanisms of oropharyngeal and pulmonary respiration (Fig. 163). Also originating independently was the replacement of bone by cartilage in the braincase in all Amphibia. Reduction of the number of dermal bones entering into the composition of the skull roof occurred similarly, although independently, in both urodele and anuran Amphibia.

Parallelism in the development of many features of organization, especially in anuran and urodele Amphibia, cannot disguise their sharply divergent evolution, however. This divergence is correlated with adaptation to a different way of life and in Anura is manifested primarily by extreme specialization of the locomotory organs. On the contrary, urodele Amphibia retained a very primitive organization in the mode of locomotion and in many other characteristics. In particular a more complex skull composition, and a very primitive structure of the whole visceral apparatus, were retained. Although the apparatus of sound transmission underwent very marked modifications in urodeles, yet, on the one hand, in the ontogeny of the Hynobiidae extremely primitive relationships, reminiscent of the hyomandibula of fishes, and on the other hand, traces of the same organization which is characteristic of the other Amphibia, Stegocephalia, and anurans, were established. Undoubtedly the variations in sound transmission apparatus are the result of divergent evolution.

The structure of the appendages of urodele Amphibia, in contrast to the appendages of anurans, is extremely primitive but is nevertheless exceptionally similar to the structure of the appendages of the Stegocephalia (Fig. 154) and also of the primitive reptiles. It is clearly derived from the general structural plan of the fin skeleton of crossopterygian osteolepids. This circumstance clearly opposes the hypothesis of a polyphyletic origin of Amphibia and terrestrial vertebrates in general.

Also opposing the hypothesis of polyphyletic origin of terrestrial vertebrates are the facts of divergent and parallel evolution on a similar structural basis in those systems which arose anew or were subjected to basic reconstruction during the transition from aquatic to terrestrial life. With such systems, in addition to the paired limbs with their girdles (in which the new iliac division of the pelvic girdle and its connection to the sacral ribs arose), there are also the organs of respiration. Both the system of dermal respiration and the mechanisms of oropharyngeal and pulmonary respiration arose only during the emergence of the animal into the aerial medium. These mechanisms are very similar in all Amphibia. With such systems belong the apparatus for taking in and partly for swallowing food, especially the tongue. These are special organs in terrestrial vertebrates, having a complex origin, but developing from similar sources both in Amphibia and in higher vertebrates.

In the sense organs new elements also originated, the similarities of which show the common root of their origin. Among these were not only the whole sound transmission apparatus but also the special receptors of terrestrial vertebrates such as the macula basilaris (which gives rise to the organ of Corti of higher forms). For Amphibia, moreover, the macula neglecta amphibiorum is characteristic, being present in both anuran and urodele Amphibia. Likewise, in direct opposition to the diphyletic hypothesis stands the presence of the special pressure regulator in the inner ear—the operculum with its muscles—in both anurans and urodeles. Such similar new organs could not have originated in different genetic lines. In the visual organs new glands arose, and new muscles: m. retractor bulbi, characteristic of all terrestrial vertebrates, and m. levator bulbi, peculiar to Amphibia and originating from a single source in both urodeles and anurans. Finally, in the olfactory system the new Jacobson's organ and nasolachrymal duct arose. The latter has a complex origin from two sources (the posterior nostril of fishes and the postorbital canal of the seismisensory system) but is nevertheless quite similar both in terrestrial vertebrates generally and in urodele and anuran Amphibia in particular. With its development the development of two dermal bones of the skull, the septomaxilla and the lachrymal, is also associated. In this respect there is a similarity between urodele and anural Amphibia (the latter lost the lachrymal secondarily).

All these organs, especially the complex organs developed from various sources, having undergone fundamental modifications or having originated anew in terrestrial vertebrates, could not have acquired such similarity in different terrestrial vertebrates if they had had independent origins from different ancestral forms lacking these organs. All morphological information indicates the origin of terrestrial vertebrates from a single root as the result of a rapid adaptive radiation of forms having conquered a new habitat. The urodele Amphibia are not exceptional in this respect. They were differentiated and became specialized extremely early, as long ago as the Carboniferous, and thereafter retained their relatively primitive organization almost unchanged.

20

Phylogenetic Relationships among the Lower Tetrapoda

The phylogenetic relationships that have been clarified in the preceding account are best illustrated in the form of a phylogenetic tree (Fig. 165). Such an arrangement is always schematic, however, and therefore needs to be explained.

The terrestrial vertebrates undoubtedly originated from crossopterygian fishes of the order Osteolepida (family Rhizodontidae). To show the precise source of their origin is impossible, although *Eusthenopteron* apparently approximates the ancestral form extremely closely.

Of the intermediate forms, the position of *Elpistostega* has not been ascertained so far, the remains being too scanty. The position of *Hesperoherpeton*, which represents some specialized side branch that did not give rise to tetrapods, is also uncertain.

The Devonian ichthyostegids are undoubtedly transitional forms that are, however, very similar to the labyrinthodonts. In skull structure the ichthyostegids are very primitive batrachomorphs. This is possibly not an obstacle to the derivation of reptiles from ichthyostegids. In some characteristics, however, they are less primitive than the Lower Carboniferous labyrinthodonts. In the ichthyostegids the intertemporal, which was present in both certain lower batrachomorphs and reptilomorphs, is absent (it is obviously fused to the parietal). In the ichthyostegids the connection of the pectoral girdle to the skull roof by means of the post-temporal, which was still present in the anthracosaurs, is not present. Of the ichthyostegids, *Acanthostega* (with paired postparietals) obviously approximates the ancestral form more closely than *Ichthyostega*. Certain Carboniferous forms—*Colosteus* and *Erpetosaurus*—also belong to the ichthyostegids. In these forms, however, there was a larger interpterygoid fenestra which is a highly specialized character.

The most primitive Carboniferous Stegocephalia, in all characteristics, are the anthracosaurs—*Eogyrinus* and *Palaeogyrinus*. The skull in these forms, however, is angustitabular. This marks the reptilomorphic line of

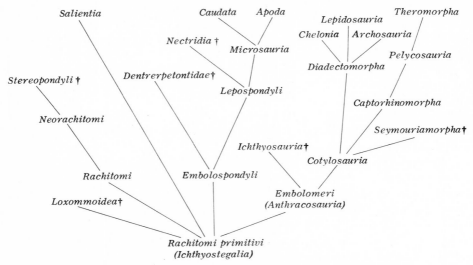

FIG. 165. The phylogenetic relationships of the lower tetrapods.

evolution. Incidentally, this is a very small difference which could have been modified in the course of evolution.

Only the ichthyostegids could have been ancestral to both lines of terrestrial vertebrates in the broadest sense, that is, could also have included forms with the intertemporal and retained the connection of the pectoral girdle to the skull roof.

The batrachomorphic forms were undoubtedly related to the ichthyostegids. In their background lay the Carboniferous ichthyostegals (*Otocratia*, *Colosteus*, and *Erpetosaurus*) and the Loxommoidea. In the latter (*Loxomma*) an intertemporal and a very primitive palate were sometimes present. In all characteristics the Dendrerpetontidae and the Edopsidae were still more primitive. Adjoining these forms are other primitive rhachitomes and beyond is a fairly continuous series of typical rhachitomes in lines leading both to the terrestrial, forms (*Micropholis, Eryops, Cacops,* and others) and also to the secondarily aquatic forms (*Archegosaurus, Trematosaurus,* and others). With the typical rhachitomes is also affiliated another series of forms leading to a secondarily aquatic life through the Neorhachitomi (*Rhinesuchus, Benthosuchus,* and others), to the stereospondylous forms (*Capitosaurus, Metoposaurus,* and others), and culminating in the broad-snouted Brachyopidae. Among the primitive rhachitomes lines also originated leading from the very primitive *Eugyrinus* to *Amphibamus* (*Miobatrachus*) and beyond, to the anuran Amphibia.

The lepospondylous Amphibia were differentiated from some very primitive Ichthyostegalia, perhaps from the same branch that led to the Dendrerpetontidae.

In the history of the lepospondylous forms probably lies the Lower Carboniferous *Dolichopareias*. From primitive amphibious forms the Nectridia arose through a return to aquatic life, and the Microsauria through adaptation to terrestrial life. The latter gradually passed into a burrowing life and gave rise to the gymnophiones (Apoda). The urodele Amphibia were differentiated from certain primitive microsaurs.

The anthracosaurs undoubtedly stand at the base of the line leading to the reptiles. However, known representatives of the anthracosaurs (*Eogyrinus* and *Palaeogyrinus*) are secondarily aquatic forms with long bodies and reduced appendages. These forms could not have given rise to reptiles. Of the embolomerous Stegocephalia only *Diplovertebron* clearly stands on the path of typical reptile evolution.

Although, since Darwin's time, paleontology has indeed achieved vast successes, it is now necessary to note the incompleteness of the geological record. Forms that are primitive in certain respects are often found to be specialized in other respects, and this prevents one from seeing in them the direct ancestors of higher forms. We still await further discoveries of Devonian Stegocephalia—Ichthyostegalia. We also await the ancestral forms of the lepospondylous Amphibia and new remains of anthracosaurs with better developed limbs.

The reptiles proper commence with the seymourians, in which the vertebral column was defintiely differentiated along this route and the first cervical vertebrae were converted into the atlas and epistropheus. The seymourias are very close to *Diplovertebron* and the Stegocephalia.

Of the typical reptiles, the cotylosaurs (especially the diadectomorphs which lead to the lepidosaurs, chelonians, and archosaurs, and thence to the birds) stand closest to *Seymouria*. The captorhinomorphs diverge a little but nevertheless are connected to the seymourians through common ancestry. They undoubtedly lead to the pelycosaurs and theromorphs and thence to the mammals. We will not delve deeply into the more advanced tetrapods here. Our task has been only to elucidate the origin of the lower terrestrial vertebrates.

References

Abel, O. (1929). "Palaobiologie und Stammesgeschichte." Jena.

Allis, E. P. (1889). The anatomy and development of the lateral line system in *Amia calva. J. Morphol.* **2.**

Allis, E. P. (1932). Concerning the nasal apertures, the lachrymal canal and the bucco-pharyngeal upper lip. *J. Anat.* **66.**

Allis, E. P. (1935). A general pattern of arrangement of the cranial roofing bones in fishes. *J. Anat.* **69.**

Allis, E. P. (1936). Comparison of the laterosensory lines, the snout, and the cranial roofing bones of the Stegocephali with those in fishes. *J. Anat.* **70.**

Amalitskii, V. P. (1921). "Dvinosauridae." Publ. Akad. Nauk S.S.S.R. (In Russian.)

Aoyama, F. (1930). Die Entwicklungsgeschichte des Kopfskelettes des *Cryptobranchus japonicus. Z. Anat. Entwicklungsgeschichte,* **93.**

Balabai, P. P. (1956). "Morphology and Phylogenetic Development of the Agnathan Groups." Kiev, Publ. Akad. Nauk, Ukr. S.S.R. (In Russian.)

Ballantyne, F. M. (1927). Air-bladder and lungs. *Trans. Roy. Soc. Edinburgh* **55.**

Berg, L. S. (1939). The pineal foramen in the Palaeoniscidae. *Dokl. Akad. Nauk SSSR* **25.**

Berg, L. S. (1940). On the systematic position of the *Polypteridae. Zool. Zh.* **19.**

Bertmar, G. (1962). Homology of ear ossicles. *Nature* **193.**

Boas, J. (1882). Ueber den Conus arteriosus und die Arterienbogen der Amphibien. *Morphol. Jahrb.* **7.**

Born, G. (1883). Die Nasenhöhlen und der Thränennasengang der amnioten Wirbeltiere. III. *Morphol. Jahrb.* **8.**

Bystrov, A. P. (1935). Morphologische Untersuchungen der Deckknochen des Schädels der Wirbelthiere. *Acta Zool.* **16.** 65–141.

Bystrov, A. P. (1938). Dvinosaurus, als neotenische Form der Stegocephalen. *Acta Zool.* **19,** 209–295.

Bystrov, A. P. (1939). Blutgefässsystem der Labyrinthodonten. *Acta Zool.* **20.**

Bystrov, A. P. (1947). Hydrophilous and xerophilous Labyrinthodonts. *Acta Zool.* **28.**

Bystrov, A. P. (1955). "Microstructure of the Armor of Agnathous Vertebrates of the Silurian and Devonian," Commemorative volume for academician L. S. Berg. Publ. Akad. Nauk S.S.S.R. (In Russian.)

Bystrov, A. P. (1956). Origin of the cyclostomes. *Ezhegodnik, Vses. Paleontol. Obshchestva* **15.** (In Russian.)

Bystrov, A. P., and Efremov, I. A. (1940). *Benthosuchus sushkini* Efr. a labyrinthodont from the Eotriassic of Shcharzhenki River. *Tr. Paleontol. Inst. Akad Nauk SSSR* **10,** 1–152.

Colbert, E. H. (1955). "Evolution of the Vertebrates." New York, London.

Cope, E. D. (1875). Synopsis of the Extinct Batrachia from the Coal Measures. *Rept. Geol. Surv., Ohio, Paleontol.* **2.**

Cope, E. D. (1882–1887). Rhachitomous Stegocephali. *Am. Naturalist* **16–21.**

Credner, H. (1881–1893). Die Stegocephalen und Saurier aus dem Rohtliegenden des Plauenschen Grundes bei Dresden. 1-X. *Z. Deut. Geol. Ges.* **33–45.**

Czopek, J. (1957). The vascularization of respiratory surfaces in *Ambystoma mexicanum* in ontogeny. *Zool. Polon.* **8.**

Czopek, J. (1959). Surface of skin and lung capillaries of amphibians. *Bull. Acad. Polon. Sci., Ser. Sci. Biol.* **7.**

Czopek, J., and Szarski, H. (1954). Oddychanie skórne plazów i jego konsequencje ewolucyjne. *Kosmos* **3.**

Dawson, J. W. (1863). Air-breathers of the coal period of Nova Scotia. *Can. Nat. Geol.* **8.**

de Beer, G. R. (1937). "The Development of the Vertebrate Skull." Oxford.

Dempster, W. T. (1930). The morphology of the amphibian endolymphatic organ. *J. Morphol.* **50.**

Dempster, W. T. (1935). The brain case and endocranial cast of *Eryops megalocephalus* (Cope). *J. Comp. Neurol.* **62.**

Druner, L. (1902). Studien zur Anatomie der Zungenbein, Kiemenbogen und Kehlkopfmuskulatur der Urodelen. II. *Zool. Jahrb., Abt. Anat. Ontog. Tiere* **15.**

Druner, L. (1904). Studien zur Anatomie der Zungenbein, Kiemenbogen und Kehlkopfmuskulatur der Urodelen. II. *Zool. Jahrb., Abt. Anat. Ontog. Tiere* **19.**

Dunn, E. R. (1923). The salamanders of the family Hynobiidae. *Proc. Am. Acad. Arts Sci.* **58.**

Eaton, T. H., Jr. (1939). The crossopterygian hyomandibular. *J. Wash. Acad. Sci.* **29.**

Eaton, T. H., Jr., and Stewart, P. L. (1960). A new order of fish-like amphibia from the Pennsylvanian of Kansas. *Univ. Kansas Publ., Museum Natu. Hist.* **12.**

Edgeworth, F. H. (1923). On the quadrate in *Cryptobranchus*, *Menopoma*, and *Hynobius*. *J. Anat.,* **57.**

Edgeworth, F. H. (1925). On the autostylism of Dipnoi and Amphibia. *J. Anat.,* **59.**

Efremov, I. A. (1933). Ueber die Labyrinthodonten der Udmurt SSR. II. Permische Labyrinthodonten, etc. *Tr. Paleontol. Inst. Akad. Nauk SSSR* **2.**

Emelyanov, S. V. (1925). Development of the ribs and their correlations with the vertebral column. *Russk. Zool.* **5.**

Emelyanov, S. V. (1938). Development of the ribs of terrestrial vertebrates. *Tr. Lab. Evol. Morfol., Akad. Nauk SSSR* **I.**

Fox, H. (1954). Development of the tail and associated structures in the Amphibia with special reference to the urodeles. *Trans. Zool. Soc. London* **28.**

Fox, H. (1959). A study of the development of the head and pharynx of the larval urodele *Hynobius* and its bearing on the evolution of the vertebrate head. *Phil. Trans. Roy Soc. London* **B242.**

Francis, E. T. B. (1934). "The Anatomy of the Salamander." Oxford.

Fritsch, A. (1883–1901). "Fauna der Gaskhole," Vols. I–IV. Prague.

Gamble, D. L. (1922). The morphology of the ribs and transversal processes in *Necturus maculatus. J. Morphoo.* **36.**

Gaupp, E. (1906). Die Entwicklung des Kopfskelettes. *In* "Handbuch der vergleichenden und experimentellen Entwicklungslehre der Wirbeltiere" (O. Hertwig, ed.), Vol. 3, Part 2. Berlin and Vienna.

Gaupp, E. (1913). Die Reichertsche Theorie (Hammer, Ambosz, and Kieferfrage). *Arch. Anat. Entwicklungsgeschichte, Anat. Abt.* **146,** Suppl. 1.

Gilyarov, M. S. (1949). "Soil Features as Habitats and Their Significance in the Evolution of Insects." Publ. Akad. Nauk S.S.S.R. (In Russian.)

Goodrich, E. S. (1907). On the scales of fish, living and extinct, and their importance in classification. *Proc. Zool. Soc. London* **2.**

Goodrich, E. S. (1908). On the systematic position of *Polypterus. Rept. Brit. Assoc. Advan. Sci., 1907.*

Goodrich, E. S. (1909). Part IX. Vertebrata craniata (First fascicle, Cyclostomes and Fishes). *In* "A Treatise on Zoology" (R. Lankester, ed.), London.

Goodrich, E. S. (1928). *Polypterus* a Palaeoniscid? *Palaeobiologica* **1.**

Goodrich, E. S. (1930). "Studies on the Structure and Development of Vertebrates." London.

Göppert, E. (1896). Die Morphologie der Amphibienrippen. *Festschr. Gegenbaur* **1.**

Götte, A. (1905). Ursprung der Lungen. *Zool. Jahrb., Abt. Anat. Ontog. Tiere* **21.**

Gregory, J. P., Peabody, F. E., and Price, L. J. (1956). Revision of the Gymnarthridae. *Bull. Peabody Museum Nat. Hist.* **10.**

Gregory, W. K. (1915). Present status of the problem of the origin of the Tetrapoda. *Ann. N.Y. Acad. Sci.* **24.**

Gregory, W. K. (1941). Studies on the origin and early evolution of paired fins and limbs. *Ann. N.Y. Acad. Sci.* **42.**

Greil, A. (1913). Entwicklungsgeschichte des Kopfes und Blutgefassystems von *Ceratodus Forsteri* Semon, Zool. Forsch. Reisen. I. *Ceratodus. Denkschr. Med.-Naturw. Ges.* **4.**

Gross, W. (1935). Histologische Studien am Aussenskelett fossiler Agnathen und Fische. *Paleontographica* **83.**

Harms, J. W. (1929). Die Realisation von Genen und die consecutive Adaption. *Z. Wiss. Zool., Abt. A* **133.**

Harms, J. W. (1934). "Wandlungen des Artegefüges." Leipzig.

Holmgren, N. (1933). On the origin of the tetrapod limb. *Acta Zool.* **14.**

Holmgren, N. (1949a). Contributions to the question of origin of tetrapods. *Acta Zool.* **30.**

Holmgren, N. (1949b). On the tetrapod limb problem again. *Acta Zool.* **30.**

Holmgren, N., and Pehrson, T. (1949). Some remarks on the ontogenetical development of the sensory lines on the cheek in fishes and amphibians. *Acta. Zool.* **30.**

Holmgren, N., and Stensiö, E. (1936). Kranium und Visceralskelett der Acranier, Cyclostomen und Fische. *In* "Handbuch der vergleichenden Anatomie der Wirbeltiere" (Bolk *et al.*, eds.), Vol. 4.

Hörstadius, S. (1950). "The Neural Crest." Oxford Univ. Press, London and New York.

Huene, F. R. (1956). "Palaeontologie und Phylogenie der neideren Tetrapoden." Jena.

Huxley, T. H. (1861). Fishes of Devonian etc. *Mem. Geol. Surv.* **12.**

Huxley, T. H. (1866, 1872). Illustrations of the structure of the crossopterygian ganoids (Coelacanthini). *Mem. Geol. Surv.* **12–18.**

Inger, R. F. (1957). Ecological aspects of the origin of the tetrapods. *Evolution* **11.**

Jarvik, E. (1942). On the structure of the snout of crossopterygians and lower gnathostomes in general. *Zool. Bidr. Uppsala* **21.**

Jarvik, E. (1944). On the dermal bones, sensory canals, and pit-lines of the skull in *Eusthenopteron foordi* etc. *Kgl. Svenska Vetenskapsakud. Handl.* [3] **21.**

Jarvik, E. (1947). Notes on the pit-lines, and dermal bones of the head in *Polypterus. Zool. Bidr. Uppsala* **25.**

Jarvik, E. (1952). On the fish-like tail in the ichthyostegid stegocephalians. *Medd. Groenland* **114.**

Jarvik, E. (1954). On the visceral skeleton in *Eusthenopteron* with a discussion of the parasphenoid and palatoquadrate in fishes. *Kgl. Svenska Vetenskapsakad. Handl.* [4] **5.**

Jarvik, E. (1955). The oldest tetrapods and their forerunners. *Sci. Monthly* **80.**

Kerr, J. G. (1907). The development of *Polypterus. Proc. Roy. Phys. Soc.* **17.**

Kingsbury, B. F., and Reed, H. D. (1909). Columella auris in Amphibia. *J. Morphol.* **20.**

Klaatsch, H. (1896). Die Brustflosse der Crossopterygier, etc. *Festschr. Gegenbaur* **1.**

Kuhn, O. (1958). "Lurche und Kriechtiere der Vorzeit." Wittenberg-Lutherstadt.

Kulczycki, J. (1960). *Porolepis* (Crossopterygii) from the Lower Devonian of the Holy Cross Mountains. *Acta Paleontol. Polon.* **5,** No. 1.

Lapage, E. O. (1928). The septomaxillary. Part 1. In the Amphibia Urodela. *J. Morphol.* **45.**

Lebedkina, N. S. (1960). Development of the parasphenoid of urodele Amphibia. *Dokl. Akad. Nauk SSSR* **133.**

Lebedkina, N. S. (1963). Development of the dermal bones of the base of the skull of urodele Amphibia. *Tr. Zool. Inst. Akad. Nauk SSSR* **33.**

Litzelman, E. (1923). Entwicklungsgeschichtliche und vergleichendanatomische Untersuchungen uber den Visceralapparat der Amphibien. *Z. Anat. Entwicklungsgeschichte* **67.**

Makushok, M. (1913). Über genetische Beziehung zwischen Schwimmblase und Lungen. *Anat. Anz.* **44.**

Marcus, H. (1933). Beiträge zur Kenntnis der Gymnophionen. *Z. Anat. Entwicklungsgeschichte* **100.**

Marcus, H., Stimmelmayr, E., and Porsch, G. (1936). Die Ossification des *Hypogeophis* Schädels. *Morphol. Jahrb.* **76.**

Maurer, F. (1888). Die Kiemen und ihre Gefasse bei anuren und urodelen Amphibien. *Morphol. Jahrb.* **14.**

Medvedeva, I. M. (1959). The Naso-lachrymal duct and its relationships to the lachrymal and septomaxillary dermal bones in *Ranodon sibiricus. Dokl. Akad. Nauk SSSR* **128.**

Medvedeva, I. M. (1960). On the relationships of the developing naso-lachrymal duct to the lachrymal and septomaxillary dermal bones in *Hynobius keyserlingii. Dokl. Akad. Nauk SSSR* **131.**

Medvedeva, I. M. (1961a). On the problem of the origin of the choana of Amphibia. *Dokl. Akad. Nauk SSSR* **137.**

Medvedeva, I. M. (1961b). Some notes on the early development of the seismosensory lines of the head in the Hynobiidae. *Dokl. Akad. Nauk SSSR* **139.**

Medvedeva, I. M. (1963). Development, origin and homology of the choana and the choanal canal of Amphibia. *Tr. Zool. Inst. Akad. Nauk SSSR* **33.**

Millot, J., and Anthony, J. (1958). Anatomie de *Latimeria chalumnae.* T. 1. Squelette, muscles et formation de soutien. C. N. R. S., Paris.

Miner, R. W. (1925). The pectoral limb of *Eryops* and other primitive Tetrapoda. *Bull. Am. Museum Nat. Hist.* **51.**

Moodie, R. L. (1908). Lateral line system in extinct amphibia. *J. Morphol.* **19.**

Moodie, R. L. (1916a). The coal measures Amphibia of North America. *Carnegie Inst. Wash. Publ.* **238.**

Moodie, R. L. (1916b). A further contribution to our knowledge of the lateral line system in extinct Amphibia. *J. Comp. Neurol.* **25.**

Moodie, R. L. (1922). The influence of the lateral system on the peripheral osseus elements of fishes and Amphibia. *J. Comp. Neurol.* **34.**

Mookerjee, H. K. (1930). On the development of the vertebral column of Urodela. *Phil. Trans. Roy. Soc. London.* **B218.**

Moroff, T. (1902). Uber die Kiemen bei Knochenfischen. *Arch. Mikroscop. Anat.* **60.**

Moy-Thomas, J. A. (1933). Notes on the development of the chondrocranium of *Polypterus senegalus. Quart. J. Microscop. Sci.* **76.**

Noble, G. K. (1925). The integumentary, pulmonary and cardiac modifications correlated with increased cutaneous respiration in the Amphibia. *J. Morphol.* **40.**

Noble, G. K. (1927). The value of life history data in the study of the evolution of the Amphibia. *Ann. N.Y. Acad. Sci.* **30.**

Noble, G. K. (1931). "The Biology of the Amphibia." New York.

Obruchev, D. V. (1945). Evolution of the Agnatha. *Zool. Zh.* **24.**

Obruchev, D. V. (1948). On the evolution of the dermal bone structure of bony fishes. *Izv. Akad. Nauk SSSR, Ser. Biol.* **3.**

Okutomi, K. (1936). Die Entwicklung des Kopfskelettes beim japanischen Krallen-Salamander. *Zool. Jahrb., Abt. Anat. Ontog. Tierre* **61.**

Pehrson, T. (1922). Some points in the cranial development of teleostomian fishes. *Acta Zool.* **3.**

Pehrson, T. (1940). The development of the dermal bones in the skull of *Amia calva. Acta Zool.* **21.**

Pehrson, T. (1947). Some new interpretations of the skull in *Polypterus. Acta Zool.* **28.**

Piveteau, J. (1937). Un Amphibien du Trias inférieur, essai sur l'origine et evolution des Amphibiens Anoures. *Ann. Paleontol.* **26.**

Platt, J. B. (1896a). The development of the cartilaginous skull and branchial and hypoglossal musculature in *Necturus. Morphol. Jahrb.* **25.**

Platt, J. B. (1896b). Ontogenetic differentiation of the ectoderm in *Necturus. Quart. J. Microscop. Sci.* **38.**

Rathke, M. (1825). Kiemen bei Vögeln. *Isis* **18.**

Rathke, M. (1838). "Entwicklungsgeschichte der Natter." Königsberg.

Rauther, M. (1937). Kiemen der Anamnier. *In* "Handbuch der vergleichenden Anatomie der Wirbeltiere"(D. D. Volk *et al.*, eds.), Vol. 4.

Reed, H. D. (1920). The morphology of the sound transmitting apparatus in caudate Amphibia and its physiological significance. *J. Morphol.* **33,** 325–387.

Regel, E. D. (1961). Traces of segmentation in the notochord division of the chondrocranium of *Hynobius keyserlingii*. *Dokl. Akad. Nauk SSSR* **140**.

Regel, E. D. (1962). The palatoquadrate cartilage and its connection to the skull axis in *Hynobius keyserlingii*. *Dokl. Akad. Nauk SSSR* **142**.

Regel, E. D. (1963). Development of the chondrocranium in *Hynobius keyserlingingii*. *Tr. Zool. Inst. Akad. Nauk SSSR* **33**.

Reinbach, W. (1950). Über den Schalleitenden Apparat der Amphibien und Reptilien (zur Schmalhausenschen Theorie der Gehorknockelchen). *Z. Anat. Entwicklungsgeschichte* **114**, 611–639.

Romer, A. S. (1933). Eurypterid influence on vertebrate history. *Science* **78**.

Romer, A. S. (1937). The braincase of the Carboniferous crossopterygian *Megalichthys nitidus*. *Bull. Museum Comp. Zool. Harvard Coll.* **82**, 1–73.

Romer, A. S. (1941). Notes on the crossopterygian hyomandibular and braincase. *J. Morphol.* **69**.

Romer, A. S. (1945). "Vertebrate Palaeontology." Chicago.

Romer, A. S. (1950a). The nature and relationships of the palaeozoic microsaurs. *Am. J. Sci.* **248**.

Romer, A. S. (1950b). Review of the Labyrinthodontia. *Bull. Museum Comp. Zool. Harvard Coll.* **99**.

Romer, A. S. (1958). Tetrapod limbs and early tetrapod life. *Evolution* **12**.

Romer, A. S., and Edinger, T. (1942). Endocranial casts and brains of living and fossil Amphibia. *J. Comp. Neurol.* **77**.

Säve-Söderbergh, G. (1932). Preliminary note on Devonian stegocephalians from East Greenland. *Medd. Groenland* **94**, 1–107.

Säve-Söderbergh, G. (1933). The dermal bones of the head and the lateral line system in *Osteolepis macrolepidotus*. *Nova Acta Regiae Soc. Sci. Upsaliensis* [4] **9**.

Säve-Söderbergh, G. (1934). Some points of view concerning the evolution of the vertebrates and the classification of this group. *Arkiv Zool.* [1] **26A**.

Säve-Söderbergh, G. (1935). On the dermal bones of the head in labyrinthodont stegocephalians and primitive Reptilia with special reference to Eotriassic stegocephalians from East Greenland. *Medd. Groenland* **98**.

Säve-Söderbergh, G. (1936). On the morphology of the Triassic stegocephalians from Spitsbergen, and the interpretation of the endocranium in the Labyrinthodontia. *Kgl. Svenska Vetenskapsakad. Handl.* [3] **16**.

Schauinsland, H. (1906). Die Entwicklung der Wirbelsäule nebst Rippen und Brustbein. *In* "Handbuch der vergleichenden und experimentellen Entwicklungslehre der Wirbeltiere" (O. Hertwig, ed.), Vol. 3, No. 2.

Schmalhausen, I. I. (1913). The unpaired fins of fishes and their phylogenetic development. *Zap. Kievskogo Obshchestva Estestvoispit.* **23**.

Schmalhausen, I. I. (1915). Development of the appendages of Amphibia. *Uch. Zap., Mosk. Gos. Univ., Otd. Nat. Hist.* **37**.

Schmalhausen, I. I. (1916a). On the functional significance of fish fins. *Zool. Zh.* **1**.

Schmalhausen, I. I. (1916b). On the problem of the morphological significance of the unpaired fins of the Dipnoi. *Zool. Zh.* **1**.

Schmalhausen, I. I. (1917a). On the dermal bones of the shoulder girdle of the Amphibia. *Zool. Zh.* **2**.

Schmalhausen, I. I. (1917b). On the appendages of *Ranidens sibiricus*. *Zool. Zh.* **2**.

Schmalhausen, I. I. (1923a). On the problem of the origin of autostyly in Dipnoi and terrestrial vertebrates. *Zool. Zh.* **3**.

Schmalhausen, I. I. (1923b). Der Suspensonalapparat der Fische und das problem der Gehörknöchelchen. *Anat. Anz.* **56**.

Schmalhausen, I. I. (1950a). On the homology of the skull roof bones of fishes and terrestrial vertebrates. *Zool. Zh.* **29**.

Schmalhausen, I. I. (1950b). On the attachment of the visceral arches to the skull axis in fishes. *Zool. Zh.* **29**.

Schmalhausen, I. I. (1951). The functional significance of the modifications of the dorsal divisions of the visceral apparatus in the transition from fishes to terrestrial vertebrates. *Zool. Zh.* **30**.

Schmalhausen, I. I. (1953a). Autostyly and the modifications of the upper divisions of the first visceral arch in lower terrestrial vertebrates. *Zool. Zh.* **32,** 1.

Schmalhausen, I. I. (1953b). Development of the arterial system of the head in urodele Amphibia. *Zool. Zh.* **32.**

Schmalhausen, I. I. (1953c). The first arterial arch and the development of the carotid artery system in Amphibia. *Zool. Zh.* **32.**

Schmalhausen, I. I. (1954). Development of gills, their blood vessels and musculature in Amphibia. *Zool. Zh.* **33.**

Schmalhausen, I. I. (1955a). Development of the visceral musculature in urodele Amphibia. *Zool. Zh.* **34.**

Schmalhausen, I. I. (1955b). The gills and gill septa of Amphibia. *Zool. Zh.* **34.**

Schmalhausen, I. I. (1955c). Distribution of the seismosensory organs in urodele Amphibia. *Zool. Zh.* **34.**

Schmalhausen, I. I. (1955d). Some notes on the ways of life of primitive Stegocephalia (Ichthyostegidae). *Tr. Zool. Inst. Akad. Nauk SSSR* **21.**

Schmalhausen, I. I. (1956a). Development of the sound transmission apparatus in urodele Amphibia of family Hynobiidae. *Zool. Zh.* **35.**

Schmalhausen, I. I. (1956b). Morphology of the sound transmission apparatus of urodele Amphibia. *Zool. Zh.* **35.**

Schmalhausen, I. I. (1957a). On the seismosensory system of urodele Amphibia in relation to the problem of the origin of terrestrial vertebrates. *Zool. Zh.* **36.**

Schmalhausen, I. I. (1957b). The sound transmission mechanism in Amphibia. *Zool. Zh.* **36.**

Schmalhausen, I. I. (1957c). Morphology of the vertebral column of urodele Amphibia I. Development of the Centra. *Zool. Zh.* **36.**

Schmalhausen, I. I. (1957d). Biological fundamentals of the origin of terrestrial vertebrates. *Izv. Akad. Nauk SSSR, Ser. Biol.* I: 3–30.

Schmalhausen, I. I. (1958a). Morphology of the vertebral column of urodele Amphibia. Origin of the Centra. *Zool. Zh.* **37,** No. 2.

Schmalhausen, I. I. (1958b). Morphology of the vertebral column of urodele Amphibia. III. Transverse processes and ribs. *Zool. Zh.* **37.**

Schmalhausen, I. I. (1958c). The naso-lachrymal duct and septomaxillary of urodele Amphibia. *Zool. Zh.* **37.**

Schmalhausen, I. I. (1958d). The nostrils of fishes and their fate in terrestrial vertebrates. *Zool. Zh.* **37.**

Schmalhausen, I. I. (1958e). History of the origin of the Amphibia. *Izv. Akad. Nauk SSSR, Series Biol.* No. 1.

Schmalhausen, I. I. (1959). The problem of monophyletism versus polyphyletism in the problem of the origin of terrestrial vertebrates. *Byull. Mosk. Obshchestva Ispytatelei Prirody, ltd. Biol.* **64.**

Schmalhausen, I. I. (1960). Biological fundamentals of the organization of crossopterygian fishes. *Paleontol. Zh.* **1.**

Schmalhausen, I. I. (1964). The position of urodele amphibia among the lower terrestrial vertebrates. *Tr. Zool. Inst. Akad. Nauk SSSR* **33.**

Schmalhausen, O. I. (1955). Development of gills in larvae of the Volga sturgeon. *Dokl. Akad. Nauk SSSR* **100.**

Schmalhausen, O. I. (1962). Morphological research on the olfactory organs of fishes. *Tr. Inst. Morfol. Zhivotn. Akad. Nauk SSSR* **40.**

Severtsov, A. N. (1922). Die Entwicklung der Kiemen una Kiemenbengefässe der Fische. *Z. Wiss. Zool., Abt. A* **121** [in collected works, Vol. 4 (1948)].

Severtsov, A. N. (1923). Die Morphologie des Visceralapparatus der Elasmobranchier. *Anat. Anz.* **56** [also in his collected works, Vol. 4 (1948)].

Severtsov, A. N. (1926). Der Ursprung der Quadrupeda. *Paleontol. Z.* **8.**

Severtsov, A. N. (1928). Skeleton and musculature of the head of *Acipenser ruthenus. Acta Zool.* **9.** [also in his collected works, Vol. 4 (1948)].

Severtsov, A. N. (1939). "Morphological Correlations of Evolution." Publ. Akad. Nauk S.S.R.R., Moskow-Leningrad.

Severtsov, A. S. (1961). On the tongue protrusion mechanism of anuran Amphibia. *Dokl. Akad. Nauk SSSR* **140.**

Smith, J. L. B. (1939). A living coelancanthid fish. *Trans. Roy. Soc. S. Africa* **28.**

Spengel, J. W. (1904). Schwimmblasen, Lungen und Kiementaschen. *Zool. Jahrb.* Suppl. 7.

Stadtmüller, F. (1924). Studien am Urodelenschädel. I. Zur Entwicklungsgeschichte des Kopf-skelettes der *Salamandra maculosa*. *Z. Anat. Entwicklungsgeschichte* **75.**

Stadtmüller, F. (1931). Varianten im Mittelohrgebiet bei *Bombinator*. *Morphol. Jahrb.* **66.** Göppert's Festschr., Hft. 1.

Stadtmüller, F. (1936). Kranium und Visceralskelett der Stegocephalen und Amphibien. *In* "Handbuch der vergleichenden Anatomie der Wirbeltiere" (Bolk *et al.*, eds.), Vol. 4.

Steen, M. S. (1934). The amphibian fauna from the South Joggins, Nova Scotia. *Proc. Zool. Soc. London* 465–504.

Steen, M. S. (1938). On the fossil amphibians from the Gas Coal of Nỳrany and other deposits in Czechoslovakia. *Proc. Zool. Soc. London* **B.108.**

Stensiö, E. A. (1921). "Triassic Fishes from Spitsbergen," Part I. Vienna.

Stensiö, E. A. (1925). On the head of macropetalichthyids with certain remarks on the head of other arthrodires. *Chicago Field Museum Nat. Hist. Publ., Geol. Ser.* [4] **232,** 87–197.

Stensiö, E. A. (1927). The Downtonian and Devonian vertebrates of Spitzbergen. *Sr. Svalbard Nordishavet* **12.**

Stensiö, E. A. (1939). A new anaspid from the upper Devonian of Scaumenac Bay in Canada, with remarks on the other anaspids. *Kgl. Svenska Vetenskapsakad. Handl.* [3] **18,** 1–25.

Stensiö, E. A. (1947). The sensory lines and dermal bones of the cheek in fishes and amphibians. *Kgl. Svenska Vetenskapsakad. Handl.* [3] **24.**

Stöhr, P. (1879). Zur Entwicklungsgeschichte des Urodelenschädels. *Z. Wiss. Zool.* **33.**

Stone, L. S. (1922). Experiments on the development of the cranial ganglia and the lateral line sense organs in *Amblystoma punctatum*. *J. Exptl. Zool.* **35.**

Stone, L. S. (1926). Further experiments on the extirpation and the transplantation of mesecto-derm in *Amblystoma punctatum*. *J. Exptl. Zool.* **44.**

Stone, L. S. (1928). Primitive lines in *Amblystoma* and their relations to the migratory lateral line primordia. *J. Comp. Neurol.* **45.**

Sushkin, P. P. (1927). On the modification of the mandibular and hyoid arches and their rela-tions to the brain case, etc. *Paleontol. Z.* **8.**

Sushkin, P. P. (1936). Notes on the pre-Jurassic Tetrapoda from USSR. III. *Dvinosaurus ama-litzki*, a perennibranchiate stegocephalian from the Upper Permian from North Dvina. *Tr. Paleontol. Inst. Akad. Nauk SSSR* **4.**

Szarski, H. (1961). "Pochodzenie plazòw." Warszawa.

Tatarinov, L. P. (1958). The evolution of the sound conducting apparatus of lower terrestrial vertebrates and the origin of the lizards. *Zool. Zh.* **37.**

Terentev, P. V., and Chernov, S. A. (1949). "A Key to the Lizards and Amphibians." "Sovet-skaya Nauka," Moskow. (In Russian.)

Thyng, F. W. (1906). Squamosal bone in tetrapodous vertebrata. *Proc. Boston Soc. Nat. Hist.* **32** (cited from Stadtmüller, 1936).

Tumarkin, A. (1949). On the evolution of the sound conducting apparatus. *J. Laryngol. Otol.* **63.**

von Baer, K. (1828, 1837). "Ueber Entwicklungsgeschichte der Tiere. Beobachtung und Re-flexion." Königsberg.

von Zittel, K. A. (1911). "Grundzüge der Paleontologie," Vol. II. Vertebrata. Munchen and Berlin.

Vorobjeva-Blokhina, E. I. (1959). A new genus of crossopterygian fishes *Platycephalichthys* from the Upper Devonian of Lovat River. *Paleontol. Zh.* 3.

Vorobjeva-Blokhina, E. I. (1962). Rhizodont crossopterygian fishes from the main Devonian localities of USSR. *Tr. Paleontol. Inst. Akad. Nauk SSSR* **44.**

Voskoboinikov, M. M. (1932). Der Apparat der Keimenathmung bei den Fischen. *Zool. Jahrb., Abt. Anat. Ontog. Tiere* **55.**

Watson, D. M. S. (1913). *Micropholis Stowi* Huxley, a temnospondylous amphibian from South Africa. *Geol. Mag.* **10,** No. 8, 340–346.

Watson, D. M. S. (1919). The structure, evolution and origin of the Amphibia I. *Phil. Trans. Roy. Soc. London* **B209,** 1–73.

Watson, D. M. S. (1926a). The Carboniferous Amphibia of Scotland. *Paleontol. Hung.* **1**, 221–252.

Watson, D. M. S. (1926b). The evolution and origin of the Amphibia. II. *Phil. Trans. Roy. Soc. London* **214.**

Watson, D. M. S. (1937). The acanthodian fishes. *Phil. Trans. Roy. Soc. London* **B228**, 49–146.

Watson, D. M. S. (1940). The origin of frogs. *Trans. Roy. Soc. Edinburgh* **60**, No. 1, 195–231.

Watson, D. M. S. (1951). "Paleontology and Modern Biology." New Haven.

Wegner, R. N. (1922). Der Stützknochen, os nariale, in der Nasenhöle etc. *Morphol. Jahrb.* **51.**

Westoll, T. S. (1943a). The hyomandibular of *Eusthenopteron* and the tetrapod middle ear. *Proc. Roy. Soc.* **B131.**

Westoll, T. S. (1943b). The origin of the tetrapods. *Biol. Rev.* **18**, 78–98.

Williams, E. E. (1959). Gadow's arcualia and the development of the tetrapod vertebrae. *Quart. Rev. Biol.* **34.**

Williston, S. W. (1909). New or little known Permian vertebrates: *Trematopus* n.g. *J. Geol.* **17.**

Wilson, J. A. (1941). The skull of *Buettneria. Contrib. Museum Geol., Univ. Mich.* **6.**

Winslow, C. M. (1898). The chondrocranium in the Ichthyopsida. *Tufts Coll. Studies* **5.**

Winterhalter, W. P. (1931). Untersuchungen über das Stirnorgan der Anuren. *Acta Zool.* **12.**

Author Index

Numbers in italics refer to pages on which the complete references are listed.

Subject Index

A

Acanthodes, 10, 155
Acanthodii, 8–11
Acanthostega, 94, 102, 121, 293
Acanthostegidae, 275
Acanthostoma, 102, 252
Acousticolateralis, complex, 45
Acipenser, 20, 82
Actinopterygian, 155
Actinopterygii, 26, 28
Adaptive radiation, 89–93
Adelogyrinus, 116, 118
Adelosponodyl, 127
Aerial respiration, in water, 51
Agamia, 203
Agnatha, 3–9
Air sacs, 16, 17
Alytes, 112
Alytes obstetricans, 114
Ambystoma, 154, 188, 207, 214, 223, 224
Ambystomidae, 154, 209, 254, 282
Amia, 16, 17, 20, 85, 143, 173, 180
Amia calva, 82, 162, 164, 175, 240
Amiurus, 195
Amniote, 175, 224, 249
Amphibamus, 104, 106–109, 240, 289, 294
Amphibia, 29, 30, 33, 44, 47, 50–52, 89, 288
    anuran, 104–115
    external gills, 22–24
    mono vs polyphyletism, 266–292
    respiration, 65
    urodele, 127–258
Amphipnous, 17
Amphipnous cuchia, 16
Amphiuma, 188, 212, 252, 258
Amphiumidae, 154
Anabas scandens, 16, 17
Anal fin, 41
Anaspida, 5–6, 8
Anlage, 222

Anocleithrum, 40, 61
Anthracosauria, 86, 119
Anthracosaurs, 266, 293
Antiarchi, 10
Anura, 75, 89, 104–115, 175, 176, 183, 210, 289
    larvae, 111–115
Anuran, 142, 165, 166, 169, 221, 237, 240, 261,
    272–274, 284, 287, 288
Aphaneramma, 96, 161
Apoda, 89, 258, 261, 289, 295
    origin, 124–126
Appendages, 75–76, 285
    anuran, 115
    crossopterygian, 40
    urodele, 252–255
Archegosaurus, 96, 110, 127, 159, 294
Arthrodira, 9, 10
Ascaphus, 112–114
Ascidia, larva, 1
Auditory organ, 68, 105
Auditory ossicles, 115
Auditory receptors, 181–221
    fish, comparison with, 193–203
    ground, transmission from, 205–206
    internal transmission, 211
    mechanisms of transmission, 203–205
    modification, 287–288
    muscles of dorsal section, 191–193
    operculum, 67–68
    reptile, comparison, 193–203
    water-sound reception, 206–211
Auditory response, 92

B

Baphetes, 95, 121
Basipterygoid, 103, 109
    articulation, 38
Batrachiderpeton, 79
Batrachosuchus, 80, 97, 161

307